Smith Book Award

presented in recognition of
outstanding achievement

Kathryne Sanserino

Canterbury School

SMITH COLLEGE · FOUNDED 1871 ·

Smith Voices

Monica Vachula '73
Illustration to *Tea with an Old Dragon* by Jane Yolen
Oil on canvas, 8 1/2" x 9 1/2"

SMITH
voices

SELECTED WORKS
by
SMITH COLLEGE ALUMNAE

edited by Patricia L. Skarda

THE SMITH COLLEGE PRESS
NORTHAMPTON, MASSACHUSETTS

Jacket illustrations

Front:
Janet Fish '60
"Herb Tea," 1995
Oil on canvas, 36″ x 60″
Smith College Museum of Art
Photograph by Beth Philips courtesy of VAGAS
Purchased with the Janet Wright Ketchem '53, Art Acquisition Fund, the Class of 1990 Art Fund, and with gifts
made in honor of President Mary Maples Dunn.

Back:
Monica Vachula '73
Oil on canvas, 3″ x 4″
Illustration to *Tea with an Old Dragon* by Jane Yolen

Table of Contents

Introduction

THE AUTHORS AND ARTISTS represented in this collection are but a few of the Smith College alumnae who have shared the products of their minds and imaginations with the public. The selections here testify to the range of interests and breadth of experiences of women who have in common both Smith College and a demonstrated love of learning that clearly never stops. The College is justifiably proud of the literary and artistic legacies of its alumnae, and current students recognize and accept the challenges inherent in being part of a long and enduring tradition of excellence.

Choosing the selections was not as easy as it may appear, for alumnae express themselves in an extraordinary variety of ways through an extraordinary number of pages and works of art. Members of the faculty and staff are steeped in Smith lore to varying degrees, and many colleagues sent along recommendations and advice. Alumnae and students, too, participated in the selection process, suggesting favorite authors and even particular passages. For the most part, I chose not to represent work by academics, though Smith College can claim a great many distinguished scholars who have shaped their respective disciplines. Wanting the book to be both interesting and entertaining, I tried to select excerpts that would have integrity standing separate from larger wholes. And, finally, I attempted to find essays that would age well. I am particularly indebted to the Smith College Museum and the Mortimer Rare Book Room staff for help in choosing the artists and the art that represents many long and distinguished careers.

My own interest in literature written by Smith alumnae began in 1974-75, the Centennial year, when I agreed to teach a student-initiated course on Smith authors. In 1989-90, at the request of the National Alumnae Admission Committee (NAAC), I worked with a committee to prepare the first edition of *Smith Voices*, which sold out much more quickly than anticipated. This collection bears only slight resemblance to that pilot volume, but its primary purpose for the admission and advancement efforts of the College remains the same.

This book has been made possible by the generosity of many loyal alumnae—writers and readers, artists and viewers. Particular and continuing thanks go to Linda Salisbury '78, whose gift in memory of her parents, Martha L. and William H. Salisbury made this volume possible.

Anne F. O'Connell '76, Chair of the National Alumnae Admission Committee (NAAC), has been an enthusiastic supporter of this project from the beginning. Carrie S. Cadwell MEd '82, Executive Director of the Alumnae Association, has endorsed and encouraged the expansion of this book to include more alumnae, both writers and artists. Both Carey Bloomfield and Karin George, Chief Advancement Officers, have recognized the value of the book to alumnae, and Nancy D. Harvin, Interim Chief Advancement Officer, made many suggestions, as did Charlotte Heartt, Principal Gifts Officer and former Director of Development. John MacMillan, editor of the *Alumnae Quarterly*, extended the resources of his office to me. And Admissions staff have looked forward to the publication of this book so that *Smith Voices* could be used for Smith Book Awards at high schools everywhere.

Through the introductions of the fifty-five alumnae in *Smith Voices*, I have tried to provide a detailed picture of the careers of individuals so that readers will run to libraries and galleries to find more to read and see by the women who are represented here. For drafting a few introductions, I am indebted to Linda Muehlig, Associate Curator of the Smith College Museum; Allison C. Deets '99, my Intern and Honors Student; Allison M. Otto '02, research assistant on the STRIDE program; and to Kaitlin K. Blazejack '99J.

Many people within the College deserve special thanks. With consistent good humor and keen aesthetic taste, M. Richard Fish, photographer for the Department of Art, provided reproductions of the works of art on campus and served as technical adviser. Elliot M. Offner, A.M. Mellon Professor of the Humanities, suggested several artists I would not otherwise have known and acted as consultant on design, as did John G. Eue, Director of Publications. Martin Antonetti, Curator of the Mortimer Rare Book Room, together with Karen Kukil, Associate Curator, and Barbara Blumenthal, Assistant Curator, helped me to find appropriate selections, to acquire permission to reprint, and to check facts. Many Smith College librarians were called to action, and I am grateful for their remarkable efficiency and assistance, especially in acquiring books and articles through interlibrary loan. Timely suggestions were made by Sherrill L. Redmon, Head of the Sophia Smith Collection; Daniel Horowitz, Sylvia Dlugasch Bauman Professor of American Studies; Ruth A. Solie, Sophia Smith Professor of Music; Ann E. Boutelle, Lecturer in English and founder of the Poetry Center; and Nanci A. Young, College Archivist.

For three semesters, my editorial intern, Allison C. Deets '99, read many more pages than were required for her classes to help in the identification of interesting texts by many alumnae. She joined me, too, in teaching an Interterm '99 class on Smith Voices, where we shared and resolved several important editorial problems. In the summer of 1998, I relied on the insight of another intern, Sarah L. Grover '99, who read long into the night, to recommend and to respond to excerpts and possibilities from the many novels, stories, poems, and essays that could have found a place in *Smith Voices*.

When the time came to prepare and proofread the manuscript, I enlisted a veritable army of students, including my other STRIDE student, Sarah Willson '02 and students in the Interterm '99 class on Smith voices—among them Sarah K. Hood '01, Lisa A. Pannone '99, Courtney Schusheim '01, and Claire Scott '01. Proofreading volunteers include Lori S. Robinson '01, Martha A. Plotz '01, Dara Weinerman '00, Rebecca Sullivan '00, Jessica M. Hannon '01, Megan A. Rodriguez '01, Allison M. Otto '02, and Allison C. Deets '99. Editing this book has been a teaching opportunity for me and learning opportunity for many students. Although the work has been shared, I remain responsible for any errors.

The designer of this book, Elizabeth Pols '75, did much more than urge this book to timely completion. Her aesthetic sensibility can be seen on every page, and her own contribution of *La Fiorentina* enriches the volume.

Smith College at its best works as a team led by President Ruth J. Simmons who listens hard and leads well. Provost and Dean of the Faculty, John M. Connolly, and Dean for Academic Development, Donald C. Baumer, helped in various ways to make possible *Smith Voices: Selected Works by Smith College Alumnae.*

I am enormously grateful to the many who helped me in this labor of love, but I am more grateful still to the spirit of Smith College for the tradition of excellence which inspired the works that follow.

MADELEINE L'ENGLE '41

Madeleine L'Engle (Madeleine Camp Franklin) spent much of her youth in Switzerland, South Carolina, and Massachusetts, but she says she grew up in New York City. After graduating cum laude from Smith, she returned to New York to work in the theater. There she met her actor husband, Hugh Franklin, best remembered as Dr. Charles Tyler in the daytime drama All My Children. Together they raised their three children in western Connecticut, where for some years they ran a general store.

While touring with productions, Madeleine L'Engle wrote her first novel, The Small Rain (1945, reissued in 1996). Four more novels emerged in close succession, and prizes followed. Meet the Austins (1960, reissued 1981), which describes the Franklin household in Connecticut, was named one of the Notable Children's Books by the American Library Association, the first of many writing awards.

With more than forty books to her credit, L'Engle is best known for the Time Trilogy: A Wrinkle in Time (1963, Newbery Medal Winner), The Wind in the Door (1973), and A Swiftly Tilting Planet (1978, American Book Award). Philosophical, paradoxical, and enchanting, L'Engle's works draw upon the traditions of Albert Einstein, Max Planck, a broad range of theologians, and upon her own experience as a wife, mother, actress, and reader. These imaginative and compelling books pit good against evil in a personal context of individual choice. Through Christian and cosmic ironies, Madeleine L'Engle repeatedly expresses her religious faith in her novels, and, in her non-fiction, she writes openly about Christianity and its attendant joy and hope. As the Writer-in-Residence at the Cathedral of St. John the Divine in New York City, she has most recently published A Live Coal in the Sea (1996), Bright Evening Star (1997), and Miracle on 10th Street and other Christmas Writings (1998).

The following selection, from L'Engle's speech given at The Library of Congress in 1983, testifies to the many sources of her inspired and inspiring creativity.

Dare to be Creative!

"DO I DARE DISTURB THE UNIVERSE?" asks T.S. Eliot's J. Alfred Prufrock. It's not an easy question, and there are no easy answers. Robert Cormier, in his cautionary tale *The Chocolate War*, has his young hero ask J. Alfred's question, and because this is not a novel of realism, as many people think, but a cautionary tale, the answer is, "You'd better not dare, because if you do, you'll get hurt." In this book, Cormier takes something which is already in existence in a small way and has it burst out into enormous proportions, in somewhat the same way that James Clavell does in *The Children's Story*, a small chill book which he was inspired to write when his daughter came home from school, having been taught by rote to say the pledge of allegiance, gabbling it with no understanding, and he saw how easily the mind of a child can be manipulated.

The writer whose words are going to be read by children has a heavy responsibility. And yet, despite the undeniable fact that children's minds are tender, they are also far more tough than many people realize, and they have an openness and an ability to grapple with difficult concepts which many adults have lost. Writers of children's literature are set apart by their willingness to confront difficult questions.

Perhaps for this reason, the content of children's books is often a matter of controversy. There are, of course, built-in restraints in the writing and publishing of a book marketed for children. Responsible editors and publishers are going to exercise these restraints by refusing to publish a book they consider pornographic, or ethnically prejudiced, or in any way potentially damaging to children. And here we come to a very fine line: what is the difference between honest editorial advice, and the manipulating of a writer?

Many years ago, when *A Wrinkle in Time* was being rejected by publisher after publisher, I wrote in my journal, "I will rewrite for months or even years for an editor who sees what I am trying to do in this book and wants to make it better and stronger. But I will not, I can not diminish it and mutilate it for an editor who does not understand it and wants to weaken it."

Now, the editors who did not understand the book and wanted the problem of evil soft-peddled had every right to refuse to publish the book, as I had, sadly, the right and obligation to try to be true to it. If they refused it out of honest conviction, that was honorable. If they refused it for fear of trampling on someone else's toes, that was, alas, the way of the world. Finally, in John Farrar and Hal Vursell I found a publisher and an editor who did understand the book and helped me to know what I needed to do to make it more the book I was trying to write.

After a book is published, we then come to the problem of outside interference. I am very wary of those individuals who are neither writers nor editors nor even, in some cases, readers, who feel that they have the right to apply their own moral criteria to the books in public and school libraries. I have enormous respect and admiration for the librarians who are rising up to protest this, because they are putting their very jobs on the line.

Recently I was lecturing in the Midwest, and the head librarian of a county system came to me in great distress, bearing an epistle composed by one woman, giving her all the reasons she should remove *A Wrinkle in Time* from the library shelves. This woman, who had obviously read neither *Wrinkle* nor the Bible carefully, was offended because she mistakenly assumed that Mrs What, Mrs Who, and Mrs Which were witches practicing black magic. I scrawled in the margin that if she had read the text she might have noted that they were referred to as guardian angels. The woman was also offended because they laughed and had fun. Is there no joy in heaven? The woman belonged to that group of people who believe that any book which mentions witches or ghosts is evil and must be banned. If these people were consistent, they would have to ban the Bible: what about the Witch of Endor and Samuel's ghost?

The woman's epistle went on to say that Charles Wallace knew things other people didn't know. "So did Jesus," I scrawled in the margin. She was upset because Calvin sometimes felt compulsions. Don't we all? This woman obviously felt a compulsion to be a censor. Finally I scrawled at the bottom of the epistle that I truly feared for this woman. If we are looking for life and love and openness and growth, we are likely to find them. If we are looking for witchcraft and evil, we'll likely find them, and we may get taken over by them.

On the other side of the censoring coin, there was an uproar in another midwestern city about the removal from the shelves of *The Best Christmas Pageant Ever* because the word *Christmas* is in the title. Do we have the right to impose our own religious beliefs, from no matter which direction they come, on the rest of the world? I don't think so.

We all practice some form of censorship. I practiced it simply by the books I had in the house when my children were little. If I am given a budget of $500 I will be practicing a form of censorship by the books I choose to buy with that limited amount of money, and the books I choose not to buy. But nobody said we were not allowed to have points of view. The exercise of personal taste is not the same thing as imposing personal opinion.

As a writer, I have to accept that books that are marketed as Young Adult Novels are also going to be read by the ten year olds. But I, too, read avidly when I was ten. I read every book I could get my hands on, suitable or unsuitable. However, when I was ten I simply skipped over the parts of the books which were not within the context of my own life. The dubious sections of the novels did not hurt me because I did not understand them and skipped over them, just as I skipped over the sermonizing in some Victorian novels in order to get on with the story.

And the stories I cared about, the stories I read and reread, were usually stories which dared to disturb the universe, which asked questions rather than gave answers.

I returned to the story, then, as now, looking for truth, for it is in the story that we find glimpses of meaning, rather than in textbooks. But how apologetic many adults are when they are caught reading a book of fiction! They tend to hide it and tell you about the "How-To" book which is what they are really reading. Fortunately, nobody ever told me that stories were untrue, or should be outgrown, and then as now they nourished me and kept me willing to ask the unanswerable questions.

I read indiscriminately, and I read what I call One-Read Books as well as Seven-Read Books. I don't think the One-Read Books did me much harm. I read them and forgot them. The Seven-Read Books—and sometimes the Ten- and Twenty-Read Books—undoubtedly did influence me. And I wonder how these beloved books would fare today with those looking for excuses to ban and burn?

Someone sent me this quotation, without giving me the source: "A book is the only place in which you can examine a fragile thought without breaking it, or explore an explosive idea without fear it will go off in your face. It is one of the few sources of information left that is served up without the silent black noise of a headline, the doomy hullabaloo of a commercial. It is one of the few havens remaining where a [person's] mind can get both provocation and privacy."

I wish we were all that open minded in our thinking and discussing.

One time I was in the kitchen drinking tea with my husband and our young son, and they got into an argument about ice hockey. I do not feel passionate about ice hockey. They do. Finally our son said, "But Daddy, you don't understand." And my husband said, reasonably, "It's not that I don't understand, Bion. It's just that I don't agree with you."

To which the little boy replied hotly. "If you don't agree with me, you don't understand."

I think we all feel that way, but it takes a child to admit it. And it's frighteningly true of those who would impose their own moral imperatives on the rest of the world, who would ban *The Best Christmas Pageant Ever* for being Christian, or *A Wrinkle in Time* for not being Christian, or the Narnia books for being pornographic.

We need to disturb the universe by not being manipulated or frightened by judgmental groups who assume the right to insist that if we do not agree with them, not only do we not understand but we are wrong. How dull the world would be if we all had to feel the same way about everything, if we all had to like the same books, dislike the same books. For my relaxing reading I enjoy English murder mysteries, but my husband prefers spy thrillers. I like beet greens and he likes beet root. We would be a society of ants if we couldn't have personal tastes and honest differences. And how sad it would be if we had to give up all sense of mystery for the limited world of provable fact. I still can't read *The Happy Prince* or *The Selfish Giant* aloud without a lump coming into my throat, but I suppose that talking statues and giants are on someone's hit list.

Perhaps some of this zeal is caused by fear. But, as Bertrand Russell warns, "Zeal is a bad mark for a cause. It was the anti-vaccinationists, not the vaccinationists, who were zealous." Yet because those who were not threatened by the idea of vaccination ultimately won out, we have eradicated the horror of smallpox from the planet.

Russell suggests that people are zealous when they are not completely certain they are right. I agree with him. When I find myself hotly defending something, when I am, in fact, zealous, it is time for me to step back and examine whatever it is that has made me so hot under the collar. Do I think it's going to disturb my comfortable rut? Make me change and grow?—and growing always causes growing pains. Am I afraid to ask questions?

Sometimes. But I believe that good questions are more important than answers, and the best children's books ask questions, and make the reader ask questions. And every new question is going to disturb someone's universe.

Writing fiction is definitely a universe disturber, and for the writer, first of all. My books push me and prod me and make me ask questions I might otherwise avoid. I start a book, having lived with the character for several years, during the writing of other books, and I have a pretty good idea of where the story is going and what I hope it's going to say. And then, once I get deep into the writing, unexpected things begin to happen, things which make me question, and which sometimes really shake my universe.

Perhaps one of the most important jobs of the writer whose books are going to be marketed for children is to dare to disturb the universe by exercising a creative kind of self-censorship.

We don't need to let it all hang out. Sure, kids today know pretty much everything that is to be known about sex, but we owe them art, rather than a clinical textbook. Probably the most potent sex scene I have ever read is in Flaubert's *Madame Bovary* where Emma goes to meet her lover, and they get in the carriage and draw the shades, and the carriage rocks like a ship as the horses draw it through the streets. How much more vivid is what the imagination can do with that than the imagination-dulling literal description!

I also want to practice self-censorship in my use of vocabulary. People who are constantly using four-letter words usually do so because of the paucity of their vocabulary. If you want to swear really elegantly, go to Shakespeare and the other sixteenth- and seventeenth-century writers; they knew how to use words. The use of limited vocabulary has always struck me as immoral: how is a child to learn vocabulary if the child is urged to stay within what the educational establishment has decided is a fourth-grade or a seventh-grade level? Certainly, in the late fifties and early sixties, when limited vocabulary was popular, the word *tesseract* was not to be found on any approved list.

We think because we have words, not the other way around, and the greater our vocabulary, the greater our ability to think conceptually. The first people a dictator puts in jail after a coup are the writers, the teachers, the librarians—because these people are dangerous. They have enough vocabulary to recognize injustice and to speak out loudly about it. Let us have the courage to go on being dangerous people.

Perhaps one of the cleverest things the communists have done is to make education in this country suspect, so that there is a strong anti-intellectual bias among many people who consider themselves patriotic. I heard someone announce, categorically, that all college professors are communists. That's a pretty ugly way to think. Perhaps education does open our eyes to injustices which make us uncomfortable; if we don't know about them, we don't have to do anything about them. Perhaps people who read and write and have enough vocabulary to think with *are* universe-disturbers. But we need to disturb the universe, if as human beings on planet earth, we are to survive. We need to have the vocabulary to question ourselves, and enough courage to disturb creatively, rather than destructively, even if it is going to make us uncomfortable or even hurt.

A librarian friend of mine told me of a woman who came to her and urged her to remove *Catcher in the Rye* from her library shelves. The woman announced that it had 7,432 dirty words in it. "How do you know the exact number?" my friend asked. "I counted them." "Did you read the book?" "No."

How dreary to spend your time counting dirty words, but not reading the book. And how revealing of the person who is counting. We do find what we look for.

So let us look for beauty and grace, for love and friendship, for that which is creative and birth-giving and soul-stretching. Let us dare to laugh at ourselves, healthy, affirmative laughter. Only when we take ourselves lightly can we take ourselves really seriously, so that we are given the courage to say, "Yes! I dare disturb the universe."

MOLLY IVINS '66

*M*olly Ivins came to Smith from Texas and returned there after getting an MA from Columbia University and attending the Institute of Political Science in Paris. Going to Smith was a family tradition, for her mother was a member of the Class of '34. But writing trenchant political commentary set Molly Ivins apart from her family and many friends. Her sharp wit and irreverent style were cultivated at the Dallas Times Herald, but she gained a national following for her essays in The Progressive, Nation, Mother Jones, Ms., GQ, Harper's, Atlantic Monthly, and The New York Times Book Review. Her first book, Molly Ivins Can't Say That, Can She? (1991), is a title that the Times Herald put on billboards with emphasis on That when Molly quipped that if a Texas state of representative's "IQ slips any lower, we'll have to water him twice a day." To Molly Ivins, Texas politics is the "finest form of entertainment ever invented." Readers don't have to live in Texas to sympathize with her sentiment. Nothin' but Good Times Ahead (1993), following the campaign of Clinton and Gore, earned her frequent spots on National Public Radio and "The NewsHour with Jim Lehrer."

Ivins broadens her scope in You've Got to Dance with Them What Brung You: Politics in the Clinton Years (1998), a collection of essays first published in the Fort Worth Star-Telegram, which she joined in 1990. She sets her own agendas and follows them with informed, interesting, and markedly uninhibited perspectives on state and national politics. The Southern vernacular endears her to her region, but her trademark good humor, even her characteristic hyperbole, speaks to the nation. Her learning is everywhere present. Moliére has much to teach religious fundamentalists with their "perfervidness"; James Madison on the separation of church and state can resolve the crêche controversy; campaign financing could be resolved with basic economics; and Rush Limbaugh needs logic and lots of research like the kind Molly Ivins regularly does.

Besides writing of the faults and foibles of politicians at home, in Washington, and abroad, Molly Ivins reveals tears in the fabric of society that can, and do, touch our hearts. She is represented here by an essay on her mother, first published in the Fort Worth Star-Telegram, 9 January 1997. Molly Ivins regularly gives heroes and heroines their due.

The Good Mother
Who Put a Shoe in the Icebox

MY MOTHER DIED THE OTHER DAY. Margaret Milne Ivins was a gay and gracious lady, and also one of the kindest people I've ever known. In eighty-four years of living, she never mastered the more practical aspects of life—I believe the correct clinical term is "seriously ditzy"—but she was nobody's fool.

She was shrewd about people and fond of fun, and at her best she could charm the birds from the trees. She was also lazy, a horrible housekeeper, somewhat depressive, and addicted to soap operas, but hey, nobody's perfect.

She believed in Education, Good Manners, and Kindness to Everyone. Actually, I believe she thought Good Manners and Kindness to Everyone were the same thing; they probably are. Her Everyone included the most hilarious cast of characters; among my mother's dear friends were the people behind the counter at the dry cleaner's, bank tellers, grocery-store clerks, and the guys at the gas station. My father used to claim that the house would look better if she would stop treating the maid like a sorority sister, but she never did.

As you can gather, she led a somewhat privileged life. Her father was well-to-do; she attended private schools, and after her graduation from Smith College (Class of '34), she went on a yearlong tour of Europe with two chums. That was in the days when one traveled on ships with steamer trunks so one could dress for dinner.

But there are different kinds of deprivation. My mother's mother died in a flu epidemic in the days before penicillin, when Mom was sixteen. I don't think she ever recovered from that sense of abandonment. She tried to comfort her grieving father and to mother her two much younger siblings, but it was too much for her. She later recalled that "my life was saved" by a caring teacher at the Roycemore School for Girls in Evanston, Illinois, who noticed that Miss Milne kept falling asleep in class from exhaustion. The teacher confronted my grandfather about it, and Mom was sent to boarding school at Walnut Hill in Massachusetts.

She went on to Smith, where her mother had gone before her and I went in my turn. (I know—this is so WASP, I'm about to urp myself.) In the midst of the Depression my grandfather couldn't afford a third year at Smith, so she spent her junior year, she always said, as "a broad in Montana," where she lived with her cousins, pledged Kappa Kappa Gamma in Missoula—later my sister's sorority—and had far too much fun. She was one of the first women ever to graduate from Smith with a degree in psychology, then considered rather a suspect field.

The evidence of that degree in her later life came in the form of her shrewd and unsparing readings of character and human relationships, including her own. She also raised her children with an unusual degree of liberality for that era; she never spanked any of us and cared not a jot for the reservations of her Texas neighbors about this college-educated Yankee lady.

Perhaps this is egocentric of me, but I think that being a mother was the central role of my mom's life. She once told me—the only one of her children never to give her a grandchild—

that to the extent (in John Donne's phrase) that no man is an island, the closest relationship one can ever have with another human being on this earth is mother/child.

Not that she regarded us as an unmitigated blessing. Like all moms, she could be a royal pain in the rear. And although she was our greatest cheerleader, she certainly took seriously her motherly duty to keep any of us from getting a swelled head.

I once had a book on the bestseller list for six months and pointed this out to her, inviting maternal approval. She said, "Yes, but I see you've slipped to last on the list." Now, that's graduate-level mothering.

I once opened our family refrigerator to find a shoe and an alarm clock inside. No wonder she could never find anything. She, of course, always claimed that we made up these stories, but as my sibs will testify, she frequently mixed up our names and, when truly flustered, would address us by the dog's name.

My mother was one of those women who are just gooey about babies. She always insisted that they smell good. As any fool knows, they frequently don't, but in my mother's ideal world, no one would ever mention bodily functions. In her endless and futile effort to turn me into a lady, she once advised my ten-year-old self that the proper response to having a horse step on your foot is, "Oh, fudge!" My mother doted shamelessly on her grandchildren and lived just long enough to meet the first great-grand and pronounce him quite the most wonderful baby there ever was.

Mother was the most teasable person I ever knew, and my brother Andy could get her to laughing so hard at her own foibles that tears would run down her cheeks. When Sara and I joined in, she would denounce us as "dreadful children, perfectly dreadful children." As my cousin Johnny said, "How can you not love a woman who loves Goo-Goo Clusters?"

My mother not only read but also traveled a great deal in her later years, usually with Smith College or Smithsonian Institution groups, venturing to China, Japan, India, Mexico, Turkey. Her succinct analysis of the world's woes was: "Too many people—the trouble with the world is too many people." The most baby-loving woman I ever knew was a great supporter of birth control and abortion rights. She had a bumper sticker on her car that said, PRO-FAMILY, PRO-CHILD AND PRO-CHOICE.

Politically, she was a lifelong Republican. She used to specify "Taft Republican" until people forgot who Taft was; then she claimed "liberal Republican" and refused to admit that it was an oxymoron. She loathed Richard Nixon on the unimpeachable grounds that he was "not a nice man."

Just a few months ago her beloved Scots terrier died. She explained how much she missed him by saying: "He had such excellent political judgment. We would watch the news together, and I would say: 'Duffie, there's that horrid Mr. Gingrich again. Isn't he an awful person?' And Duffie would thump his tail on the floor in agreement. He was a terribly smart dog."

What, peculiar? My mom?

A friend of mine claims that my mother must have been the model for the Helen Hokinson cartoons in *The New Yorker*. O.K., that was her type, but she was as shrewd as she was ditzy. It was like living with a combination of Sigmund Freud and Gracie Allen. Looking on the bright side, at least we'll never have to eat turnip fluff again.

When it came to the "memorials preferred" on the obit form, we put in her favorite causes, but if you truly wanted to memorialize my mother, you would eat a piece of fudge today, hug someone you love, and be blindingly pleasant to a total stranger.

SUSAN ALLEN TOTH '61

*S*usan Allen Toth grew up in Ames, Iowa, richly celebrated in her first book of *essays*, Blooming: A Small-Town Girlhood (1981). Her second book, Ivy Days: Making My Way Out East (1984), *recalls with ironic nostalgia her years at Smith, ending with* magna cum laude, *and continuing on to her 1963 MA from the University of California at Berkeley. She went on to receive a PhD in English from the University of Minnesota in 1969, for her work on New England women writers, whose "luminous significance" of detail informs all Toth's own essays. Her third book,* How to Prepare for Your High School Reunion and Other Midlife Musings (1988), *reveals the texture of her own life as Professor of English at Macalester College, mother, writer, and wife. The crosssection of her memories richly expresses the rings of time as well as the growth of her determined independence and fertile intelligence. With essays frequently in* The New York Times (both Book Review *and* Travel section), Redbook, Ms., Harper's, Cosmopolitan, *she has acquired a significant reputation as a writer of nonfiction.*

She gradually resigned her position at Macalester to write full time, beginning with A House of One's Own: An Architect's Guide to Designing the House of Your Dreams (1991) *with architect husband James Stageberg, who designed Wind Whistle, their country home. With John Coughlan, lover of librar- ies, she collected writers' descriptions of reading in public libraries in* Reading Rooms (1991). *Always an Anglophile, she goes to England often enough to gen- erate a continuing series of travel essays:* My Love Affair With England: A Traveler's Memoir (1992), England As You Like It: An Independent Traveler's Companion (1995), *and* England For All Seasons (1997).

The memorable Class Day Speech here was given in 1994, the day before the Smith Commencement of her daughter Jennifer, whose work is represented in the art portfolio.

Smith Class Day Speech

IT IS A STRANGE FEELING—exhilarating and a little unnerving—to be standing here today on the stage of John M. Greene. As a student at Smith, I was usually facing the other direction, half-listening to what was happening on stage or wondering, as I slumped irritably in my seat, why I'd bothered to come, and occasionally straining to see or hear a compelling lecture or performance. I once sat here in the late 1950s trying very hard to understand a rambling lecture by the writer Aldous Huxley. (I think he was touting the wonders of hallucenogenic drugs, which most of us had never then heard of.) I whistled and clapped with a jammed auditorium when Ella Fitzgerald sang like an exotic warbling bird at President Thomas Mendenhall's inaugural celebration in 1959. I remember proudly adjusting my cap and gown at the Rally Day convocation in the spring of 1961 when we seniors appeared in our full glory for the first time.

I was here a lot, because all students were expected to attend weekly chapel in John M., unless excused in advance by the student body president. It was an honor system offense to skip chapel. In my senior year, when my suite-mate was president, her phone rang non-stop early every Friday morning with calls from students asking to be excused. John M. Greene meant serious business.

Standing here in John M. today, I am not only assailed by memories, but I am also caught in a time warp. That always happens to me on those rare occasions when I return to Smith. I forget how old I am. I half-expect to see my former professors—still in their vigorous thirties or forties or fifties—walking across campus. Passing the door of Lawrence house, I look curiously at the girls hurrying down the porch stairs as if I might somehow recognize their faces.

And I can almost too easily imagine myself here in John M. for opening convocation in the fall of 1957. Just off the train from Ames, Iowa, where I'd lived all my life, and which was an inconceivable distance from Northampton, Massachusetts, I was scared and lonely, but also very impressed as I looked around me. Each class sat together, everyone dressed in white, with a sash in the appropriate class color draped across one's chest (or, as I flinch to think, what we called one's "buz," short for "bosom"). So John M. was a sea of white shot through with bands of color, rather like an enormous garden, which was probably the effect intended. Young ladies were supposed to resemble graceful tulips then, though at Smith, I felt most of the time more like a stray dandelion.

As everyone stood up to the majestic but rollicking strains of "Gaudeamus Igitur," the faculty marched in, with an assortment of flashy hoods that were meant to advertise the glamorous universities where they'd gotten their PhD's. I sang as loud as I could, mangling the Latin, but believing as I sang that I had now been inestimably privileged to join an academic tradition stretching back to the Middle Ages. I remember feeling sure that after my four years at Smith, which, as I looked ahead, seemed as if they would last forever, I would become a completely educated woman, not to mention sophisticated and self-confident. That was certainly how all the seniors looked to me.

Then, suddenly, four fast years later, I was ready to graduate. To my intense disappointment, I had to admit that I was *not* completely educated, or anywhere near it. In my mind, I could run over the courses in which I'd coasted, or taken half-hearted notes, or crammed for tests at the last minute. Already I'd forgotten what little I'd once known on some subjects I'd studied for a whole semester or even a year. What could I really recall of economics? What had happened to all the dates I'd memorized for Modern European History? Why had the French subjunctive sunk into a deep black hole? As for "sophisticated" or "self-confident," although Smith had given me a pretty good act, I was depressingly aware that anyone with a little moxie would probably find me out in minutes.

All of my Commencement weekend was disorienting. My friends and I watched with barely disguised disdain as the alumnae trooped onto campus and took over our houses. Even though they looked unbelievably old and frumpy, they behaved like teen-agers. They shouted and laughed and hugged each other and sat, giggling and gossiping, for hours in *our* living rooms, ignoring those of us whose campus it really was. What a bunch of silly middle-aged women! We seniors tacitly agreed that we would *never* become alumnae.

At Commencement itself, our class listened respectfully to James Reston, a Washington columnist and commentator for the *New York Times*, who was then at the peak of his career. (Note that in 1961, we had not only a white male president but also a white male commencement speaker.) As we sat in the bright sunshine of the Quad, we waited for Mr. Reston to dispense wisdom. I was in a weird state that day—hot, tired, happy, unhappy, confused, excited but disconcertingly numb at the same time. Mostly what I remember is being hot, steaming away in my black gown on a humid Massachusetts afternoon. I couldn't quite believe this was happening to me. Me, graduating. Me, supposedly grown up. Me, leaving my few friends, perhaps forever. Me, with a future I found it impossible to envision. Although I suppose Mr. Reston spoke with force and earnestness about the many challenging opportunities open to all of us, he was talking, in my case, to someone who merely had very sweaty palms.

As I was thinking about coming to Smith this weekend, and about meeting with you today, I felt, rather dizzily, as if I were three women at once, who kept blurring back and forth into each other. I was that eager and hopeful freshman, looking in awe around John M. Greene at the full panoply of an assembled Smith College. I was also that uneasy graduating senior. And I was myself right now, a woman of fifty-three, who had somehow become, in what seemed like the time it takes to walk from the library to Lawrence House, both a middle-aged alumna and the enormously proud parent of a member of the Class of 1994, a daughter whom I love very much, and whom, in 1961, I couldn't have begun to conjure up.

So I decided to give up trying to prepare a single coherent message for you and instead to let these different women talk to each other a little. "Well," the entering first-year asked the middle-aged woman, "did you ever get completely educated?" Certainly not. I realize now that will never happen. Think for a moment of the course catalogue you all studied in the fall of your first year here. If you were like me, you found so many courses that sounded appealing, or even essential, that you wondered how you could possibly take everything in just four years. And of course you couldn't.

But what Smith should do is give you the assurance that you can go right on, browsing forever in a course catalogue of your own devising, compiling your own reading lists, and taking your own notes. At home I always have heaps of books, waiting to be read, stacked on shelves and tables. Some of them are already getting dusty, and others may eventually be transferred, unread, to a higher shelf, where I keep thinking I'll get back to them. Smith women never have enough time. But they always do have plans.

When I looked a few days ago at the current pile on the small bedroom table where I keep most of my recent acquisitions, I thought it said something about the intellectual freedom to explore that Smith encouraged and nurtured: Andrew Harvey's *Journey to Ladakh*, Peter Kramer's *Listening to Prozac*, Art Spiegelman's *Maus*, Mollie Hardwick's murder mystery, *Malice Domestic*; Thomas Moore's *The Care of the Soul*; Buchwald, Fletcher, and Roth's *Transforming a Rape Culture*; Isabel Huggan's collection of stories, *You Never Know*; Susan Powter's *Stop the Insanity* and *The Field of Greens Cookbook*, a contradictory pair; the Knopf guide to Istanbul; and Margery Fish's *We Made a Garden*. My revered history advisor at Smith, a remarkable and fine-spirited woman called Jean Wilson, once told me she feared I might become an intellectual butterfly. But she, and others like her, had shown me where the flowers were, and I've been off and flying ever since.

So I am not completely educated, I'd say to that inquiring first-year student, and I never will be, which is just fine. The graduating senior, who thought she was much more knowing than her first-year self, then brought up a question that lay not far below her uneasy thoughts on Commencement Day. "So now you're in your fifties. Tell me," she said wistfully to the middle-aged alumna, "when did you find yourself?" Well, I never did, exactly.

The question itself says something about the expectations I had at twenty-one. I suppose I thought I had an ideal self hiding somewhere. Perhaps she was studiously taking notes in the Berkeley library, where I began graduate school; or she might be preparing *coq au vin* for her first dinner party as a married woman; or she was teaching and living in London with her small daughter. Perhaps all I had to do was search enough likely places, and I'd eventually find her. When I did, I'd recognize her instantly, and there I'd be: found! I didn't realize that I'd be making new discovering, and changing my ideas of myself, all my life.

As a graduating senior, I also assumed that at some definable point, perhaps a few years away, but absolutely and certainly before I turned thirty, I would know with assurance what I ought to be doing with my life. Everything would have worked out. I would be settled and happy.

Let's take "settled" first. Five years ago, after twenty-odd years of college teaching, I voluntarily gave up my tenure, choosing instead a riskier temporary appointment, with an indefinitely long leave from teaching, so I could stay home and write. But I did not always think I'd be a writer. I didn't publish my first book until I was forty-one. Once, soon after I'd graduated from Smith, I decided I wanted to read my recommendations. A friend told me about a sneaky way to do this—which, of course, I can't officially encourage: Have them sent to a member of your family or to a trusted friend with a business-like title. So I did. One of my English professors had commented, "Miss Allen has the potential to be a fine scholar. I highly recommend her for postgraduate study. She has the makings of a critic; all she lacks is the creative gift herself." Only after my third book did I feel I could safely call myself a writer, and even now, I tend to say it with a certain self-deprecation, in case a *real* writer might overhear me.

Nor am I always sure, even now, writing is what I should be doing. Although I find it engrossing and addictive, writing can also be frustrating and exhausting. But, when I stop to consider alternatives, I actually don't want to be doing anything else. When too much time goes by without my being able to write, I feel uncomfortable. I always have more projects than I ever have time to start or complete. Writing seems to be what I do. Is this what it means to be "settled"?

As for the word "happy," it sounds to me like such a sweeping generalization, covering every aspect of life, that I am very suspicious of using it. Once, some years ago, after I'd written my first memoir, *Blooming*, I had a phone call from an old high-school friend I'd barely thought of in twenty years. After he had identified himself on the phone, and we'd exchanged greetings, he got right to the point: "Tell me, Sue," he said, "are you happy?" I didn't answer right away. Smith trained me to break down generalizations. Did he mean this very moment, I wondered? Or yesterday, or this year? Happy in my job? As a mother? As a single divorced woman? What *was* "happy," anyway?

"Ummm," I said to my caller, trying to achieve the same intonation—thoughtful, considering, and fully prepared—that I used to strive for when a Smith professor asked in class about a part of the chapter I hadn't finished. "Ummm," I said, "Well, that is a *very* interesting question. Let me see. I need to think about that a bit. There are many ways one could approach that problem. It all depends probably on one's point of view. It isn't necessarily a simple answer. Could you give me some more time to think about it?"

As I've grown older, life has not become any easier to summarize. A friend of mine recently told me, "When I graduated from college, I thought life would unroll before me like a seamless carpet. It's not that I knew precisely what the pattern would be, but I was sure it would unroll in a straight line. No bumps, no sudden breaks, no ditches. No detours. And I guess I also thought someone would always be moving ahead of me, picking off the lint." We both laughed.

In the many years we've known each other, my friend and I have both experienced marriage, divorce, re-marriage, job changes, the pleasures and perils of being parents, and many other ordinary cataclysms. We've finally learned, I think, that sometimes we must simply concentrate on putting one foot ahead of another, taking a breath and another step, then another breath, another step.

At least I know I'm not on a carpet, but a path, which is much more interesting, even if I can't always tell where I'm going, and at any moment, I may sink ankle-deep into the mud again. Mostly, I try not to worry too much about what's around the next turning, and I keep moving. The scenery is sometimes bleak and sometimes beautiful. It is always utterly absorbing.

What I didn't expect about life was that it would turn out to be so wildly unpredictable. I don't think my twenty-one-year-old self would have found that comforting, but now I do. Awful things happen, and wonderful things happen. No matter how well you plan and prepare, they happen when you are eighteen, and twenty-one, and thirty, and forty-four, and fifty, and, I presume, right on to the end.

That may sound as if I'm advising you to relax, sit back and wait for the next event. Not at all. Most of you couldn't do that, anyway, because after four years at Smith, you have undoubtedly lost the knack of relaxing, sitting back, and waiting. What I'm suggesting instead—what I wish I could have told myself at sixteen or twenty-one—is that, almost always, no matter what happens, you will survive. In my study I keep a framed quotation from Philip Roth, who is definitely not my favorite writer, but who knows about survival. Here it is: "We writers are lucky: nothing truly bad can happen to us. It's all material." I like that. You take what happens to you and do something with it. And even if you're not a writer, it's still all material, the stuff of which you use to go on creating your life, which turns out, in the end, to be your own complicated and unique story.

At this point I can tell that the first-year and the graduating senior who began talking to the middle-aged alumna have begun exchanging glances. "Let's get out of here," they say wordlessly. "She's starting to lecture. Who needs this?" The middle-aged alumna gets defensive. She doesn't want to seem like one of those hopelessly outdated and frumpy women who clogged up the campus on her own Commencement weekend. But of course, that's exactly who she is, in a way: one of the huggers, gossipers and gigglers, who like to sit around and share those complicated stories we've made of our lives.

But, she thinks to herself as her younger selves head out the door, they're right to go. I was getting to the point where I thought I ought to say something succinct and memorable about the meaning of it all, the kind of summing up an older woman is supposed to be able to do with the equanimity of age. But I can't. I'm still struggling to make sense of what has happened, and continues to happen, not only to me, but to the confusing, turbulent world around me, which presses more insistently on my consciousness all the time. I don't have easy answers. Fortunately, if I learned anything at all at Smith, I learned to distrust easy answers.

Once in a bookstore, I picked up a book by best-selling psychologist Sheldon Kopp called, *If You Meet the Buddha on the Road, Kill Him!* Then and now, I disliked the show-offiness and implicit violence of the title, but I browsed through the book to see what it was about. The title seemed to refer to Kopp's belief that everyone needs to find out the spiritual truths of life for him or herself. No one, he argued, should merely accept another's truth without taking the required journey to find it.

Another book I haven't read—I am hoping that my admission of all these books I *haven't* read will relieve some of you of guilt in years to come—is Leonard Woolf's memoir, *The Journey Not the Arrival Matters.* I love that title. It reminds me that, in fact, we are all on a journey. When I was a student at Smith, I never thought of myself as on a spiritual search, but it is here, beginning on that first day in John M. Greene, that I really began to learn to value the whole process of searching, inquiring, questioning, and wondering.

Journeys do have stages, and sometimes even brief pauses. Several weeks ago, on a Sunday morning in San Francisco, my husband James and I went for a long walk in Golden Gate Park. It was a glorious spring morning, fresh and damp, with the rare bright sunshine that always makes San Francisco, my favorite American city, shine as if it had just been washed clean. The Botanical Garden in the park was bursting with bloom, from azaleas to California poppies. As we walked along the paths, we brushed aside fallen magnolia petals. We were approaching a small dell in the park, a kind of sunken garden, when I first heard the music. At first it was a disembodied melody floating somewhere in the morning air. But as we drew close to the dell, I could see a young man standing near a pool. He had his back to us. He was not looking for an audience, but he was playing the flute with skill and ease. A clear bright line of Bach rose from the pool and flowers into the blue sky. He played for a long while, and indeed, he was playing when he left, playing, it seemed, for the sheer joy of it. That was the kind of magic that sometimes occurs in life, a pause that gives meaning to the journey.

Today is a kind of pause too. I want to thank the seniors of the Class of 1994 for letting me come here today for a moment and consider my own journey, as well as yours. As I have looked both backwards and forwards, I have realized once again how critically important, influential, and far-reaching my four years at Smith really were. Notice, please, I said they were important, *not* especially pleasant. Those of you who have read *Ivy Days* know all about my struggles here. I've always felt that anyone who refers to the college years as "happy and carefree" is either kidding, doesn't remember, or just plain doesn't notice much. As for anyone who calls them "the best years of my life," I figure those people must have had pretty lousy lives.

What I think I can assure you is that from now on, your experiences will become richer, fuller, more complex, and ever more interesting. Tomorrow, when you finish one chapter and begin another, you cannot possibly know everything that will happen in the next one. Enjoy what you can—have fun whenever possible, play the flute just for the joy of it—and remember, the rest is all material. In five years, ten, twenty—at each reunion you choose to attend—you will all have surprising stories to tell each other. As I writer, I only wish I could be here to listen to all of them.

BARBARA BUSH '47

*B*arbara Pierce came to Smith College's Tyler House from Rye, NY, in *1943. Though neither her classmates nor her family knew it, she was already engaged to George Bush, a Navy pilot and the future forty-first President of the United States. Barbara Bush left Smith after the war-time summer session in 1944, and she and George were married in January of 1945. For the next eight months she followed her husband as he traveled with the Navy, and after World War II they moved to New Haven, CT, where George attended Yale University. Their son George was born in 1946 in New Haven, and their daughter Pauline (Robin) in 1949 in California. After moving back to George Bush's hometown of Midland, Texas, they had four more children, John (Jeb), Neil, Marvin, and Dorothy.*

During her years as First Lady, Barbara Bush devoted considerable energy to promoting literacy in America. Her first large-scale contribution to literacy organizations in the United States was a book called C. Fred's Story (1984), about one of the Bush dogs, which raised money for the Literacy Volunteers of America and Laudbach Literacy Action. The Barbara Bush Foundation for Family Literacy was established in 1989, and supported in part by funds from sales of Millie's Book, As Dictated to Barbara Bush (1990). At the 1989 Opening Convocation, Smith College presented her with an honorary degree. Wellesley followed Smith's lead in 1990 when she spoke at its commencement with Raisa Gorbachev.

Barbara Bush currently supports the Ronald McDonald House and the Boys and Girls Clubs of America, among many other philanthropic organizations. She also maintains her positions as AmeriCares ambassador-at-large, a Mayo Clinic Foundation board member, and an honorary chairperson of the Leukemia Society of America. In this selection from her 1994 book Barbara Bush: A Memoir, she describes her daughter Robin's sudden illness from leukemia and her death in 1953 at Memorial Sloan-Kettering Hospital in New York. Barbara's first serious volunteer work began by forming support groups for the parents of leukemia victims, and in Robin's memory she and George Bush established the Bright Star Foundation for leukemia research.

Robin

FROM *Barbara Bush: A Memoir*

So I am glad not that my loved one has gone,
But that the earth she laughed and lived on was my earth, too.
That I had known and loved her,
And that my love I'd shown.
Tears over her departure?
Nay, a smile
That I had walked with her a little while.

JEB WAS JUST A FEW WEEKS OLD when Robin woke up one morning and said, "I don't know what to do this morning. I may go out and lie on the grass and watch the cars go by, or I might just stay in bed." I didn't think that sounded like a normal three-year-old and decided she must have what my mother called "spring fever." I took her to our excellent pediatrician, Dr. Dorothy Wyvell. She examined Robin, took some blood, and told me she would call me after the test results were in. She suggested I might want to come back without Robin, but with George. That sounded rather ominous to me, but I wasn't too worried. Certainly Robin had no energy, but nothing seemed seriously wrong.

Dr. Wyvell called, and George met me at her office in the late afternoon. Dorothy was not one to pull any punches. She told us Robin had leukemia. Neither of us had ever heard of it, and George asked what the next step was; how did we cure her? She talked to us a little about red and white blood cells and told us as gently as possible that there was no cure. Her advice was to tell no one, go home, forget that Robin was sick, make her as comfortable as we could, love her—and let her gently slip away. She said this would happen very quickly, in several weeks. We talked a little more, and George asked her if she would talk to his uncle, Dr. John Walker, at Memorial Sloan-Kettering Hospital in New York City. She readily agreed. Uncle John also thought Robin had little chance to live, but he thought we should by all means treat her and try to extend her life, just in case of a breakthrough.

I drove home, and George had to return to the office for just a minute. On the way, he stopped at Liz and Tom Fowler's house and asked Liz please to come over to be with me. By that evening our living room was filled with close friends, all offering to help. I remember being so surrounded by love that I did not really believe what the doctor had told us was true. She just had to be wrong. But either way, we knew we had to do everything we could to save our beautiful child.

It's funny how you remember such unimportant things at moments of stress. Our minister, Dr. Matthew Lynn, and his wife popped in. They were offered a drink, and I will always remember his answer. He said, "Not *now*, thank you, George." Tommy and Matthew Lynn would no more take a drink than fly, but by saying "now," he made everyone feel comfortable. Such a silly, small thing to remember.

The very next day George and I flew to New York City, leaving Georgie and Jebby with different friends, and checked Robin into Memorial Sloan-Kettering on Sixty-eighth Street. At first, no one there believed that our little hospital in Midland had done the testing correctly. Robin's white blood cell count was just too high—the highest they had ever heard. Unfortunately, it was correct, and they immediately put Robin on medication. We moved into Ganny and Gampy Walker's beautiful apartment on Sutton Place in New York and stayed there off and on until October 1953, when our little one passed away with both of us standing by her side.

It was an extraordinary experience, and in a strange kind of way, we learned how lucky we were. We met people there who had only one child. We had three. We met people who did not love each other. We loved each other very much. (I learned later that 70 percent of people who lose a child get divorced. I suspect this is because their love for each other was found wanting and they did not communicate.) We had the most supportive family, and we shared. We had friends who helped us. Financially, we were very lucky, as our insurance covered almost everything.

And last, but not least, we believed in God. That has made an enormous difference in our lives, then and now.

GEORGE WAS JUST GETTING STARTED in business, so he rushed back and forth between Midland and New York. He came east whenever he could, and we talked on the phone every evening. I missed my baby Jeb and Georgie at home, but George was with them as much as possible.

Friends and family made such a difference. There were so many who cared and helped. Lud Ashley, George's classmate and great friend from Yale days, was a bachelor then living in New York City. He quietly checked in all the time. I did not know just how much until very early one morning a night nurse said, "What does your husband do, Mrs. Bush? I meet him every morning around 2 a.m. when he comes in to check on Robin before going to bed." I said that it couldn't have been my husband because he was in Texas. It was Lud Ashley.

One day, when Robin was very ill, I remember going out onto the cold roof off the parents' room to be alone for a tear or two. I found Lud huddled outside, freezing. He hadn't wanted to intrude, but he wanted to be there if needed.

Back in Midland, George dropped by church every morning at 6:30 a.m. and prayed for Robin. He said at first only the custodian was there. Then one morning he felt a presence, and our minister, Matthew Lynn, had started joining him. They never talked, just prayed. That meant a lot to George.

Robin was wonderful. She never asked why this was happening to her. She lived each day as it came, sweet and loving, unquestioning and unselfish. How we hated bone marrow tests. They were so agonizing for all ages. She had many painful blood transfusions, and family and friends quietly slipped into the hospital and replaced the blood supply. Several times I was called to come pick up my sister or a friend who had passed out while giving blood. The hospital asked people to try to get replacements for the blood that was used, and thanks to many dear people, I honestly think we fulfilled our obligation.

Robin would go into remission, and once in a great while, we were able to take her as an outpatient to Ganny Walker's. Gampy Walker was a scary old man, but he was putty in Robin's hands. He taught her to play a simplified game of Gin Rummy, which she misunderstood to be Gin Mummy. She then changed it to Gin Poppy, after her beloved father.

Sometimes we went to the Bush house in Greenwich, and in the summer, we went to Maine for a brief period and Robin got to see her brothers. She had their pictures taped to her headboard at Sloan-Kettering and every single doctor and nurse heard about those "superman" brothers of hers.

We took her home to Midland for a short stay. That was the farthest the hospital had ever allowed a patient to go, but the doctors knew Dorothy Wyvell could take care of Robin. Still, it was scary to be so far from the hospital. Hugh Liedtke and George were building their new business, and George must have been exhausted with work, worry, and travel, but somehow he managed to do it all. Hugh's wife, Betty, who had children of her own, saved my life. She spent hours each day with us, thinking up ways to get Robin to eat and make her laugh. She was loving and funny and no matter how bad it got, she came. I don't know how she knew, but if I got frightened, she was there.

Leukemia was not a well-known disease. Many people thought it was catching and did not let their children get near Robin. In those days, cancer in general was only whispered about, and some people just couldn't cope with a dying child. It was not an easy time for our friends or us.

I made up my mind that there would be no tears around Robin, so I asked people who cried to step out of her room. I didn't want to scare our little girl. Poor George had the most dreadful time and could hardly stand to see her get a blood transfusion. He would say that he had to go to the men's room. We used to laugh and wonder if Robin thought he had the weakest bladder in the world. Not true. He just had the most tender heart.

Rightly or wrongly, we did not tell six-year-old Georgie that his sister was dying. We hated that, but we felt it would have been too big a burden for such a little fellow. On the other hand, there could be no more roughhousing since leukemia patients easily hemorrhage, so we had to keep a close watch on them when they were together.

One day, back in New York, George's father asked me to go with him to the graveyard in Greenwich. He wanted me to see where he would be buried. The lot he picked was lovely, on a nice hillside with trees. He was such a dear man, and he picked out a modest headstone that said BUSH—about three feet tall and four feet wide. On one side of the headstone was a freshly planted lilac bush; on the other side, a dogwood tree. It was a sunny, bright day, and Dad pointed out some enormous mausoleum-type buildings or large headstones. Then he said, "I knew old so-and-so. He certainly thought highly of himself, didn't he, Bar?" That darling man bought that lot so Robin would have a place to rest.

Eventually the medicine that was controlling the leukemia caused other terrible problems. We called George, and by the time he got there after flying all night, our baby was in a coma. Her death was very peaceful. One minute she was there, and the next she was gone. I truly felt her soul go out of that beautiful little body. For one last time I combed her hair, and we held our precious little girl. I never felt the presence of God more strongly than at that moment.

WE CALLED OUR FAMILIES and told them the news and went to Greenwich for a memorial service. (There would be no funeral; we had signed papers giving Robin's body to research.) Those few days are a little vague, but several things come to mind.

The day after Robin died, George and I went to Rye to play golf with Daddy, at his suggestion. As we drove out on the parkway, I was shocked that the leaves were at the peak of their fall beauty. I remember realizing life went on, whether we were looking or not. I also remember changing my shoes in the ladies' locker room and seeing a childhood friend, Marilyn Peterson.

We talked briefly, and I did not mention Robin. I wondered later if she thought it was strange that we were playing golf the day after our baby died. I, for one, was numb.

The next day there was a memorial service for Robin with family and only a few dear friends. Upstairs in our bedroom, I could hear the family gathering below and told George I did not think I could face all that. He was so dear and special and became the rock of our family. For one who allowed no tears before her death, I fell apart, and time after time during the next six months, George would put me together again. He looked out the window, and seeing my sister, Martha, and her husband, Walt, walking up the driveway, said, "Sure, and with the O'Raffertys, it is going to be a grand wake." Sounds dumb now, but believe me, it did the trick. I giggled through my tears and went down.

The minute the service was over, George and I raced home to Midland. (George's mother and Lud Ashley laid our little Robin to rest several days later when the hospital released her body.) We wanted to be the ones to break the news to Georgie. As we drove up to his school, Georgie was walking down the covered walk carrying something into his classroom. He ran and asked his teacher, "My mom, dad, and sister are home. Can I go see them?" We felt devastated by what we had to tell him. As I recall, he asked a lot of questions and couldn't understand why we hadn't told him when we had known for such a long time.

We picked up Jebby at Betty and Hugh's, and George made us all go by several friends' houses just to say hello and get over that first awful moment of seeing each other after a death. That started the most painful period of adjusting to life after Robin.

We awakened night after night in great physical pain—it hurt that much. I hated that nobody mentioned her; it was as if she had never been. I know now that it was because our friends did not want to hurt us, but you don't think too clearly after a death. Several times Georgie helped break the ice. At a football game George had taken him to, Georgie suddenly said he wished he were Robin. George told me all his friends stiffened with uncomfortable embarrassment. When he asked Georgie just why he wished he were Robin, he said, "I bet she can see the game better from up there than we can here." Another time, he asked his dad if we had buried Robin lying down or standing up. Again, shocked silence. George said that he wasn't sure, but why did Georgie want to know. He said he had just learned that the earth rotated, and he wanted to know if she spent part of her time standing on her head, and wouldn't that be neat? He made it okay for our friends to mention her, and that helped us a great deal.

Midland was a small town, and many, many people called on us. It was exhausting, and once I complained to George about it. People I hardly knew came by. I caught one friend practicing in front of a mirror her sad facial expressions and what she was going to say to me. I backed out of the living room and came in again. She struggled through something that came out like this: "At least it wasn't your firstborn and a boy at that." I was speechless. George pointed out that it wasn't easy for them and that I should be patient. He was right. I just needed somebody to blame.

I wanted to get back to real life, but there is a dance that you have to go through to get there. When I wanted to cut out, George made me talk to him, and he shared with me. What a difference that makes. He made me remember that the loss was not just mine. It was his, Georgie's, and Jeb's, our friends' who loved her, and all our family's so far away. He did it subtly, but with love. Many times he held me in his arms and let me weep myself to sleep. In those days there was no Hospice program, which I certainly needed. Thank heavens George was always there for me.

Hugh Liedtke came up with the brilliant idea of setting up a foundation for leukemia research in Robin's name, which helped me enormously. We called it the Bright Star Foundation.

I devoted my time to our children, spending every single moment with Jebby, and then with Georgie when he came home from school. One lovely, breezy day I was in our bedroom when I heard Georgie talking to a neighbor child who wanted him to come over and play. Georgie said he wanted to, but he couldn't leave his mother. She needed him. That started my cure. I realized I was too much of a burden for a little seven-year-old boy to carry.

For a year I devoted my time to starting a little women's exchange shop for the Junior Service League. I worked at that project night and day, and everyone helped me. We made very little money for the league, and when I retired in 1955 to have yet again another baby, the store closed. I think the shop was just another way that our supportive hometown helped me cope with death.

We named our beautiful, smiling little boy after Neil Mallon. Less than two years later, in 1956, Neil was followed by Marvin, named after my dad. Just as an observation—men are funny. We wanted to name the other boys after Daddy, but he always said that we should not because Marvin was a dreadful name. Well, when George and I called and told him that in spite of him, we were going to name the baby Marvin Pierce Bush, he cried. He really had not meant it when he said no.

GEORGE AND I LOVE AND VALUE every person more because of Robin. She lives on in our hearts, memories, actions, and through the Bright Star Foundation. I don't cry over her anymore. She is a happy, bright part of our lives.

After George's mother died in 1992, I was given an envelope with George's name on it. It contained the following letter, which George had written his mother several years after Robin died and which she had saved all these years:

Dear Mum,

I have jotted down some words about a subject dear to your heart and mine. It is fun to fool around and try in one form or another to express thoughts that suddenly come up from way down deep in one's heart. Last night I went out on the town and on my way home—late—I said to myself, "You could well have gone to Greenwich tonight" . . . this thought struck me out of the blue, but I felt no real sense of negligence. The part I like is to think of Robin as though she were a part, a living part, of our vital and energetic and wonderful family of men and Bar.

Bar and I wonder how long this will go on. We hope we will feel this genuine closeness when we are 83 and 82. Wouldn't it be exciting at that age to have a beautiful 3 1/2-year-old daughter . . . she doesn't grow up. Now she's Neil's age. Soon she'll be Marvin's—and beyond that she'll be all alone, but with us, a vital living pleasurable part of our day-to-day life. I sometimes wonder whether it is fair to our boys and to our friends to "fly-high" that portrait of Robin which I love so much; but here selfishness takes over because every time I sit at our table with just our candlelight, I somehow can't help but glance at this picture you gave us and enjoy a renewed physical sensation of closeness to a loved one.

This letter . . . is kind of like a confessional . . . between you and me, a mother and her little boy—now not so little, but still just as close, only when we are older, we hesitate to talk from our hearts quite as much.

There is about our house a need. The running, pulsating restlessness of the four boys as they struggle to learn and grow; their athletic chests and arms and legs; their happy noises as the world embraces them . . . all this wonder needs a counterpart. We need some starched crisp frocks to go with all our torn-kneed blue jeans and helmets. We need some soft blond hair to offset those crew cuts. We need a doll house to stand firm against our forts and rackets and thousand baseball cards. We need a cut-out star to play alone while the others battle to see who's "family champ." We even need someone . . . who could sing the descant to "Alouette," while outside they scramble to catch the elusive ball aimed ever roofward, but usually thudding against the screen.

We need a legitimate Christmas angel—one who doesn't have cuffs beneath the dress.

We need someone who's afraid of frogs.

We need someone to cry when I get mad—not argue.

We need a little one who can kiss without leaving egg or jam or gum.

We need a girl.

We had one once—she'd fight and cry and play and make her way just like the rest. But there was about her a certain softness.

She was patient—her hugs were just a little less wiggly.

Like them, she'd climb in to sleep with me, but somehow she'd fit.

She didn't boot and flip and wake me up with pug nose and mischievous eyes a challenging quarter-inch from my sleeping face.

No—she'd stand beside our bed till I felt her there. Silently and comfortably, she'd put those precious, fragrant locks against my chest and fall asleep.

Her peace made me feel strong, and so very important.

"My Daddy" had a caress, a certain ownership which touched a slightly different spot than the "Hi Dad" I love so much.

But she is still with us. We need her and yet we have her. We can't touch her, and yet we can feel her.

We hope she'll stay in our house for a long, long time.

Love, Pop

ANNE MORROW
LINDBERGH '28

Going to Smith was a Morrow family tradition. Anne Morrow's mother, Elizabeth Cutter Morrow, Class of 1896, was a trustee for thirty-five years and Acting President for one; her sister Constance Morrow Morgan, Class of 1935, was a trustee for fifteen years; and her sister Elisabeth Reeve Morrow Morgan graduated in 1925. Yet when time came for Anne Morrow to decide where she would go to college, she decided on Vassar, exercising her independence at a young age. She came to Smith, however, earning prizes for her literary work and, after meeting Charles A. Lindbergh in Mexico where her father was ambassador, flying occasionally from Mt. Tom Airport near Northampton. Anne Morrow Lindbergh married "the Colonel" in 1929, just two years after his solo flight from New York to Paris, and became an aviation pioneer in her own right, joining her husband on many of his survey flights and recording their adventures in her extraordinary diaries and letters and in books like North to the Orient (1935).

Private pain at the kidnapping and death of their first child Charles in 1932 was made painfully public, so public, in fact, that the Lindberghs raised their other five children—Jon, Land, Anne, Scott, and Reeve—in protective privacy, first in England, then on an island off the northern coast of Brittany, later in Connecticut, and from time to time on the island of Maui, Hawaii, where Colonel Lindbergh died of lymphatic cancer in 1974. Colonel Lindbergh's stand on isolationism before World War II wrongly branded him as anti-Semitic, as new books by his daughter Reeve Lindbergh and A. Scott Berg make clear.

Regardless of politics and distorting publicity, Anne Morrow Lindbergh convincingly articulates a woman's need for privacy, self-sufficiency, and personal peace in Gift From the Sea (1955), still in print and still serving its readers. In an interview with Julie Nixon Eisenhower '73, recorded in Special People (1977), Anne Morrow Lindbergh says, "Fame separates you from life," but being alone restores it. In "Moon Shell," the second of five essays from Gift From the Sea, Anne Morrow Lindbergh writes of a woman's need for inner serenity in the midst of the distractions of life. Here a sensitive and original mind authenticates in careful cadences the still point of strong self in a turning universe.

Moon Shell

FROM *Gift from the Sea*

THIS IS A SNAIL SHELL, round, full and glossy as a horse chestnut. Comfortable and compact, it sits curled up like a cat in the hollow of my hand. Milky and opaque, it has the pinkish bloom of the sky on a summer evening, ripening to rain. On its smooth symmetrical face is pencilled with precision a perfect spiral, winding inward to the pinpoint center of the shell, the tiny dark core of the apex, the pupil of the eye. It stares at me, the mysterious single eye—and I stare back.

Now it is the moon, solitary in the sky, full and round, replete with power. Now it is the eye of a cat that brushes noiselessly through long grass at night. Now it is an island, set in ever-widening circles of waves, alone, self-contained, serene.

How wonderful are islands! Islands in space, like this one I have come to, ringed about by miles of water, linked by no bridges, no cables, no telephones. An island from the world and the world's life. Islands in time, like this short vacation of mine. The past and the future are cut off; only the present remains. Existence in the present gives island living an extreme vividness and purity. One lives like a child or a saint in the immediacy of here and now. Every day, every act, is an island, washed by time and space, and has an island's completion. People, too, become like islands in such an atmosphere, self-contained, whole and serene; respecting other people's solitude, not intruding on their shores, standing back in reverence before the miracle of another individual. "No man is an island," said John Donne. I feel we are all islands—in a common sea.

We are all, in the last analysis, alone. And this basic state of solitude is not something we have any choice about. It is, as the poet Rilke says, "not something that one can take or leave. We *are* solitary. We may delude ourselves and act as though this were not so. That is all. But how much better it is to realize that we are so, yes, even to begin by assuming it. Naturally," he goes on to say, "we will turn giddy."

Naturally. How one hates to think of oneself as alone. How one avoids it. It seems to imply rejection or unpopularity. An early wallflower panic still clings to the word. One will be left, one fears, sitting in a straight-backed chair *alone*, while the popular girls are already chosen and spinning around the dance floor with their hot-palmed partners. We seem so frightened today of being alone that we never let it happen. Even if family, friends, and movies should fail, there is still the radio or television to fill up the void. Women, who used to complain of loneliness, need never be alone any more. We can do our housework with soap-opera heroes at our side. Even day-dreaming was more creative than this; it demanded something of oneself and it fed the inner life. Now, instead of planting our solitude with our own dream blossoms, we choke the space with continuous music, chatter, and companionship to which we do not even listen. It is simply there to fill the vacuum. When the noise stops there is no inner music to take its place. We must re-learn to be alone.

It is a difficult lesson to learn today—to leave one's friends and family and deliberately practice the art of solitude for an hour or a day or a week. For me, the break is the most difficult.

Parting is inevitably painful, even for a short time. It is like an amputation, I feel. A limb is being torn off, without which I shall be unable to function. And yet, once it is done, I find there is a quality to being alone that is incredibly precious. Life rushes back into the void, richer, more vivid, fuller than before. It is as if in parting one did actually lose an arm. And then, like the star-fish, one grows it anew; one is whole again, complete and round—more whole, even, than before, when the other people had pieces of one.

For a full day and two nights I have been alone. I lay on the beach under the stars at night alone. I made my breakfast alone. Alone I watched the gulls at the end of the pier, dip and wheel and dive for the scraps I threw them. A morning's work at my desk, and then, a late picnic lunch alone on the beach. And it seemed to me, separated from my own species, that I was nearer to others: the shy willet, nesting in the ragged tide-wash behind me; the sandpiper, running in little unfrightened steps down the shining beach rim ahead of me; the slowly flapping pelicans over my head, coasting down wind; the old gull, hunched up, grouchy, surveying the horizon. I felt a kind of impersonal kinship with them and a joy in that kinship. Beauty of earth and sea and air meant more to me. I was in harmony with it, melted into the universe, lost in it, as one is lost in a canticle of praise, swelling from an unknown crowd in a cathedral. "Praise ye the Lord, all ye fishes of the sea—all ye birds of the air—all ye children of men—Praise ye the Lord!"

Yes, I felt closer to my fellow men too, even in my solitude. For it is not physical solitude that actually separates one from other men, not physical isolation, but spiritual isolation. It is not the desert island nor the stony wilderness that cuts you from the people you love. It is the wilderness in the mind, the desert wastes in the heart through which one wanders lost and a stranger. When one is a stranger to oneself then one is estranged from others too. If one is out of touch with oneself, then one cannot touch others. How often in a large city, shaking hands with my friends, I have felt the wilderness stretching between us. Both of us were wandering in arid wastes, having lost the springs that nourished us—or having found them dry. Only when one is connected to one's own core is one connected to others, I am beginning to discover. And, for me, the core, the inner spring, can best be refound through solitude.

I walked far down the beach, soothed by the rhythm of the waves, the sun on my bare back and legs, the wind and mist from the spray on my hair. Into the waves and out like a sandpiper. And then home, drenched, drugged, reeling, full to the brim with my day alone; full like the moon before the night has taken a single nibble of it; full as a cup poured up to the lip. There is a quality to fullness that the Psalmist expressed: "My cup runneth over." Let no one come—I pray in sudden panic—I might spill myself away!

Is this then what happens to woman? She wants perpetually to spill herself away. All her instinct as a woman—the eternal nourisher of children, of men, of society—demands that she give. Her time, her energy, her creativeness drain out into these channels if there is any chance, any leak. Traditionally we are taught, and instinctively we long, to give where it is needed—and immediately. Eternally, woman spills herself away in driblets to the thirsty, seldom being allowed the time, the quiet, the peace, to let the pitcher fill up to the brim.

But why not, one may ask? What is wrong with woman's spilling herself away, since it is her function to give? Why am I, coming back from my perfect day at the beach, so afraid of losing my treasure? It is not just the artist in me. The artist, naturally, always resents giving himself in small drops. He must save up for the pitcher-full. No, it is also the woman in me who is so unexpectedly miserly.

HERE IS A STRANGE PARADOX. Woman instinctively wants to give, yet resents giving herself in small pieces. Basically is this a conflict? Or is it an over-simplification of a many-stranded problem? I believe that what woman resents is not so much giving herself in pieces as giving herself purposelessly. What we fear is not so much that our energy may be leaking away through small outlets as that it may be going "down the drain." We do not see the results of our giving as concretely as man does in his work. In the job of home-keeping there is no raise from the boss, and seldom praise from others to show us we have hit the mark. Except for the child, woman's creation is so often invisible, especially today. We are working at an arrangement in form, of the myriad disparate details of housework, family routine, and social life. It is a kind of intricate game of cat's-cradle we manipulate on our fingers, with invisible threads. How can one point to this constant tangle of household chores, errands, and fragments of human relationships, as a creation? It is hard even to think of it as purposeful activity, so much of it is automatic. Woman herself begins to feel like a telephone exchange or a laundromat.

Purposeful giving is not as apt to deplete one's resources; it belongs to that natural order of giving that seems to renew itself even in the act of depletion. The more one gives, the more one has to give—like milk in the breast. In our early pioneer days and recently in war-time Europe, difficult as it was, woman's giving was purposeful, indispensable. Today, in our comparative comfort, many women hardly feel indispensable any more, either in the primitive struggle to survive or as the cultural font of the home. No longer fed by a feeling of indispensability or purposefulness, we are hungry, and not knowing what we are hungry for, we fill up the void with endless distractions, always at hand—unnecessary errands, compulsive duties, social niceties. And for the most part, to little purpose. Suddenly the spring is dry; the well is empty.

Hunger cannot, of course, be fed merely by a feeling of indispensability. Even purposeful giving must have some source that refills it. The milk in the breast must be replenished by food taken into the body. If it is woman's function to give, she must be replenished too. But how?

Solitude, says the moon shell. Every person, especially every woman, should be alone sometime during the year, some part of each week, and each day. How revolutionary that sounds and how impossible of attainment. To many women such a program seems quite out of reach. They have no extra income to spend on a vacation for themselves; no time left over from the weekly drudgery of housework for a day off; no energy after the daily cooking, cleaning and washing for even an hour of creative solitude.

Is this then only an economic problem? I do not think so. Every paid worker, no matter where in the economic scale, expects a day off a week and a vacation a year. By and large, mothers and housewives are the only workers who do not have regular time off. They are the great vacationless class. They rarely even complain of their lack, apparently not considering occasional time to themselves as a justifiable need.

HEREIN LIES ONE KEY TO THE PROBLEM. If women were convinced that a day off or an hour of solitude was a reasonable ambition, they would find a way of attaining it. As it is, they feel so unjustified in their demand that they rarely make the attempt. One has only to look at those women who actually have the economic means or the time and energy for solitude yet do not use it, to realize that the problem is not solely economic. It is more a question of inner convictions than of outer pressures, though, of course, the outer pressures are there and make it more difficult. As far as the search for solitude is concerned, we live in a negative atmosphere as invisible, as all-pervasive, and as enervating as high humidity on an August afternoon. The world today does not understand, in either man or woman, the need to be alone.

How inexplicable it seems. Anything else will be accepted as a better excuse. If one sets aside time for a business appointment, a trip to the hairdresser, a social engagement, or a shopping expedition, that time is accepted as inviolable. But if one says: I cannot come because that is my hour to be alone, one is considered rude, egotistical or strange. What a commentary on our civilization, when being alone is considered suspect; when one has to apologize for it, make excuses, hide the fact that one practices it—like a secret vice!

Actually these are among the most important times in one's life—when one is alone. Certain springs are tapped only when we are alone. The artist knows he must be alone to create; the writer, to work out his thoughts; the musician, to compose; the saint, to pray. But women need solitude in order to find again the true essence of themselves: that firm strand which will be the indispensable center of a whole web of human relationships. She must find that inner stillness which Charles Morgan describes as "the stilling of the soul within the activities of the mind and body so that it might be still as the axis of a revolving wheel is still."

This beautiful image is to my mind the one that women could hold before their eyes. This is an end toward which we could strive—to be the still axis within the revolving wheel of relationships, obligations, and activities. Solitude alone is not the answer to this; it is only a step toward it, a mechanical aid, like the "room of one's own" demanded for women, before they could make their place in the world. The problem is not entirely in finding the room of one's own, the time alone, difficult and necessary as this is. The problem is more how to still the soul in the midst of its activities. In fact, the problem is how to feed the soul.

For it is the spirit of woman that is going dry, not the mechanics that are wanting. Mechanically, woman has gained in the past generation. Certainly in America, our lives are easier, freer, more open to opportunities, thanks—among other things—to the Feminist battles. The room of one's own, the hour alone are now more possible in a wider economic class than ever before. But these hard-won prizes are insufficient because we have not yet learned how to use them. The Feminists did not look that far ahead; they laid down no rules of conduct. For them it was enough to demand the privileges. The exploration of their use, as in all pioneer movements, was left open to the women who would follow. And woman today is still searching. We are aware of our hunger and needs, but still ignorant of what will satisfy them. With our garnered free time, we are more apt to drain our creative springs than to refill them. With our pitchers, we attempt sometimes to water a field, not a garden. We throw ourselves indiscriminately into committees and causes. Not knowing how to feed the spirit, we try to muffle its demands in distractions. Instead of stilling the center, the axis of the wheel, we add more centrifugal activities to our lives—which tend to throw us off balance.

Mechanically we have gained, in the last generation, but spiritually we have, I think, unwittingly lost. In other times, women had in their lives more forces which centered them whether or not they realized it; sources which nourished them whether or not they consciously went to those springs. Their very seclusion in the home gave them time alone. Many of their duties were conducive to a quiet contemplative drawing together of the self. They had more creative tasks to perform. Nothing feeds the center so much as creative work, even humble kinds like cooking and sewing. Baking bread, weaving cloth, putting up preserves, teaching and singing to children, must have been far more nourishing than being the family chauffeur or shopping at super-markets, or doing housework with mechanical aids. The art and craft of housework has diminished; much of the time-consuming drudgery—despite modern advertising to the contrary—remains. In housework, as in the rest of life, the curtain of mechanization has come down between the mind and the hand.

The church, too, has always been a great centering force for women. Through what ages women have had that quiet hour, free of interruption, to draw themselves together. No wonder woman has been the mainstay of the church. Here were the advantages of the room of her own, the time alone, the quiet, the peace, all rolled into one and sanctioned by the approval of both family and community. Here no one could intrude with a careless call, "Mother," "Wife," "Mistress." Here, finally and more deeply, woman was whole, not split into a thousand functions. She was able to give herself completely in that hour in worship, in prayer, in communion, and be completely accepted. And in that giving and acceptance she was renewed; the springs were refilled.

The church is still a great centering force for men and women, more needed than ever before—as its increasing membership shows. But are those who attend as ready to give themselves or to receive its message as they used to be? Our daily life does not prepare us for contemplation. How can a single weekly hour of church, helpful as it may be, counteract the many daily hours of distraction that surround it? If we had our contemplative hour at home we might be readier to give ourselves at church and find ourselves more completely renewed. For the need for renewal is still there. The desire to be accepted whole, the desire to be seen as an individual, not as a collection of functions, the desire to give oneself completely and purposefully pursues us always, and has its part in pushing us into more and more distractions, illusory love affairs, or the haven of hospitals and doctors' offices.

The answer is not in going back, in putting woman in the home and giving her the broom and the needle again. A number of mechanical aids save us time and energy. But neither is the answer in dissipating our time and energy in more purposeless occupations, more accumulations which supposedly simplify life but actually burden it, more possessions which we have not time to use or appreciate, more diversions to fill up the void.

In other words, the answer is not in the feverish pursuit of centrifugal activities which only lead in the end to fragmentation. Woman's life today is tending more and more toward the state William James describes so well in the German word, "Zerrissenheit—torn-to-pieces-hood." She cannot live perpetually in "Zerrissenheit." She will be shattered into a thousand pieces. On the contrary, she must consciously encourage those pursuits which oppose the centrifugal forces of today. Quiet time alone, contemplation, prayer, music, a centering line of thought or reading, of study or work. It can be physical or intellectual or artistic, any creative life proceeding from oneself. It need not be an enormous project or a great work. But it should be something of one's own. Arranging a bowl of flowers in the morning can give a sense of quiet in a crowded day—like writing a poem, or saying a prayer. What matters is that one be for a time inwardly attentive.

Solitude, says the moon shell. Center-down, say the Quaker saints. To the possession of the self the way is inward, says Plotinus. The cell of self-knowledge is the stall in which the pilgrim must be reborn, says St. Catherine of Siena. Voices from the past. In fact, these are pursuits and virtues of the past. But done in another way today because done consciously, aware, with eyes open. Not done as before, as part of the pattern of the time. Not done because everyone else is doing them; almost no one is doing them. Revolutionary, in fact, because almost every trend and pressure, every voice from the outside is against this new way of inward living.

Woman must be the pioneer in this turning inward for strength. In a sense she has always been the pioneer. Less able, until the last generation, to escape into outward activities, the very limitations of her life forced her to look inward. And from looking inward she gained an inner strength which man in his outward active life did not as often find. But in our recent efforts to emancipate ourselves, to prove ourselves the equal of man, we have, naturally enough perhaps, been drawn into competing with him in his outward activities, to the neglect of our own inner springs. Why have we been seduced into abandoning this timeless inner strength of woman for the temporal outer strength of man? This outer strength of man is essential to the pattern, but even here the reign of purely outer strength and purely outward solutions seems to be waning today. Men, too, are being forced to look inward—to find inner solutions as well as outer ones. Perhaps this change marks a new stage of maturity for modern extrovert, activist, materialistic Western man. Can it be that he is beginning to realize that the kingdom of heaven is within?

MOON SHELL, WHO NAMED YOU? Some intuitive woman I like to think. I shall give you another name—Island shell. I cannot live forever on my island. But I can take you back to my desk in Connecticut. You will sit there and fasten your single eye upon me. You will make me think, with your smooth circles winding inward to the tiny core, of the island I lived on for a few weeks. You will say to me "solitude." You will remind me that I must try to be alone for part of each year, even a week or a few days; and for part of each day, even for an hour or a few minutes in order to keep my core, my center, my island-quality. You will remind me that unless I keep the island-quality intact somewhere within me, I will have little to give my husband, my children, my friends or the world at large. You will remind me that woman must be still as the axis of a wheel in the midst of her activities; that she must be the pioneer in achieving this stillness, not only for her own salvation, but for the salvation of family life, of society, perhaps even of our civilization.

ERNESTINE
GILBRETH CAREY '29

*E*rnestine Gilbreth Carey grew up in Montclair, NJ, with six brothers and five sisters, the dozen children of parents who became the century's foremost efficiency experts. Her mother, Lillian Moller Gilbreth, who provided for her children after her husband's early death, was the first woman elected to the National Academy of Engineering. She wrote her own autobiography, As I Remember (1998), and is now the subject of a biography, Managing On Her Own (1998). Frank Bunker Gilbreth, a motion study expert, used his children as laboratory guinea pigs to test his time-saving devices for everything from bathing, to typing, to tonsillectomies. In Cheaper by the Dozen (1949), written with her brother, Frank B. Gilbreth, Jr., Ernestine Gilbreth Carey describes the "Gilbreth System," a concept of time and motion study that controlled the dozen children in the Gilbreth family and revolutionized theories of work management and productivity.

After graduating from Smith College in 1929, Ernestine Gilbreth married Charles Everett Carey, and together they raised a daughter and son, while pursuing their own careers. After working as a buyer for Macy's and other stores, Ernestine Gilbreth Carey began her distinguished writing career with Cheaper by the Dozen, the first and the most popular of her six books, recipient of the French International Humor Award. The sequel, Belles on Their Toes (1950), also written in collaboration with her brother Frank, continues the adventures of the remarkable Gilbreth family into young adulthood. Both books were made into successful movies by Twentieth-Century Fox in 1950 and 1952, respectively, and a contemporary remake of Cheaper by the Dozen is in process. Her experiences in retailing and of marrying and raising a family resulted in Jumping Jupiter (1952), Rings Around Us (1956), and Giddy Moment (1958). Cheaper by the Dozen, from which "Nantucket" has been drawn, has been translated into over fifty languages, and has sold more than three million copies.

Nantucket

FROM *Cheaper by the Dozen*

W E SPENT OUR SUMMERS AT NANTUCKET, Massachusetts, where Dad bought two lighthouses, which had been abandoned by the government, and a ramshackle cottage, which looked as if it had been abandoned by Coxey's army. Dad had the lighthouses moved so that they flanked the cottage. He and Mother used one of them as an office and den. The other served as a bedroom for three of the children.

He named the cottage *The Shoe*, in honor of Mother, who, he said, reminded him of the old woman who lived in one.

The cottage and lighthouses were situated on a flat stretch of land between the fashionable Cliff and the Bathing Beach. Besides our place, there was only one other house in the vicinity. This belonged to an artist couple named Whitney. But after our first summer at Nantucket, the Whitneys had their house jacked up, placed on rollers, and moved a mile away to a vacant lot near the tip of Brant Point. After that, we had the strip of land all to ourselves.

Customarily, en route from Montclair to Nantucket, we spent the night in a hotel in New London, Connecticut. Dad knew the hotel manager and all of the men at the desk, and they used to exchange loud and good-natured insults for the benefit of the crowds that followed us in from the street.

"Oh, Lord, look what's coming," the manager called when we entered the door. And then to an assistant. "Alert the fire department and the house detective. It's the Gilbreths. And take that cigar cutter off the counter and lock it in the safe."

"Do you still have that dangerous guillotine?" Dad grinned. "I know you'll be disappointed to hear that the finger grew in just as good as new. Show the man your finger, Ernestine."

Ernestine held up the little finger of her right hand. On a previous visit, she had pushed it inquisitively into the cigar cutter, and had lost about an eighth of an inch of it. She had bled considerably on a rug, while Dad tried to fashion a tourniquet and roared inquiries about whether there was a doctor in the house.

"Tell me," Dad remarked as he picked up a pen to register in the big book, "do my Irishmen come cheaper by the dozen?"

"Irishmen! If I were wearing a sheet, you'd call them Arabs. How many of them are there, anyway? Last year, when I went to make out your bill, you claimed there were only seven. I can count at least a dozen of them now."

"It's quite possible there may have been some additions since then," Dad conceded.

"Front, boy. Front, boy. Front, boy. Front, boy. You four boys show Mr. and Mrs. Gilbreth and their seven—or so—Irishmen to 503, 504, 505, 506, and 507. And mind you take good care of them, too."

W HEN WE FIRST STARTED GOING TO NANTUCKET, which is off the tip of Cape Cod, automobiles weren't allowed on the island, and we'd leave the Pierce Arrow in a garage at

New Bedford, Massachusetts. Later, when the automobile ban was lifted, we'd take the car with us on the *Gay Head* or the *Sankaty*, the steamers which plied between the mainland and the island. Dad had a frightening time backing the automobile up the gangplank. Mother insisted that we get out of the car and stand clear. Then she'd beg Dad to put on a life preserver.

"I know you and it are going into the water one of these days," she warned.

"Doesn't anybody, even my wife, have confidence in my driving?" he would moan. Then on a more practical note. "Besides, I can swim."

The biggest problem, on the boat and in the car, was Martha's two canaries, which she had won for making the best recitation in Sunday school. All of us, except Dad, were fond of them. Dad called one of them Shut Up and the other You Heard Me. He said they smelled so much that they ruined his whole trip, and were the only creatures on earth with voices louder than his children. Tom Grieves, the handyman, who had to clean up the cage, named the birds Peter Soil and Maggie Mess. Mother wouldn't let us use those full names, she said they were "Eskimo." (Eskimo was Mother's description of anything that was off-color, revolting, or evil-minded.) We called the birds simply Peter and Maggie.

On one trip, Fred was holding the cage on the stern of the ship, while Dad backed the car aboard. Somehow, the wire door popped open and the birds escaped. They flew to a piling on the dock, and then to a roof of a warehouse. When Dad, with the car finally stowed away, appeared on deck, three of the younger children were sobbing. They made so much noise that the captain heard them and came off the bridge.

"What's the trouble now, Mr. Gilbreth?" he asked.

"Nothing," said Dad, who saw a chance to put thirty miles between himself and the canaries. "You can shove off at any time, captain."

"No one tells me when to shove off until I'm ready to shove off," the captain announced stubbornly. He leaned over Fred. "What's the matter, son?"

"Peter and Maggie," bawled Fred. "They've gone over the rail."

"My God," the captain blanched. "I've been afraid this would happen ever since you Gilbreths started coming to Nantucket."

"Peter and Maggie aren't Gilbreths," Dad said irritatedly. "Why don't you just forget about the whole thing and shove off?"

The captain leaned over Fred again. "Peter and Maggie who? Speak up, boy!"

Fred stopped crying. "I'm not allowed to tell you their last names," he said. "Mother says they're Eskimo."

The captain was bewildered. "I wish someone would make sense," he complained. "You say Peter and Maggie, the Eskimos, have disappeared over the rail?"

Fred nodded. Dad pointed to the empty cage. "Two canaries," Dad shouted, "known as Peter and Maggie and by other aliases, have flown the coop. No matter. We wouldn't think of delaying you further."

"Where did they fly to, sonny?"

Fred pointed to the roof of the warehouse. The captain sighed.

"I can't stand to see children cry," he said. He walked back to the bridge and started giving orders.

Four crew members, armed with crab nets, climbed to the roof of the warehouse. While passengers shouted encouragement from the rail, the men chased the birds across the roof, back to the dock, onto the rigging of the ship, and back to the warehouse again. Finally Peter and Maggie disappeared altogether, and the captain had to give up.

"I'm sorry, Mr. Gilbreth," he said. "I guess we'll have to shove off without your canaries."

"You've been too kind already," Dad beamed.

Dad felt good for the rest of the trip, and even managed to convince Martha of the wisdom of throwing the empty, but still smelly, bird cage over the side of the ship.

The next day, after we settled in our cottage, a cardboard box arrived from the captain. It was addressed to Fred, and it had holes punched in the top.

"You don't have to tell *me* what's in it," Dad said glumly. "I've got a nose." He reached in his wallet and handed Martha a bill. "Take this and go down to the village and buy another cage. And after this, I hope you'll be more careful of your belongings."

OUR COTTAGE HAD ONE SMALL LAVATORY, but no hot water, shower, or bathtub. Dad thought that living a primitive life in the summer was healthful. He also believed that cleanliness was next to godliness, and as a result all of us had to go swimming at least once a day. The rule was never waived, even when the temperature dropped to the fifties, and a cold, gray rain was falling. Dad would lead the way from the house to the beach, dog-trotting, holding a bar of soap in one hand, and beating his chest with the other.

"Look out, ocean, here comes a tidal wave. Brrr. Last one in is Kaiser Bill."

Then he'd take a running dive and disappear in a geyser of spray. He'd swim under water a ways, allow his feet to emerge, wiggle his toes, swim under water some more, and then come up head first, grinning and spitting a thin stream of water through his teeth.

"Come on," he'd call. "It's wonderful once you get in." And he'd start lathering himself with soap.

Mother was the only non-swimmer, except the babies. She hated cold water, she hated salt water, and she hated bathing suits. Bathing suits itched her, and although she wore the most conservative models, with long sleeves and black stockings, she never felt modest in them. Dad used to say Mother put on more clothes than she took off when she went swimming.

Mother's swims consisted of testing the water with the tip of a black bathing shoe, wading cautiously out to her knees, making some tentative dabs in the water with her hands, splashing a few drops on her shoulders, and, finally, in a moment of supreme courage, pinching her nose and squatting down until the water reached her chest. The nose-pinch was an unnecessary precaution, because her nose never came within a foot of the water.

Then, with teeth chattering, she'd hurry back to the house, where she'd take a cold water sponge bath, to get rid of the salt.

"My, the water was delightful this morning, wasn't it?" she'd say brightly at the lunch table.

"I've seen fish who found the air more delightful than you do the water," Dad would remark.

As in every other phase of teaching, Dad knew his business as a swimming instructor. Some of us learned to swim when we were as young as three years old, and all of us had learned by the time we were five. It was a sore point with Dad that Mother was the only pupil he ever had encountered with whom he had no success.

"This summer," he'd tell Mother at the start of every vacation, "I'm really going to teach you, if it's the last thing I do. It's dangerous not to know how to swim. What would you do if you were on a boat that sank? Leave me with a dozen children on my hands, I suppose! After all, you should have some consideration for me."

"I'll try again," Mother said patiently. But you could tell she knew it was hopeless.

Once they had gone down to the beach, Dad would take her hand and lead her. Mother would start out bravely enough, but would begin holding back about the time the water got to her knees. We'd form a ring around her and offer her what encouragement we could.

"That's the girl, Mother," we'd say. "It's not going to hurt you. Look at me. Look at me."

"Please don't splash," Mother would say. "You know how I hate to be splashed."

"For Lord's sakes, Lillie," said Dad. "Come out deeper."

"Isn't this deep enough?"

"You can't learn to swim if you're hard aground."

"No matter how deep we go, I always end up aground anyway."

"Don't be scared, now. Come on. This time it will be different. You'll see."

Dad towed her out until the water was just above her waist. "Now the first thing you have to do," he said, "is to learn the dead man's float. If a dead man can do it, so can you."

"I don't even like its name. It sounds ominous."

"Like this, Mother. Look at me."

"You kids clear out," said Dad. "But, Lillie, if the children can do it, you, a grown woman, should be able to. Come on now. You can't help but float, because the human body, when inflated with air, is lighter than water."

"You know I always sink."

"That was last year. Try it now. Be a sport. I won't let anything happen to you."

"I don't want to."

"You don't want to show the white feather in front of all the kids."

"I don't care if I show the whole albatross," Mother said. "But I don't suppose I'll have another minute's peace until I try it. So here goes. And remember, I'm counting on you not to let anything happen to me."

"You'll float. Don't worry."

Mother took a deep breath, stretched herself out on the surface, and sank like a stone. Dad waited a while, still convinced that under the laws of physics she must ultimately rise. When she didn't, he finally reached down in disgust and fished her up. Mother was gagging, choking up water, and furious.

"See what I mean?" she finally managed.

Dad was furious, too. "Are you sure you didn't do that on purpose?" he asked her.

"Mercy, Maud," Mother sputtered. "Mercy, mercy, Maud. Do you think I like it down there in Davey Jones' locker?"

"Davey Jones' locker," scoffed Dad. "Why you weren't even four feet under water. You weren't even in his attic."

"Well, it seemed like his locker to me. And I'm never going down there again. You ought to be convinced by now that Archimedes' principle simply doesn't apply, so far as I am concerned."

Coughing and blowing her nose, Mother started for the beach.

"I still don't understand it," Dad muttered. "She's right. It completely refutes Archimedes."

DAD HAD PROMISED BEFORE WE CAME TO NANTUCKET that there would be no formal studying—no language records and no school books. He kept his promise, although we found he was always teaching us things informally, when our backs were turned.

For instance, there was the matter of the Morse code.

"I have a way to teach you the code without any studying," he announced one day at lunch.

We said we didn't want to learn the code, that we didn't want to learn anything until school started in the fall.

"There's no studying," said Dad, "and the ones who learn it first will get rewards. The ones who don't learn it are going to wish they had."

After lunch, he got a small paint brush and a can of black enamel, and locked himself in the lavatory, where he painted the alphabet in code on the wall.

For the next three days Dad was busy with his paint brush, writing code over the whitewash in every room in *The Shoe*. On the ceiling in the dormitory bedrooms, he wrote the alphabet together with key words, whose accents were a reminder of the code for the various letters. It went like this: A, dot-dash, a-BOUT; B, dash-dot-dot-dot, BOIS-ter-ous-ly; C, dash-dot-dash-dot, CARE-less CHILD-ren; D, dash-dot-dot, DAN-ger-ous, etc.

When you lay on your back, dozing, the words kept going through your head, and you'd find yourself saying, "DAN-ger-ous, dash-dot-dot, DAN-ger-ous."

He painted secret messages in code on the walls of the front porch and dining room.

"What do they say, Daddy?" we asked him.

"Many things," he replied mysteriously. "Many secret things and many things of great humor."

We went into the bedrooms and copied the code alphabet on pieces of paper. Then, referring to the paper, we started translating Dad's messages. He went right on painting, as if he were paying no attention to us, but he didn't miss a word.

"Lord, what awful puns," said Anne. "And this, I presume, is meant to fit into the category of 'things of great humor.' Listen to this one: 'Bee it ever so bumble there's no place like comb.'"

"And we're stung," Ern moaned. "We're not going to be satisfied until we translate them all. I see dash-dot-dash-dot, and I hear myself repeating CARE-less CHILD-ren. What's this one say?"

We figured it out: "When igorots is bliss, 'tis folly to be white." And another, by courtesy of Mr. Irvin S. Cobb, "Eat, drink and be merry for tomorrow you may diet." And still another, which Mother made Dad paint out, "Two maggots were fighting in dead Ernest."

"That one is Eskimo," said Mother. "I won't have it in my dining room, even in Morse code."

"All right, boss," Dad grinned sheepishly. "I'll paint over it. It's already served its purpose, anyway."

Every day or so after that, Dad would leave a piece of paper, containing a Morse code message, on the dining room table. Translated, it might read something like this: "The first one who figures out this secret message should look in the right hand pocket of my linen knickers, hanging on a hook in my room. Daddy." Or: "Hurry up before someone beats you to it, and look in the bottom, left drawer of the sewing machine."

In the knickers' pocket and in the drawer would be some sort of reward—a Hershey bar, a quarter, a receipt entitling the bearer to one chocolate ice cream soda at Coffin's Drug Store, payable by Dad on demand.

Some of the Morse code notes were false alarms. "Hello, Live Bait. This one is on the house. No reward. But there may be a reward next time. When you finish reading this, dash off like mad so the next fellow will think you are on some hot clue. Then he'll read it, too, and you won't be the only one who gets fooled. Daddy."

As Dad had planned, we all knew the Morse code fairly well within a few weeks. Well enough, in fact, so that we could tap out messages to each other by bouncing the tip of a fork on a butter plate. When a dozen or so persons all attempt to broadcast in this manner, and all of us preferred sending to receiving, the accumulation is loud and nerve-shattering. A present-day equivalent might be reproduced if the sound-effects man on *Gangbusters* and Walter Winchell should go on the air simultaneously, before a battery of powerful amplifiers.

The wall-writing worked so well in teaching us the code that Dad decided to use the same system to teach us astronomy. His first step was to capture our interest, and he did this by fashioning a telescope from a camera tripod and a pair of binoculars. He'd tote the contraption out into the yard on clear nights, and look at the stars, while apparently ignoring us.

We'd gather around and nudge him, and pull at his clothes, demanding that he let us look through the telescope.

"Don't bother me," he'd say, with his nose stuck into the glasses. "Oh, my golly, I believe those two stars are going to collide! No. Awfully close, though. Now I've got to see what the Old Beetle's up to. What a star, what a star!"

"Daddy, give us a turn," we'd insist. "Don't be a pig."

Finally, with assumed reluctance, he agreed to let us look through the glasses. We could see the ring on Saturn, three moons on Jupiter, and the craters on our own moon. Dad's favorite star was Betelgeuse, the yellowish red "Old Beetle" in the Orion constellation. He took a personal interest in her, because some of his friends were collaborating in experiments to measure her diameter by Michelson's interferometer.

When he finally was convinced he had interested us in astronomy, Dad started a new series of wall paintings dealing with stars. On one wall he made a scale drawing of the major planets, ranging from little Mercury, represented by a circle about as big as a marble, to Jupiter, as big as a basketball. On another, he showed the planets in relation to their distances from the sun, with Mercury the closest and Neptune the farthest away—almost in the kitchen. Pluto still hadn't been discovered, which was just as well, because there really wasn't room for it.

Dr. Harlow Shapley of Harvard gave Dad a hundred or more photographs of stars, nebulae and solar eclipses. Dad hung these on the wall, near the floor. He explained that if they were up any higher, at the conventional level for pictures, the smaller children wouldn't be able to see them.

There was still some wall space left, and Dad had more than enough ideas to fill it. He tacked up a piece of cross-section graph paper, which was a thousand lines long and a thousand lines wide, and thus contained exactly a million little squares.

"You hear people talk a lot about a million," he said, "but not many people have ever seen exactly a million things at the same time. If a man has a million dollars, he has exactly as many dollars as there are little squares on that chart."

"Do you have a million dollars, Daddy?" Bill asked.

"No," said Dad a little ruefully. "I have a million children, instead. Somewhere along the line, a man has to choose between the two."

He painted diagrams in the dining room showing the difference between meters and feet, kilograms and pounds, liters and quarts. And he painted seventeen mysterious-looking symbols, representing each of the Therbligs, on a wall near the front door.

The Therbligs were discovered, or maybe a better word would be diagnosed, by Dad and Mother. Everybody has seventeen of them, they said, and the Therbligs can be used in such a way as to make life difficult or easy for their possessor.

A lazy man, Dad believed, always makes the best use of his Therbligs because he is too indolent to waste motions. Whenever Dad started to do a new motion study project at a factory, he'd always begin by announcing he wanted to photograph the motions of the laziest man on the job.

"The kind of fellow I want," he'd say, "is the fellow who is so lazy he won't even scratch himself. You must have one of those around some place. Every factory has them."

Dad named the Therbligs for himself—Gilbreth spelled backwards, with a slight variation. They were the basic theorems of his business and resulted indirectly in such things as foot levers to open garbage cans, special chairs for factory workers, redesign of typewriters, and some aspects of the assembly line technique.

Using Therbligs, Dad had shown Regal Shoe Company clerks how they could take a customer's shoe off in seven seconds and put it back on again and lace it up in twenty-two seconds.

Actually, a Therblig is a unit of motion or thought. Suppose a man goes into the bathroom to shave. We'll assume that his face is all lathered and he is ready to pick up his razor. He knows where the razor is, but first he must locate it with his eye. That is "search," the first Therblig. His eye finds it and comes to rest—that's "find," the second Therblig. Third comes "select," the process of sliding the razor prior to the fourth Therblig, "grasp." Fifth is "transport loaded," bringing the razor up to the face, and sixth is "position," getting the razor set on the face. There are eleven other Therbligs—the last one is "think!"

When Dad made a motion study, he broke down each operation into a Therblig, and then tried to reduce the time taken to perform each Therblig. Perhaps certain parts to be assembled could be painted red and others green, so as to reduce the time required for "search" and "find." Perhaps the parts could be moved closer to the object being assembled, so as to reduce the time required for "transport loaded."

Every Therblig had its own symbol, and once they were painted on the wall Dad had us apply them to our household chores—bedmaking, dishwashing, sweeping, and dusting.

Meanwhile, *The Shoe* and the lighthouses had become a stop on some of the Nantucket sightseeing tours. The stop didn't entail getting out of the carriages or, later, the buses. But we'd hear the drivers giving lurid and inaccurate accounts of the history of the place and the family which inhabited it. Some individuals occasionally would come up to the door and ask if they could peek in, and if the house was presentable we'd usually show them around.

Then, unexpectedly, the names of strangers started appearing in a guest book which we kept in the front room.

"Are these friends of yours?" Dad asked Mother.

"I never heard of them before. Maybe they're friends of the children."

When we said we didn't know them, Dad questioned Tom Grieves, who admitted readily enough that he had been showing tourists through the house and lighthouses, while we were at the beach. Tom's tour included the dormitories; Mother's and Dad's room, where the baby stayed; and even the lavatory, where he pointed out the code alphabet. Some of the visitors, seeing the guest book on the table, thought they were supposed to sign. Tom stood at the front door as the tourists filed out, and frequently collected tips.

Mother was irked. "I never heard of such a thing in all my born days. Imagine taking perfect strangers through our bedrooms, and the house a wreck, most likely."

"Well," said Dad, who was convinced the tourists had come to see his visual education methods, "there's no need for us to be selfish about the ideas we've developed. Maybe it's not a bad plan to let the public see what we're doing."

He leaned back reflectively in his chair, an old mahogany pew from some church. Dad had found the pew, disassembled, in the basement of our cottage. He had resurrected it reverently, rubbed it down, put it together, and varnished it. The pew was his seat of authority in *The Shoe*, and the only chair which fitted him comfortably and in which he could place complete confidence.

"I wonder how much money Tom took in," he said to Mother. "Maybe we could work out some sort of an arrangement so that Tom could split tips from future admissions . . ."

"The idea!" said Mother. "There'll be no future admissions. The very idea."

"Can't you take a joke? I was only joking. Where's your sense of humor?"

"I know." Mother nodded her head. "I'm not supposed to have any. But did you ever stop to think that there might be some women, somewhere, who might think their husbands were joking if they said they had bought two lighthouses and . . ."

Dad started to laugh, and as he rocked back and forth he shook the house so that loose whitewash flaked off the ceiling and landed on the top of his head. When Dad laughed, everybody laughed—you couldn't help it. And Mother, after a losing battle to remain severe, joined in.

"By jingo," he wheezed. "And I guess there are some women, somewhere who wouldn't want the Morse code, and planets, and even Therbligs, painted all over the walls of their house, either. Come over here, boss, and let me take back everything I ever said about your sense of humor."

Mother walked over and brushed the whitewash out of what was left of his hair.

JULIA CHILD '34

*J*ulia McWilliams Child was born and raised in Pasadena, CA. She followed
her mother, Class of '00, to Smith, majoring in history. She lived in Hubbard
House, returning to celebrate its centennial in 1975. She also designed and super-
vised the inaugural feast for President Mary Maples Dunn in 1985. But loyalty
to the College is not what endears this self-effacing chef to cooks around the world.
On the cover of U.S. News & World Report *in September* 1997, Julia Child
laughs over lettuce, while the headline promises to tell "How Julia Child Invented
Modern Life." And so she did, as Karen Lehrman's essay and Noël Riley Finch's
biography, Appetite for Life, *attest.*

*After she graduated, she began a career in public relations, but, with the out-
break of World War II, volunteered for the Office of Strategic Services, and was
sent to Ceylon, where she met her future husband, Paul Child. After the war, her
husband joined the State Department and was posted to Paris. There Julia Child
studied at the Cordon Bleu and with private chefs to learn the art of French cuisine.
She was the only woman among the aspiring chefs. Later she met Simone Beck and
Louisette Bartholle, with whom she opened her own cooking school, L'École des
Trois Gourmandes, and wrote the first of eight cookbooks,* Mastering the Art of
French Cooking (1961). *Upon her husband's retirement, she settled in Cambridge, MA, and there, in 1962, WGBH, the public television station in Boston,
proposed a television cooking series to her. In only a few years, her show, "The
French Chef," won both the George Foster Peabody Award (1965) and an Emmy
(1996), as well as a wide audience. After the successful 39-part series "Baking
with Julia," her newest television venture is a 22-part series with Jacques Pepin. It
will air in the fall of 1999, and is a technique-based program aimed at both the
serious home cook and aspiring chef.*

The following selection, from The French Chef Cookbook (1968),
describes the earliest days of her first famous television program.

About the Television Series

FROM *The French Chef Cookbook*

"H OW IN THE WORLD did you ever manage to get on television?" is a question frequently asked me. It was purely by accident. My husband, Paul, had resigned from the diplomatic service in 1961, after almost twenty years. We had settled in our great gray pre-Victorian house in Cambridge with its comfortable kitchen, and *Mastering the Art of French Cooking* had just been published. He was planning to write, paint, and photograph; I was to cook, write, and teach. We had even bought ourselves a budget television set, which was so ugly we hid it in an unused fireplace.

One evening a friend we had known in Paris, Beatrice Braude, who was then working at Boston's educational television station, WGBH-TV, suggested it would be a useful push for *Mastering* if I could appear on one of the station's book-review programs. Always happy to do anything for the book, I agreed that it might well be worth thinking about. She persuaded the station and the interview took place with a bit of conversation about food and France, and at one point I beat some egg whites in a large French copper bowl to enliven the talk. The program brought numerous requests for some kind of a cooking program, and WGBH-TV asked me if I would be willing to try three pilots, or experimental half-hour shows, to see whether there might be a real cooking audience out there over the air waves. Paul and I accepted the challenge, although we knew nothing at all about television and had hardly watched a program.

The studio assigned Russell Morash, producer of "Science Reporter," as Producer-Director. Assistant Producer was Ruth Lockwood, who had been working on the Eleanor Roosevelt shows. Because Channel 2's studio had burned almost to the ground a few months before, The Boston Gas Company loaned us its display kitchen. The budget was minute.

Ruth, Paul, and I blocked out a rough sequence of events for three programs: French omelettes, *coq au vin*, and a noncollapsible soufflé, which provided a varied and not-too-complicated sampling of French cooking. After thinking up dozens of titles for the show, we could find nothing better than "The French Chef"; it was short and told a story. Ruth dug around somewhere and came up with the anonymous but spritely musical theme song we are still using. As our own kitchen had enough equipment to furnish a small restaurant, there were no problems in that quarter.

It was out of the question for us to film a live show since we had only two cameras attached by long cables to a mobile bus. Besides, with an absolutely amateur performer, it would have been far too risky. We decided, however, that it would be taped as though it were live. Unless the sky fell in, the cameras failed, or the lights went off, there would be no stops, and no corrections—just a straight thirty minutes from start to finish. This was a good fundamental decision, I think. I hate to stop. I lose that sense of drama and excitement which the uninterrupted thirty-minute limitation imposes. Besides, I would far prefer to have things happen as they naturally do, such as the mousse refusing to leave the mold, the potatoes sticking to the skillet, the apple charlotte slowly collapsing. One of the secrets of cooking is to learn to correct something if you can, and bear with it if you cannot.

The day in June for our first taping, "The French Omelette," Paul and I packed our station wagon with pots, pans, eggs, and trimmings and were off to the Gas Company. Parking was difficult in downtown Boston, so he off-loaded inside the main entrance, and I stood over our mound until he returned. How were the two of us to get everything down to the basement of that imposing office building? There was nobody to help, as we were hours ahead of our WGBH camera crew. Office girls and business-suited executives looked disapprovingly at our household pile as they rushed in and out. A uniformed elevator operator said, "Hey, get that stuff out of this lobby!" Eventually Paul located a janitor with a rolling cart and we clanked down to the basement where we unpacked, setting up our wares according to the master plan we had worked out.

Ruth arrived shortly to arrange a dining room setup for the final scene, and to go over our sequence of events. Then came Russ and our camera crew. After a short rehearsal to check lighting and camera angles, Russ said, "Let's shoot it!" And we did. Within the next week, following the same informal system, we taped the other two shows. I still have my notes. There is the map of the free-standing stove and work counter: "Simmering water in large alum. pan, upper R. burner." "Wet sponge left top drawer." "6 eggs in nest of 3 alum. plates w. ramekin." Paul, who was acting as invisible helper, had made himself a sheet of instructions: "When J. starts buttering, remove stack molds." "When soufflé is cheesed, take black saucepan."

On July 26, 1962, after we all had eaten a big steak dinner at our house, we pulled the television set out of hiding and turned it on at 8:30. There was this woman tossing French omelettes, splashing eggs about the place, brandishing big knives, panting heavily as she careened around the stove, and WGBH-TV lurched into educational television's first cooking program. Response to the three shows indicated that there was indeed an audience in New England, Channel 2 suggested we try a series of twenty-six programs, and "The French Chef" was underway. We were to start taping in January, and the first show would be on the air February 11, 1963.

What to pack into each of those thirty minutes? If we showed dishes that were too complicated, we would scare off all but a handful of people. Yet if we remained in the kindergarten, we would soon be a bore. Ruth, Paul, and I decided to start out with a few audience catchers, dishes that were famous, like *boeuf bourguignon*, but easy to make, and then gradually work into the subject. We also wanted to vary the weekly menu and take time to show French techniques, such as how to wield the knife, bone the lamb, clean the leek, whip and fold the egg whites. The idea was to take the bugaboo out of French cooking, to demonstrate that it is not merely good cooking but that it follows definite rules. The simplicity of a *velouté* sauce, for instance, is butter, flour, and seasoned liquid, but the rule is that the flour is cooked in the butter before the liquid is added. Why? (I, myself, will not do anything unless I know why.) "If you don't cook the flour in the butter, your sauce will have the horrid pasty taste of uncooked flour"—I have certainly given tongue to that one a hundred times. Finally we agreed on our program of twenty-six shows, starting with *"Boeuf Bourguignon"* and "French Onion Soup," ending with "Lobster *à l'Américaine*" and *"Crêpes Suzette."*

In January when we started taping four shows a week, WGBH-TV still had no studio. The shows, like the three pilots, would have to be done where the mobile bus could park and string out cables to its two cameras. Fortunately for us, the Cambridge Electric Company offered their display kitchen located in a large loft room, with ample parking space nearby. We could reach it by a front stairway, by a freight elevator from two floors below, or by an outside iron fire escape that descended into the parking lot. Though our lighting arrangements were make-shift and the sound track was likely to mingle with the roar of the freight elevator, the cooking facilities were fine. The ceiling was high enough for us to hang a mirror over the stove that the camera could peer into when it needed the inside view of a pot. Best of all, we had the whole place to ourselves.

Although we were now an actual and official enterprise, our budget remained small. Paul and I did all the shopping and precooking, and he continued to act as porter and unpacker, as well as chief dishwasher, until we got some volunteer cleaner-uppers for the taping days. Tues-days and Thursdays were the long cooking rehearsals for the two shows scheduled the follow-ing days. Nobody at WGBH had the slightest idea what we were cooking in our loft until the cameras were lugged up the outside fire escape at 10 o'clock on Wednesdays and Fridays, to begin the tapings. We depended on Paul for advice when we were doubtful, and Russ for great openings and closings as well as all the techniques of camera and direction. Otherwise, Ruth Lockwood and I had complete freedom to work up anything we wished and to present it in any manner we chose.

The general pattern of the first three pilot shows seemed to fit my style, so we continued it, perfecting details as we went along. I found I had no sense of timing whatsoever, 1 minute or 5 minutes meant nothing to me as sadly illustrated by our second show and first try at "Onion Soup." I had to show the proper professional way to slice onions fast, the first cooking to soften them, the second cooking to brown them, the several ways to serve the soup; then there was *croûton*-making and gratinéing. I rushed through that program like a madwoman but I got every-thing in, only to find that when I carried the onion soup to the dining room I had gone so fast we still had 8 minutes left. Agony. I had to sit there and talk for all that time. Russ erased the tape back to about the 15-minute point, but after it happened again, Ruth devised the plan of breaking up the recipe into blocks of time. I could go as fast or slow as I wanted in the allotted time block, but I could not go into the next step until I got the signal.

Signals to the performer are written on placards known as "idiot cards." They are handed to the floor manager, who, by earphones, is plugged into one of the television cameras so he can hear and talk to the director who is shut away in the control room. The floor manager holds the idiot card just under the camera lens, and the performer appears to be gazing right into your eyes but is really reading that message: "Turn on burner number three!" In our case, the floor manager has a big looseleaf book, and flips the pages according to a time schedule carefully worked out on a stop watch by Ruth. For the onion soup we were very simple: "The Knife & 1st Cook 5 min," "Browning and Simmering 4 min," "Soup in Bowls 2 min," and so forth. Later we became more elaborate, and put key words onto the idiot cards so I would not forget important points. I remember when we did *brioches*, we opened with a shot of three of them: the great big grandfather *brioche*, the middle-sized mother *brioche*, and the little baby *brioche*; we had obviously fallen into the story of Goldilocks and the Three Brioches. The idiot cards read like an Indian massacre—"This Baby; Remove head," "Punch Grandpa," "Slash Mother," "30 sec. Before Wash Hands." Often I am faced with Ruth's helpful reminders: "Stop gasping," "Wipe face," "Don't gallop."

The nonstop taping we have always continued, and in only a few instances, after the disaster of the first onion soup show, have we had to break off, erase, and pick up again. I can remember only half a dozen occasions, some of which were due to electrical failures, others due to me. Once, doing the "Lobster *à la Américaine*," every time I touched the cooktop I got a short-circuit in the microphone against my chest, and kept clutching my breast in a very odd fashion. It felt like a bee sting. We wiped out back to the worst clutch, and were able to continue in mid-stream. Another time, "The Flaming Soufflé" collapsed in its dish on the way to the dining room; I had forgotten to put in the cornstarch. We merely waited for the standby soufflé to come out of the oven and used that. Otherwise we let the gaffes lie where they fell, and on the whole it is just as well.

About halfway through, at the "Beef Gets Stewed Two Ways" show, WGBH-TV moved into its fine new building and we had a beautiful set with the most modern lighting, sound, and equipment. Wonderful as it is, we miss our old loft. It had an intimate atmosphere. We were a happy and independent family of twenty-four, we could eat up all the food ourselves, and even throw a party on occasion. But we could never have done color television there. In the new series, there are no more gray strawberries, pale and sickly veal, livid lettuce or pallid pickles. Even the tongue is utterly lifelike as it licks the *mousse au chocolat* off the spoon, and "The French Chef" has a new dimension.

MOIRA CRONE '74

Moira Crone came to Smith College from the tobacco country of North Carolina, a setting she frequently employs in her short stories. As an undergraduate she won a number of prizes for her short fiction, and following graduation, she attended the Writing Seminars at Johns Hopkins University, where she won the Coleman Award and earned her MA (1977). In 1982, she published her first collection, The Winnebago Mysteries and Other Stories.

Since 1981, Moira Crone has been teaching English and creative writing in the graduate program at Louisiana State University in Baton Rouge, where her husband, Rodger Kamenetz, a poet and essayist, also teaches. She has enjoyed extended stays out of the country—in France in 1983 and Jerusalem in 1986. Shortly after the publication of her first novel, A Period of Confinement (1986), the story of a young woman artist, she received a fellowship from the Mary Ingraham Bunting Institute of Radcliffe College to work on her fiction. Her stories have appeared in the New Yorker, Mademoiselle, The Ohio Review, The Boston Globe, The North American Review, and The Southern Review, among other periodicals, and has been represented in several anthologies, including American Made (1986), New Stories by Southern Women (1991), and New Stories from the South: The Year's Best (1995). The title story from her most recent collection, Dream State (1995), won the Collin C. Diboll short story prize from the Pirate's Alley Faulkner Society, and in 1995 she was awarded a fellowship from the Ragdale Foundation. She is working on a collection of stories set in North Carolina in the fifties and sixties, called Where What Gets Into People Comes From, and she has also been publishing parts of a dystopian novel set in New Orleans called Elysian Nights. She has been named series editor for original fiction from the University Press of Mississippi, and since 1997 has been the director of the Louisiana State University MFA in Creative Writing.

"Oslo," the short story shown here, was originally published in the New Yorker in May 1984. It demonstrates the stark realism of the themes recurrent in Crone's work, of individuation, separation, betrayal, and forgiveness.

Oslo

ONE SATURDAY IN DECEMBER, my husband told me that he wanted to find a place to live that meant something to him. I told him I knew Baton Rouge was still strange to us, but that was not official, it was patter. I wanted to ask him how he broke up with his first wife, for reference. But every time he answers that question the response is different. So we talked about other people: why did the visiting Norwegian artist we liked so much leave town before her stay was properly over? Why did she abandon all her paintings? The recent ugly abstracts and the early works with sheep, some haystacks, tundras in the sun, even fjords but not hokey, were stored hastily in our friends the Richardses' garage.

She had hung out with the Richardses and us, and had planned to leave almost a month later, and take her stuff, of course. Roll up the canvases, weigh everything, ship it. Instead, she just took off for the airport Friday morning in a cardigan, her hair curled under at the chin—so pretty, everybody thought—heading for Oslo.

The next day, Nadine Richards came over on a bicycle, in brilliant sweatpants, and sat on a tiled step in our new house, trembling. She called her husband, Jordan, a cad and a creep. He too was silent. He hoarded himself. She didn't know him anymore. He didn't think he wanted to ever have kids. She hated him. And he was in love, she had figured out, with the lady painter who left.

Jordan is a good guy—to this everyone agreed. Even my husband agreed, and he is harsh on people and places. He hates Baton Rouge, for instance. We've lived here a year and a half, and before this San Antonio. We could live somewhere else. Mark is a computer writer. He gives good manual, as he says. He admitted he hated our life before I asked him how he left his first wife. Was his exit gradual or abrupt? Did he know in February and wait until June to do it? Did he know in May and in a week break it off for good? When did he know why he had done it? A year later? At the time? When he met me? Mark answered that he wanted to live either in San Francisco or in Jerusalem. What an address Jerusalem would be, but maybe you wouldn't understand, he told me.

"Oslo," Nadine said loudly, Sunday, over some jazz we had put on the stereo. In her aerobic pink pants, she seemed to shimmer around the edges–a first-day-of-the-rest-of-your-life look, something in a movie. "I swear I'm telling him to go this time," she then announced. "I know he was in love with her." She picked at the cranberry bread I'd baked, but she wasn't really eating. "I just took it all in on Friday, when he got back from taking her to the airport. She had insisted she was leaving because she couldn't cope with the looks of the subtropics. This town, this place was frightening to her. The banana trees, the catalpas. The lizards that come into your house. Swamps. Such palaver, really. She had to get back to her native landscape. She was losing her connection to things, felt out of time, couldn't paint. I stayed up nights listening to this crock."

It is awfully hot in south Louisiana sometime in December, I was thinking, watching Nadine perspire. It climbs into the eighties, then there's a cold snap.

Monday morning, I saw Jordan at a sandwich counter next door to the bookstore he manages, and his eyes were dark, as usual, but with new gray circles. He was wearing a white cotton sweater Nadine had knitted, which swallowed him. He felt furtive about seeing even me. I guess I was too well versed in the reasons Nadine and he should split. And I wanted to go up to him and hold his hand, tell him we were there—Mark and I—if he wanted to talk to someone. He sat four seats away from me at the counter and said the merest hello. While I was eating a wet avocado salad, I realized that Jordan had never started a sentence in my presence with the word "I" and gone on to elaborate how he felt. It wasn't in his makeup. What did he know about himself that he couldn't tell anybody?

On Wednesday, I called Nadine and told her she should leave Jordan. Or at least lock him out. She replied that she was going to—going to do the right thing.

"You don't know the half of it," she went on. "He loves to love women he hardly knows. Once he almost left me for a woman whose book he had read. He fell for her through photos and letters. This lady painter will get him to Oslo. Then, once he's there, he'll start hoarding his heart again. It's the proximity he hates."

"So lock the door," I said.

"He won't deny it—he doesn't care what I know," Nadine said. "Won't say it, either." She sucked on a cigarette. (She is the only person left I know who smokes.) "He's got a house key."

"Face it. It's over. He hurts you. You know that," I said. "You've been gong on about this for so long. Remember the chalet in Alabama?"

The four of us took a vacation there. It was supposed to be brisk in the southern Appalachians in June. She told me once at breakfast there that he grabbed her at night like a cool pillow—then, in the morning, nothing.

"I know," she said now. "I know it. I've been talking about it for months. Maybe even a year. However long we've been friends. I've got no idea why he likes me, even. I'm not his type."

Then I told Nadine she was being stupid. She is beautiful. Her features are unusual and piquant; her hair is full and well cut. And besides, she is good-natured. She trusts people.

On Thursday, my husband said that Jordan, who is his only friend in town, was just bored. I said Nadine said he was a cad, and then I thought how old-fashioned, Edwardian even, to know a cad. Handsome, black-eyed, ruthless a little, interested in distance in his women, not pleasure. I would love Jordan if he liked me, almost, I thought.

That afternoon, Nadine called me and I told her again to set up barriers. It was the only way. I said I was speaking from experience. Everybody wants what he can't have. I told her to be martial. She couldn't go on as she had been. I mentioned self-respect. She responded that Jordan had admitted he was planning to go to Oslo but that the woman had got skittish about the plan at the end and run away. Then she said, "He doesn't know what he wants. He came home this morning. Had spent the night out. Sat around like an object. Said nothing. Wouldn't even say where he had slept. Do you know? I told him to move out next month. He said he'd look for a place. But we get along, you know. I don't know how to cook."

"Take yourself seriously," I told her.

"I do," she said. "We're serious. We're just not planning to do it tomorrow. We both work. It's a lot of trouble."

Then I realized Nadine wasn't as angry as she pretended to be. She was just too sad. She was by herself, in her open kitchen, and her husband, Jordan, was in some part of the house, probably sitting under a floor lamp looking at some of the other woman's color slides. He is so large and good-looking that I had a hard time imagining he was also sad. Nadine went on explaining. It didn't matter that he had slept with the painter, it was that he'd kept everything from her. Held back. "Making me the heart police," she said. "And I'm becoming this cold person, somebody I don't even like. This isn't life."

While Nadine was talking to me I was thinking that the rooms in my house were clean and interesting, and that I was kind of happy even though we live in Baton Rouge. I had been planning to buy one of the Norwegian woman's paintings to hang on the brick above our working fireplace. My husband thought the woman talked too much. She reminded him of Liv Ullmann in those Bergman movies. She had odd ideas, and she repeated herself. He asked what did Jordan see in her. Then I thought about having bright blue furniture and living in Jerusalem. We have two cars and inch-wide blinds; these things took on nuance whenever I thought of giving them up. An image of my husband and me sitting down in Israel, near a little balcony, appeared once in a dream of my husband's ex-wife. She was very tall and always had few men to choose from. Even after their divorce, she wanted Mark badly, and snatched him away from me at gallery openings or parties when we were all there together. Yet she had this dream, which she called him about once, early in the morning—woke us up to tell us. It was so vivid, she said, that it seemed painted. She saw my husband and me living in a small white apartment in Jerusalem, with a view of the sea, among cushions the color of lapis lazuli. Mark told her there isn't any sea in Jerusalem. Then he hung up, like that. I knew the history of their unhappiness, the reasons for it, but I could never see him just shut down with her one day and say no more, goodbye. The first several months I knew him, after he had left her, his heart was packed in ice. I finally told him to thaw or abuse somebody else, and since then he's been at room temperature, with lapses.

Almost at midnight on Thursday, the same day, Nadine called back and said she had been crying. "It's pitch dark in Oslo at this time of year," she said. "Night all the time now. How could a painter go there in December? I bet she's not going to paint anymore. I know it. That's why she left all her work out in our garage. What did Jordan *do* to her? I just realized this. It has taken all week, almost, for it to sink in. I'll feel sorry for her even if he goes to her. Especially if he goes to her. Am I crazy?" she asked, then paused, giving me a chance to catch up and say something, but I didn't; I was thinking about other things. "I feel so far away from this," she continued. "We are in Louisiana and Jordan is in love with this woman who is sitting in a room somewhere six hours into tomorrow, and it is still dark there anyway. And I feel so far away. I could be on the moon tonight. I don't even know if he is sleeping here or going out, is he in the house or not."

"Take a look," I said. "You are okay. Maybe I will come over. Nobody is satisfied. Mark wants to move to Jerusalem. It is a place, he says. You know where you are when you are there. It's a good city to be buried in—lots of company. The world could end there, even. History in the streets. I think he wants to get rid of me. I always thought we had it down."

"I was in Oslo once," Nadine answered. "I was sixteen, on a trip with my parents, who went off on their own, so I walked around on these endless sunny evenings and met polite boys. One of them took me to a museum full of those paintings by Edvard Munch. I knew nothing then, wasn't prepared. On the whole second floor of this museum are pictures the size of double doors filled with people in one kind of obvious pain or another. The figures are so hard and flat and separate. All of them are standing in interiors with harsh colors behind them—this citron yellow representing light from lamps. Hideous. It was as if the backgrounds were mean to them and so they were starting to turn into rocks. Munch and Grieg, the two other artists from Norway. It must feel crucial to be there. Maybe where you were born is essential. Maybe she was telling the truth. In the summer, the sun is relentless; then it just goes out. I don't know. I think I am going crazy. I don't feel like locking Jordan out. I want to send him on. Here there are no seasons at all. It only matters what the day is like. It never goes by the week, even. Tonight it is cold, for once. Jordan's on the porch; I can see him now. I don't know if he's coming in or going out. I can see his breath. I never saw Jordan's breath once in the two years we've lived here. Do I mean that I love him?" She exhaled into the phone.

"Oh, let it be one way or the other," I said. The next thing I said felt vital. "Tell him it is going down to freezing tonight. Go, tell him."

Then Nadine told me I was being a romantic—me.

WENDY KAMINER '71

*W*endy Kaminer has been called "one of the most brilliant essayists alive and writing in America today." Her penetrating wit has been displayed in books and essays of far-ranging social criticism. Kaminer's position as president of National Coalition Against Censorship and as a public policy fellow at Radcliffe College have provided current and relevant material for her probing examination of cultural issues. She is frequently read in the Atlantic Monthly and heard as a commentator on "Morning Edition" for National Public Radio.

After Smith, Kaminer went on to Boston University Law School for her JD (1975). Her early experience as a lawyer is reflected in her descriptive evaluations of societal trends and raging issues from recovery movements and victimology in I'm Dysfunctional, You're Dysfunctional: The Recovery Movement and Other Self-Help Fashions (1992) to the death penalty debate in It's All the Rage: Crime and Culture (1995). She has stretched from consideration of Volunteering: The Pleasure, Pain, and Politics of Unpaid Work From 1830 to the Present (1984) to True Love Waits: Essays and Criticism (1996), which takes on everything from feminism and sex to free speech, gun control, and "The Shrunken Reality of Lives in Therapy."

Regarded as a revolutionary in feminist thought and taking a position as an equal-rights and not a difference feminist, Kaminer believes that sexual equality can be achieved only by reducing gender separation and special treatment for women. In A Fearful Freedom: Women's Flight From Equality (1991), Kaminer examines the ways in which measures intended to protect or promote women may actually slow their advancement by perpetuating the image of the fragile, delicate female. She takes on single-sex education, and questions the prudence of teaching and encouraging women by sheltering them. In doing so, her articles enter into the debates over gender segregation of public schools and fitness centers as well as schools and colleges. She first outlined these views in her Rally Day address at Smith in 1998, concluding, "Only as the sexes have become less separate have women become more free."

In 1993 Wendy Kaminer was awarded both a Guggenheim Fellowship and the Exceptional Media Merit Award from the National Women's Political Caucus. This September 1997 essay from Atlantic Monthly presents her view that "criticism sometimes expresses greater respect than praise."

A Civic Duty to Annoy

WHAT IS THERE ABOUT being in a room filled with people who agree with me that makes me want to change my mind? Maybe it's the self-congratulatory air of consensus among people who consider themselves and one another right-thinking. Maybe it's the consistency of belief that devolves into mere conformity. Maybe it's just that I can no longer bear to hear the word "empower."

At self-consciously feminist gatherings I feel at home in the worst way. I feel the way I do at family dinners, when I want to put my feet up on the table and say something to provoke old Uncle George. To get George going, I defend affirmative action or the capital-gains tax. To irritate my more orthodox feminist colleagues, I disavow any personal guilt about being born white and middle-class. I scoff every time I hear a Harvard student complain that she's oppressed.

I'm not alone in my irreverence, but feminist pieties combined with feminine courtesy keep most of us in line. Radcliffe College, where I am based, is devoted to nurturing female undergraduates. We're supposed to nod sympathetically, in solidarity, when a student speaks of feeling silenced or invisible because she is female, of color, or both. We're not supposed to point out that Harvard students are among the most privileged people in the universe, regardless of race or sex.

I don't mean to scoff at the discrimination that a young woman of any color may have experienced or is likely to experience someday. I do want to remind her that as a student at Harvard/Radcliffe or any other elite university she enjoys many more advantages than a working-class white male attending a community college. And the kind of discrimination that students are apt to encounter at Harvard—relatively subtle and occasional—is not "oppression." It does not systematically deprive people of basic civil rights and liberties and is not generally sanctioned by the administration.

Besides, everyone is bound to feel silenced, invisible, or unappreciated at least once in a while. Imagine how a white male middle manager feels when he's about to be downsized. Like laments about dysfunctional families, complaints about oppression lose their power when proffered so promiscuously. Melodramatic complaints about oppression at Harvard are in part developmental: students in their late teens and early twenties are apt to place themselves at the center of the universe. But their extreme sensitivity reflects frequently criticized cultural trends as well. An obsession with identity and self-esteem has encouraged students to assume that every insult or slight is motivated by racist, sexist, or heterosexist bias and gravely threatens their well-being. What's lost is a sense of perspective. If attending Harvard is oppression, what was slavery?

Sometimes nurturing students means challenging their complaints instead of satisfying their demands for sympathy. I've heard female students declare that any male classmate who makes derogatory remarks about women online or over the telephone is guilty of sexual harassment and should be punished. What are we teaching them if we agree? That they aren't strong enough to withstand a few puerile sexist jokes that may not even be directed at them? That their male classmates don't have the right to make statements that some women deem offensive? There would be no feminist movement if women never dared to give offense.

When nurturing devolves into pandering, feminism gives way to femininity. Recently a small group of female students called for disciplinary proceedings against males wearing "pornographic" T-shirts in a dining hall. They found it difficult to eat lunch in the presence of such unwholesome, sexist images. Should we encourage these young women to believe that they're fragile creatures, with particularly delicate digestive systems? Should we offer them official protection from T-shirts? Or should we point out that a group of pro-choice students might someday wear shirts emblazoned with words or images that pro-life students find deeply disturbing? Should we teach them that the art of giving and taking offense is an art of citizenship in a free society?

That is not a feminine art. Radcliffe, for example, is an unfailingly polite institution. Criticism and dissatisfaction are apt to be expressed in a feminine mode, covertly or indirectly. It's particularly hard for many of us not to react with great solicitude to a student who declares herself marginalized, demeaned, or oppressed, even if we harbor doubts about her claim. If she seeks virtue in oppression, as so many do, we seek it in maternalism.

We tend to forget that criticism sometimes expresses greater respect than praise. It is surely more of an honor than flattery. You challenge a student because you consider her capable of learning. You question her premises because you think she's game enough to re-examine them. You do need to take the measure of her self-confidence, and your own. Teaching—or nurturing—requires that you gain students' trust and then risk having them not like you.

Sometimes withholding sympathy feels mean, insensitive, and uncaring; you acquire all the adjectives that aren't supposed to attach to women. You take on the stereotypically masculine vices at a time when the feminine virtue of niceness is being revived: Rosie O'Donnell is the model talk-show host, civility the reigning civic virtue, and communitarianism the paradigmatic political theory. Communities are exalted, as if the typical community were composed solely of people who shared and cared about one another and never engaged in conflict.

In fact communities are built on compromise, and compromise presupposes disagreement. Tolerance presupposes the existence of people and ideas you don't like. It prevails upon you to forswear censoring others but not yourself. One test of tolerance is provocation. When you sit down to dinner with your disagreeable relations, or comrades who bask in their rectitude and compassion, you have a civic duty to annoy them.

BETTY FRIEDAN '42

When Betty Goldstein Friedan arrived at Smith College in the fall of 1938, she carried with her memories of personal experiences that had sensitized her to society's prevalent prejudices and injustices against women and Jews. In particular, her childhood and adolescence in Peoria, IL, offered her a keen awareness of sexism and anti-Semitism—forces of oppression that had often made her feel like an outcast. This personal knowledge, combined with Friedan's profound ability to witness and capture vividly the world around her in prose, propelled her into a life spent fighting inequality through action and written words. After completing her formal education, which included a psychology major summa cum laude from Smith in 1942 and graduate study at the University of California at Berkeley, Friedan began to work in New York as a labor journalist, where she campaigned for social justice. Soon afterward she married, had three children, and, as a suburban housewife limited by her position to a set locale and social group, started to write about the binding conventions that held women captive.

The results of Friedan's work appear in The Feminine Mystique (1963), a book which, because of its radical call for recognition of the essential equality of women, served as the catalyst for what is now called the women's movement. In 1966, Betty Friedan began her career as a feminist organizer, contributing to the foundation of the National Organization for Women, the National Women's Political Caucus, and later, the National Abortion Rights Action League. The articles, speeches, and reflections from this period of her life appear in Friedan's second book, It Changed My Life: Writings on the Women's Movement (1977). More recently, she has published The Second Stage (1981) and The Fountain of Age (1993). Throughout all of these works, Betty Friedan has remained faithful to her ongoing mission of promoting equality and justice.

"The Scapegoat," published by Bettye Goldstein in the October 1941 edition of the Smith College Monthly, captures the essence of the type of covert anti-Semitism that Friedan herself witnessed and experienced, and sets an early example of the passionate intensity with which Friedan continues to fight for equality.

The Scapegoat

But the goat, on which the lot fell to be the scapegoat, shall be presented alive before the Lord, to make an atonement with him, and to let him go for a scapegoat into the wilderness. (Leviticus 16:10)

I DON'T THINK I NOTICED SHIRLEY much during the first few weeks of college. We were all trying to get adjusted and feeling very strange and uneasy; none of us knew each other very well then; she was just one of the fourteen freshmen in the house. I remember that she came in and helped me unpack because her trunk hadn't come so she didn't have much to do. She was nice enough, I guess: I mean, fundamentally there was nothing wrong with her. I had a blind date with a Harvard man that fall who asked me if I knew her. He thought she was a swell kid and a lot of fun. But she didn't seem to fit in at Ransom House. After the first month it was obvious that no one liked her. There was something objectionable about her, I don't know what it was. I don't think the fact that she was Jewish had anything to do with it. There were several other Jewish girls in the house, and we all got along quite well. Certainly that would have nothing to do with *my* feeling for her. And when I asked Phyl and Katy about it, they said, "Absolutely not. We wouldn't like her, regardless. And after all, you're Jewish, and Alice, and we like you, silly." They are always very frank. So I don't think you could call it race prejudice.

Naturally, we were all nice enough to her. But we didn't want her hanging around with us. I don't know why, but she got on our nerves. We couldn't help feeling that way. We began to notice the way she talked, and the way she swung her hips when she walked, and the moist messy way she smoked cigarettes, and the way she bit her fingernails so low that it nauseated you to look at them. She had a pretty face, but she was short and plump and always wore her hair in the sort of tight sausage curls that were obviously rolled on curlers the night before. And she wore too much make-up for college—rouge, mascara, eye-shadow. She had an affected little giggle, and she stuck out her little finger when she drank, and there was something about the way she chewed gum. . . .

She was very friendly though, and affectionate in an eager sort of way. I remember not long after college opened her mother sent her some food. She asked Alice and me to come up that night. We didn't want to go very much, but we couldn't be rude. There was a chicken. It was very greasy. She showed us a large still-life her father had painted. It wasn't very good. She said she was crazy about Smith, but it was awfully large, and didn't we think it was hard to get to know people. Maybe it was New England, but she'd never known people who were so stand-offish before. It was just at first, of course; she was sure they'd be swell as soon as you got to know them. And we three would be very good friends, naturally.

Alice said, "I don't think one should be in too much of a hurry to become good friends with anyone at a place like this. It takes time to know with whom you really want to be friends. I don't believe in rushing into things. One has to be careful." She didn't look at Shirley when she said this. Shirley didn't say anything. Then I glanced at my watch and said, "I think I'd better go. I have an English theme to do. Thank you very much, Shirley."

Shirley said, "But it's so early. We haven't really gotten acquainted or talked or anything. Why don't you stay and do your theme in here?"

I said, "No, I really have to go." Then Alice remembered that she had some math to do. So we both left. Shirley seemed a little hurt; we had stayed only twenty minutes.

A L AND I WERE WALKING DOWN THE HALL and Al said, "I'm glad the rest weren't there. All that greasy food." She wrinkled up her nose, and then she looked at me as if she wanted to say something but didn't know whether to or not. Finally just as we got to my door she blurted out, "You don't suppose the others think we're like her, do you? Just because we're all three. . . ."

"Well, they certainly see that we're different from her," I said, "At least, I hope they do. And I don't see how they could help it. But I don't like the idea of her having just you and me up there tonight. As if we naturally belonged with her. It's people like her that cause segregation, really. They ask for it."

Alice said, "I know. And I guess for our own good we ought to make it clear that we don't intend to be a little threesome with her." Then she looked embarrassed, and said goodnight.

After that we were both careful not to sit at the same table with Shirley at dinner, and the next time she asked us into her room, we said we had to study. She offered to get us blind dates several times; she seemed to have plenty of men. We always found some excuse.

Pretty soon Al and I got to be good friends with Phyl and Katy and Liz and Janice and Marty and Jill. We all enjoyed each other's company and didn't want Shirley following us around and trying to push into things. She didn't seem to be able to take a hint. For instance, one night we were all going to the movies. We had decided about it when Shirley wasn't around. She had a habit of assuming that she was included whenever she knew we were going to do something, so this was the only way to prevent her from coming. But she must have guessed or something, because at dinner she asked, very casually, "Has anyone seen the Calvin? It's supposed to be swell."

Katy said no in an impatient tone of voice, and the rest of us started talking about something else very fast. Then Shirley said, "Let's all go tonight."

We all looked at each other and raised our eyebrows. Phyl muttered something about not having decided yet what we were going to do that evening. No one else said anything. Then Shirley said in a stilted, self-conscious way, "Well, let me know if you decide to go."

We said we would, and then we went into the living room to play bridge. Shirley said she was dying for a good game of bridge and did anyone need a fourth? No one did. So she giggled and said, "I guess I'll kibitz. Who wants the honor of my excellent advice?"

No one paid any attention. So she said she had some studying to do and went upstairs. But she walked into Marty's room just as she was putting on her coat and asked where she was going. Marty said, "Oh, to the corner or some place. Can I get you something, Shirley?"

Shirley said, "No, I don't think so." And then, as if it had just occurred to her, "Maybe I'll go with you. I haven't been out yet tonight, and I could use some coffee."

Marty became very polite and insisted that it would be no trouble at all to bring some coffee back, so she really need not bother to come along.

Shirley said, "No, I really think I'd like to go."

The rest of us were waiting for Marty downstairs, and when Shirley came down with her, we all looked at each other, and Phyl said, "Well really!"

Katy said, "Oh, I forgot to tell you, Shirley. We decided to go to the movies after all. Or did you know?" You couldn't help smiling, Katy said this with such a suave pointedness. Shirley tried to look nonchalant, but she didn't succeed very well. I should think she would have had more pride than to insist on coming when it was so obvious that we didn't want her. And she might just as well have gone alone: no one paid any attention to her. Except for Liz's imitating her walk on our way home. We howled; it was really a scream. Shirley turned around and asked what was so funny. Phyl said, "Oh, nothing much."

ONCE IN A WHILE we used to talk about how heavenly it would be if Shirley moved out of the house at the end of the year. But in a way it was exciting to dodge her. And it made us feel more close to each other. There was a togetherness, a warm shared feeling when we were all in someone's room griping about the way Shirley followed us around. And it was nice, whenever Shirley committed one of her characteristic *faux pas*, to look at someone and know she was thinking the same thing you were. I used to wonder what would happen if she weren't there. It would be ghastly to be in her place. Our group was swell: we had fun together, we were friends, we would do anything for each other. But this was on the inside. It would be horrible to be on the outside suddenly. But this would not happen to any of us. Shirley was different.

In a way I think it was rather helpful to Alice and me, having Shirley in the house. Everyone was always so disgusted with her that they almost seemed to forget that we were Jewish, too. The things they said without any self-consciousness when we two were in the room showed that. So it was nice for us.

We were quite surprised at the end of the year when we found out that Shirley had no intention of moving. I guess she had no friends in any of the other houses so she thought she might as well stick it out in Ransom. And maybe she was determined not to admit there was any situation to move away from.

SOPHOMORE YEAR we were all rather busy. We hardly noticed Shirley; she didn't annoy us any more. We were engrossed in our own affairs and didn't think much about her, one way or the other. For the most part we didn't even bother to be witty about her idiosyncrasies. We said hello when we saw her.

She must have found this absolute indifference unnerving. I think I should have found it much more frustrating than the obvious dislike of the year before. It was less warm, less tangible. What can you do if the people around you cease to recognize your existence? You cannot penetrate finality.

I think Shirley tried to. She made some pretty undisguised pleas for attention. She bought five or six symphonies and played them obtrusively for hours at a time on the living room victrola. We used to laugh at this sudden passion for culture, or whatever you want to call it. The living room would be full of people sitting at tables or on the floor, talking or playing bridge. And Shirley would sit in the big chair by the victrola and change the records, one after the other. But I guess she couldn't just sit there and do nothing, and no one ever talked to her or asked her to play bridge. I wonder what she thought about when she sat there after every meal and played records while the rest of us talked and laughed. It was almost as if she weren't in the room at all, except as a sort of furniture. Like the thing they discuss in philosophy—is there a noise if a book drops off a table in an empty room, is there thunder when it storms in the middle of the ocean, does a tree exist where there is no one to see it?

She was getting desperate, I guess. She began to go in for drinking and sex in a big way. I'll never forget the Saturday night Dick Freel, a man I knew at Yale Law, came up. We had come back from Toto's a little early and were sitting on the porch talking with Katy and Jack and Phyl and her man, when Shirley came up with a town boy, both of them dead drunk. Shirley was singing an extremely risqué song at the top of her voice, and when she saw us, she came over, plopped herself on Dick's lap, and slobbered, "H'lo, Dickie baby. D'you want to know a cute joke, cutie pie?" Then she started to whisper something in his ear. He looked awfully embarrassed. More and more people were coming up; it was almost twelve. I felt horribly conspicuous. Everyone was watching us. This person Shirley had picked up kept saying, "Come on, baby, kiss me good-night," and trying to pull her off Dick's lap. But she wouldn't stop whispering in Dick's ear. It was horrible. I prayed for twelve o'clock to come so we would have to go in. Finally the town boy pulled away and Dick straightened his tie and lit a cigarette. He said, "Who the hell is she anyway? A friend of yours?" I said, "No. She's an impossible girl in our house. No one likes her. I hope she didn't embarrass you too much, Dick. I'm really very sorry."

The next morning Alice and I went into her room and told her a few simple truths. We said we didn't care what kind of reputation she got for herself but that she had to stop that sort of thing in public, if not for her sake then for ours. Shirley was very sullen and said she didn't care what people thought—she'd do as she damn pleased, and we should mind our own business.

She would get sickening mushy postcards full of x's and leave them around on the mail table for days. And once she came back from a Dartmouth weekend and told everyone in the living room how she had spent the night in some hotel with a man she had just met. She said she'd had a lot to drink and so had he. She told us in graphic detail how he seduced her. I wondered if it really happened, or if she were just talking to seem glamorous or exciting or something. Alice said to me that night, "Really, one can see why people become anti-Semitic."

Whenever anyone moved into the house, Shirley immediately claimed her as a bosom friend. There was a transfer named Dotty Simpson. She was nice to Shirley at first, and Shirley clung to her with a smothering sort of adoration. She came into Dotty's room every night to talk about how misunderstood and mistreated she was, how we abused her, and how bravely she was bearing it. We all wondered how long Dotty would be able to take it. No one, not even the kindest person, could endure that devotion for long: it was so desperate, so avid, it made one embarrassed, ashamed. Dotty told us about it later, when we took her into our crowd. She said that she felt very sorry for Shirley, but that there was something horrible about her over-affectionateness, her obsequiousness. It made her so uncomfortable that she finally couldn't stand it any longer. Just because she didn't mind being nice to the girl, it didn't mean that she wanted to spend every minute with her. We told her she'd have to be pretty pointed to get Shirley to see this.

Shirley should never have come back that year. I admire her determination. But I think she carried it too far. All this was doing something to her. I guess she had been fairly likable at first, outside of the several characteristics that grated on us. But now there was something grotesque about her. Even if she aroused one's pity, by now it could only be an objective, intellectual sort of pity. One could not force oneself to be with her, listen to her talk, be her friend, even if one knew that lack of these things was making her warped and cringing, even if one had been willing to risk sharing her ostracism. The whole affair was very depressing. Sometimes I wonder how I should have reacted if I had been in her place. Sometimes I wonder what sort of a person I should have been after several years of that treatment. It is a horrible thing to think about.

By spring Shirley had stopped making those desperate bids for attention, stopped forcing her affection on new girls, stopped whining about herself. For days at a time no one saw her. She stayed in her room, I guess. And when she was around, she didn't speak to anyone. We were all so used to ignoring her that we hardly noticed this withdrawal, or whatever you want to call it. Once Katy remarked that Shirley was much less of a nuisance now, and we all agreed. I remember Dotty's mentioning that Shirley had complained of bad headaches, from her eyes or something, and that she couldn't sleep. She didn't get those postcards any more, and all of her men seemed to have disappeared.

At dinner one night around the first of May I asked if Shirley were in the infirmary. I hadn't seen her around for ages. Dotty said that her mother had come and that she had gone away with her—several days ago. It seems queer that I hadn't known about it: she lived three doors down the hall from me. I went into her room and all her things were gone except for her trunk, which was labeled to be sent to her. We found out later that she had a nervous breakdown.

We talked about it pretty much that week. Once I said that we were fools not to have seen it coming, that no one could stand the treatment she received and not be affected violently by it. I said that in the last analysis we were to blame for her nervous breakdown, or that at least we might have prevented it. But the others didn't agree with me. In fact, they became rather angry. Phyl said, "I don't see how you can say we were to blame. We couldn't help it if we didn't like her. She was simply impossible, and you know it."

And Katy said, "She never should have come to Smith. She didn't belong here. When she found it out—and you can't tell me she didn't realize it—she should have left."

Then Liz looked at me speculatively and said, "What are you getting so worked up for? I didn't notice you going out of your way to be nice to her."

And so I didn't say any more. The others might think I was on Shirley's side because I was Jewish too. They might think I was afraid . . . afraid that the same thing might happen to me now that Shirley was gone. I think I know how Shirley must have felt.

And so I didn't say any more. I really hadn't liked her either, from the first.

SALLY QUINN '63

Sally Quinn came to Smith from Savannah, GA. After working as a translator, secretary, public relations agent, librarian, dancer, and social secretary to the Algerian ambassador, Cherif Guellal, in 1969 she joined the staff of the Washington Post, writing profiles and covering every event from birthday parties to political soirées. Her coverage of Washington's elite became the talk of the town, and she quickly emerged as a well-known and often controversial reporter. She took a leave from the Post to serve as co-anchor of the "CBS Morning News" in 1972-73, an experience she recounts with wisdom and acerbity in her book We're Going to Make You a Star (1975). After her return, Sally Quinn wrote features on the national and international political scene in Washington and covered political conventions and campaigns throughout the country. In 1978 she married the then executive editor of the Washington Post, Benjamin C. Bradlee; the couple currently live in Washington, DC, with their son Josiah Quinn.

As a contributor to Vogue, Esquire, Harper's Bazaar, Atlantic Monthly, and frequently to the New Yorker, Sally Quinn has established a distinguished career as a journalist and novelist. Her first fiction, chosen as a Literary Guild selection, is Regrets Only (1986), the sequel to which is Happy Endings (1991), both rippling with witty satire on power and influence and rare insight into sexual politics. In both her books and her articles, Sally Quinn explores the cultural and social world of Washington, DC, giving the reader a close look at life behind the newspaper stories. Nora Ephron was quoted in Vanity Fair saying that Sally Quinn "could go to a dinner party and . . . tell you who was about to be fired — just on the basis of the seating plan!" In her most recent work, The Party: A Guide to Adventurous Entertaining (1997), excerpted here, Sally Quinn demonstrates why she has been so successful in the social and political system of the nation's capital.

The Point

FROM *The Party: A Guide to Adventurous Entertaining*

THERE ARE A THOUSAND REASONS TO HAVE A PARTY or to entertain, but as far as I'm concerned there is only one legitimate one. And that is to have a good time. If you don't care about having fun, then have a meeting. I'm dead serious about this. The late Pamela Harriman, hostess and ambassador to France, once said that one should never have a party unless one had a serious agenda. That's ridiculous. A party is its own excuse, and the most successful way to further a "serious agenda" is to make sure all the guests enjoy themselves.

It is true that, in Washington, dinner parties have always had a special place in entertaining, mainly because they are often working events, no matter what the stated purpose. This must be true in New York or Chicago or Hollywood too, though not so easily recognized.

These dinners have always been a place where information and ideas are exchanged among the "power elite" of the capital. Henry Kissinger once wrote of Washingtonians that "it is at their dinner parties and receptions that the relationships are created without which the machinery of government would soon stalemate itself."

Translated, this means that people in different spheres need to get to know one another. But it doesn't mean they have to be bored to death doing it. Certainly people (not only in Washington but everywhere) have parties to further themselves professionally and socially. There's nothing new about that. What is important is how it is done. You have to be either extremely subtle or completely forthright about what you are doing. And you should actually like the people you are honoring or hosting, or you will soon earn a reputation for being a phony and a climber.

I once did a profile on a young would-be host, the late Steve Martindale, who was making quite a splash in Washington. He had recently had a party that both Alice Roosevelt Longworth and Henry Kissinger, then secretary of state, attended, and he had the rest of the town's A list as well.

How did he do it, this little unknown thirty-year-old from Pocatello, Idaho?

"Easy," he said. "I called up Alice Longworth and told her I was having a party for Henry Kissinger and then I called up Henry Kissinger and told him I was having a party for Alice Roosevelt Longworth."

Steve was a personable guy and was actually pretty good at it for a while, but he was just too obvious and it ruined him socially. It's never a good idea to be duplicitous. You always get found out in the end.

YEARS AGO I FOUND MYSELF in a desolate situation. I had lost several jobs, broken up with my boyfriend, moved to California, been unhappy there, and moved back to Washington. I was living with my parents, and I was completely broke at age thirty. In other words, I had bottomed out. What was a girl to do?

Why, have a party.

Basically what I needed to do was announce that I was back in town and available for work. It so happened that Barry Goldwater Jr. had just been elected to Congress, and his parents were my parents' best friends. It was agreed by everyone that if I had a party for Barry Jr., who was attractive and fun, it would serve to introduce him to many of my friends in town and serve also as a sort of want ad for me. My parents bankrolled me. I sent out festive invitations to about two hundred of my "closest" friends, bought sexy one-shouldered white lace pajamas, and called the society columnists (that's what they were called in those days. Sort of like "society hostess"). It turned out that the combination of Barry Jr. and Barry Sr. was an irresistible draw. The columnists and photographers came in droves, the party was a huge success, and the next day I got a phone call.

"Hello," said this gravelly voice on the other end of the line. "Sally, you don't know me, but I'm Ben Bradlee and I would like to talk to you about a job at the *Washington Post*. Would you be interested?"

I was hired the next day. It seems that Ben had read the social columns and decided I was just the right person to cover parties for the newly created "Style" section.

So this party actually had two elements that I think are essential for success. It was great fun, and it had a reason, which I'll get to in a moment. The ostensible reason was to honor Barry Jr., but I have to say that I was pretty frank with my friends about the fact that it was essentially a job placement program for me as well.

Parties are usually more fun if there is a reason to have them. A "reason" is different from Pam Harriman's "serious agenda." Generally having a party just to have a party doesn't work as well as having a party for something or somebody. Even if you owe everybody in the world and have to have a payback party, you can always have it on or near a holiday or have it for a friend from out of town, just to give it a little more spark.

Actually, the only party I've ever had for no apparent reason was my own wedding reception. I had wanted a huge wedding with all the frills—twelve bridesmaids, flower girls, ring bearers, a beautiful dress with a six-foot train, a fabulous reception with at least three hundred people, the throwing of the bouquet, a limousine with a JUST MARRIED sign on the back, and a grand exit with rice being thrown as we headed for a romantic honeymoon destination. Ben did not. He had been married twice before and felt that it would be too much. Since we had been living together for five and a half years, I acquiesced, and we got married in a judge's chambers in Washington with only our immediate family and our attendants, *Washington Post* publisher Kay Graham as my matron of honor, and as best men, humorist and columnist Art Buchwald and lawyer Edward Bennett Williams.

I had arranged a small dinner party for about thirty or forty friends at our house afterward, with a wedding cake and white lilies everywhere. But Ben didn't want to tell anyone what the party was for beforehand because he didn't want to get scooped by the opposition newspaper, the *Washington Star*. (We were in a very competitive newspaper war.) This caused big problems for me because, as it turned out, Margaret and Peter Jay, the British ambassador and his wife, were having a dinner party that night and had invited us as well as half our friends. When I called everyone to invite them to "dinner," they all declined, and I had to coerce them into coming without revealing why. *What's it for? Who's the guest of honor?* they all wanted to know, and I was forced to demur. What I did was tell them in my sternest voice that I was calling in my chits, that this was extremely important and I wanted them to get out of the Jays' party and come to mine. They must have heard the resolve in my voice because they did it.

We had to contend with a number of grudging guests at the beginning of the evening, but once they saw the wedding cake and the white lilies everywhere, heard a few mushy toasts, and drank several glasses of champagne, they were mollified, and it turned out to be a wonderful evening. But I will never again have another party without an apparent reason.

P.S. We beat the *Star* on the wedding announcement.

NOBODY REALLY CARES what the reason for a party is, but it does help to have one. You could have a Leap Year party and invite women and ask them to bring a man of their choice. That sounds silly, but it's already an amusing concept and there's nothing wrong with grown-ups being silly every now and then. I once had a Valentine's Day party in February (of course), when the weather and people's mood tend to be cold and dreary. Guests were greeted at the door with "love potions." God knows what was in them, but after about an hour men in black tie and women in evening dresses were reclining all over the living room floor giggling.

I got somebody to read palms and tell people about their love lives. Many of the guests were what you might call important and powerful Washington types, but the line for the palmist in the upstairs bedroom, which included the director of the CIA, formed at the bottom of the stairs. I could just as easily have had a regular dinner party, but it wouldn't have been nearly as much fun.

Having a party for no reason doesn't mean that people won't come. It's just that they usually can't figure out why they went in the first place. Two close journalist friends of mine, very much sought after as guests, recently went to a dinner party given by some newcomers who were clearly on the make. They complained bitterly to me afterward about what a tedious evening it had been.

"Well, why on earth did you go?" I asked them. They looked puzzled for a moment and finally one of them replied, "Because we were asked." . . .

The point of the story, though, is that they will never go back.

ANN M. MARTIN '77

Ann Matthews Martin was born in Princeton, NJ, where she enjoyed an imaginative childhood as the daughter of New Yorker cartoonist, Henry Read Martin, and a teacher, Edith Martin. At Smith Ann M. Martin majored in psychology and education and graduated with honors. She taught for a year, but she soon found her way to New York to work for Pocket Books, Bantam, and then for Scholastic Inc., now her principal publisher. Her first book, Bummer Summer (1983), is one of nearly twenty apart from the series books. Others include Leo the Magnificat (1996), a picture book story about a cat who lives in a church, a story based on a real cat from her aunt's Kentucky church. But the series books together number over three hundred. According to Publishers Weekly, Ann M. Martin "just might be queen of the children's bestsellers," for what began in August 1986 as a miniseries is now a mini-industry, with well over 150 million books in print in several series, including the Baby-Sitters Club, Baby-Sitters Little Sisters, and California Diaries. The idea for the series came from Jean Feiwel, editor-in-chief of the Book Group at Scholastic, who asked Ann to write the pilots. When the sixth book of the series hit number one on the B. Dalton Juvenile Bestseller list, sometime in 1987, Martin stepped up the schedule to one book every other month and eventually one every month. The pace gets her up at 5:30 and keeps her at work all day every day. Her most devoted readers are girls between the ages of eight and twelve.

Ann M. Martin is co-founder of the Lisa Novak Community Libraries, which sends books to libraries in day-care centers and under-funded facilities, and founder of the Ann M. Martin Foundation, which benefits children, education and literacy programs, and homeless people and animals. She practices the ethics she writes about so well. Margot Becker's biography of Ann Martin (1993) highlights the generous spirit of this shaper of a generation of women, who read her books and live by her values.

"Belle Teal" is a new story based on her mother who has Alzheimer's. Belle Teal and Adele are family names, but the story is pure imagination. Now Ann M. Martin is expanding "Belle Teal" into a novel for young readers.

Belle Teal

WELL, IT'S JUST BEEN MAMA AND GRAN AND ME for as long as I can remember. Daddy, he died before I turned one, and Grandpop was gone before Mama married Daddy. But Mama and Gran and me make a very cozy family. And I like a family that is all women. When boys get into the picture they spoil things. Fast too. Some people—Her Royal Highness Vanessa Mathers, for one—might say that a family like mine is not a real family. When Gran hears something like that, she says to me, "And Belle Teal, if someone told you the moon was made of cheese, would you believe it?" So Gran, she is a firm believer that we are a fine family. And so am I.

Me and Gran are real close. We spend a lot of time together, since Mama works two to three jobs all at once, depending on the time of year. Waitressing, bartending, whatever kind of work she can find down in Mechanicsville. I am even named after Gran, who is really Gran Belle, and whose full married name is Belle Teal Rodes. I am Belle Teal Harper. HRH Vanessa says, "What kind of a stupid name is Belle Teal?" and I don't have an answer for a question put like that.

I don't look a thing like Gran, though. Gran is all skinny and birdish. Tiny too. And before her hair went white it was pure blonde. I've seen pictures of her as a girl. Me, I'm darker, like Mama, and just a bit on the plump side. Plus, I'm growing as fast as a weed right now. Soon I'll be taller than Gran.

Mama and Gran are the strongest women I know. Mama, she says, "We have faced lots of hardships, Belle Teal, but we can take care of ourselves. We do whatever is necessary." It seems to me, though, that Gran is the strongest of all of us. She takes care of Mama and me. While Mama is at work, Gran runs things at home. She plants our vegetable garden and cans the fruit from our trees. The chickens are my responsibility, but Gran is the one with the egg business.

Gran generally has answers. She knows about all sort of things, especially things that have to do with our hills. Gran has lived in these hills all her whole life. She can tell you everything about them—their weather and their trees and their animals. She reads the weather with one finger and her nose. Every morning she stands on our front porch, holds up one thin pointer finger, and sniffs the air. "Hot today," she'll say. Or, "Snow coming." Or, "No rain yet." Lately, though, I've noticed that when she predicts the weather she doesn't always make much sense. For instance, she'll stand on that porch shivering in the little light summer nightie that is the only one she'll wear anymore, and she'll look at our broken thermometer, the one that's been stuck on sixty degrees for three years now, and say, "My land, sixty already. It's going to be a scorcher today for sure."

Now Gran knows as well as Mama and I that that thermometer is broken. Plus she's actually shivering, so I don't know what's got into her head. Also, I know for a fact that we have never had a scorcher in these hills in November. Not once. It's a good thing I pick up on facts pretty easy because lately I have to sort out the facts from Gran's new brand of fiction. Like yesterday when she was reading the paper and saw the article on Fog Hollow and just up and announced that she had never in her life been there.

"Why, Gran," I said, "you were *born* over in Fog Hollow."

Gran laughed. "Oh, I don't think so, Belle Teal."

"Okay, where were you born?" I hardly ever challenge Gran, but this was too much. I was all prepared to show her her birth certificate, if necessary, since I know where Mama keeps our important pieces of paper.

"Well . . . I don't know," Gran replied vaguely.

And then Mama called to tell me I was about to miss the bus again and she would NOT drive me to school one more time, and Gran started assembling the ingredients for the year's fruitcakes, which she and I were going to make on the day after Thanksgiving. I might have given a bit more thought to Gran's statement about Fog Hollow, but I was having trouble with HRH Vanessa *and* it was the day Miss Casey had said we could plan our class Christmas program, so I had plenty on my mind.

I rushed around our house, gathering my books and lunch things, kissed our kitten Mewy good-bye, let Mama's gentle arms encircle me for a moment, then Gran's, and lit outside just as the school bus came lurching along the road. The road is not dirt anymore (it got paved at least four years ago), but it's so full of potholes that it might as well be a cow track.

HRH Vanessa, she can't believe that she got stuck on my bus route and has to trundle around in the hills twice a day in order to get an education. I can only think that landing on this route is one of the worst things that has ever befallen her because she makes comments about the hills, my road, my house, and my clothes every single time we are on the bus. Most days I sit in the very backseat with Clarice, and her and I, we just ignore Vanessa until that nearly drives her crazy. But occasionally I am unable to let one of Vanessa's comments slide by me.

That day, for instance, the moment I stepped onto the bus, Vanessa began humming the theme song to *The Beverly Hillbillies*. Several kids laughed.

I rolled my eyes at Clarice and plopped down next to her. Then I started in on the theme song to *Green Acres*, which was a brand-new show and which I had seen once or twice on Clarice's TV.

"You're stuck here for good, Vanessa," I yelled toward the front of the bus. "Just like that city lady who's allergic to everything."

Vanessa took more offense at that than even I had thought she would. "That tacky blonde? I am nothing like her," she said, whipping her head around just long enough to speak, then whipping it back again.

See, here is the thing about HRH Vanessa. It is entirely too easy to get her riled up. Which is why I only bother to do so every now and then. I believe that a person can have too much of a good thing.

Vanessa is new to our school this year. New in September. Her family moved here from over by Stone Ridge, which is like the city of New York compared to Mechanicsville. And to hear Vanessa talk, you'd think she did come from New York. Vanessa doesn't live right in town, she lives at the foot of my mountain. But she makes like she lives in town. And she has nothing but scorn for the mountains.

Vanessa and I have hated each other since the moment I stepped on the school bus on September 6th.

Vanessa actually snorted when she saw me. She was sitting in the front seat of the bus, right up behind the driver, all dressed up—but not so dressed up as anyone could make fun of her. The best feature, in my opinion, was the yellow-and-white striped ribbon in her hair.

I climbed on the bus wearing the green shift Gran had made me at the beginning of the summer. It hadn't been the best-looking shift then, and three months later, I was starting to pop out of it in a few key places. Sort of straining at the seams (which I hoped Gran had double-stitched for safety). On my feet were hiking boots, which I wear purely for comfort, even in hot weather. Of course, I had no ribbon in my hair. I wasn't even sure when I had last washed my hair.

Anyway, I stepped onto that bus and two things happened at once: Clarice waved to me from the backseat, and Vanessa snorted.

"Nice dress," she whispered as I passed by her.

I stopped and gave her a stare. "Who are you?" I asked. (Gran, she says it's generally best to be direct with people.)

At first Vanessa didn't answer me. I shrugged and took another step toward Clarice and the friendly back of the bus, and Vanessa finally said, "I'm Vanessa Mathers, and I come from Stone Ridge."

"Good for you," I replied and once again headed for Clarice.

So that was how me and Vanessa started off with each other.

Now I am not one to be rude, but Vanessa sure is hard to do nice by. So I've taken to ignoring her. I'm an expert at walking right by her, not looking her way, no matter what she's wearing or what I'm wearing.

"My mama says it's not nice to ignore people," Vanessa said to me one day.

"*My* mama says it's not nice to . . ." (I was going to say that she says it's not nice to look down on those less fortunate than you, but at the last moment I changed my mind) ". . . to snort like a piggy," I finished up, since Vanessa has snorted at just about every outfit I've worn all fall.

Clarice laughed loudly at this, and Vanessa blushed, and as you can imagine, things got no better between HRH and me.

AFTER THAT RIDE WITH VANESSA on the first day of school, Clarice and me, we skittered off the bus and ran inside Coker Creek Elementary and directly to our classroom. We were brimming with excitement because our teacher, Miss Casey, was the best teacher in the whole school and we had been hoping we would wind up in her class. When we had gotten our teacher assignments at the end of fourth grade we had been overjoyed. The blanks on both of our forms had been filled out in exactly the same way: Report to Room 12, Miss Casey, on September 6th.

Miss Casey is young and pretty and not yet married, even though she is twenty-four years old. She's exotic. Every kid and every teacher in Coker Creek loves her. I had a crush on her in fourth grade when she wasn't even my teacher yet.

On that first day of school this year, Clarice and me tore into Room 12 and slid into two seats next to each other in the front row. (The back row is better in the bus; the front row is better in school, especially if you have a crush on your teacher.) A few other kids were in the room, clustered around Miss Casey's desk. Clarice and I were deciding whether to join them—which would look unruly but be a lot of fun—or to sit primlike at our desks to show Miss Casey our adultness, when who should walk through the door but HRH Vanessa Mathers herself. She looked dead straight at me and smiled a fake smile and I smiled a fake one back at her and she plopped herself down at the desk next to mine. Luckily the first thing Miss Casey did when school got underway was assign seats. Everyone got switched around, and Vanessa and me ended up on opposite sides of the room.

That morning, after the Pledge of Allegiance and taking milk orders and all, Miss Casey stood in front of the blackboard and said, sounding all formal, "Boys and girls, we have a student who is new to our school this year. Her name is Vanessa Mathers. Please make her feel at home. Vanessa, would you come up here and tell us a few things about yourself?"

Vanessa slid out of her seat and stood next to Miss Casey, who put her arm around her, which made me jealous. Then Her Royal Highness looked at our whole class, taking each of us in with her eyes, and said, "Bonjour, mes amis. In case you don't know, that's French. French for 'Hello, my friends.'"

"Who does she think she is? The queen?" whispered Clarice, who was sitting directly behind me. I was too astonished to laugh.

Vanessa waved one hand in the air, regal-like, and said, "I hail from Stone Ridge. I have lived my entire life there. I have a younger brother named . . ."

". . . Prince Heraldium," Clarice supplied, all whispery.

". . . Joseph Crew Mathers, and my full name is Vanessa Amy Winona Mathers. I am named for my beautiful mama. My daddy manages the grain company in Stone Ridge. It is a very important job. We hope to be happy here in the little town of Mechanicsville. I am sure I am going to enjoy being a student at Coker Creek Elementary School. Thank you."

"Thank you, Vanessa," said Miss Casey. "You may sit down now."

I imagined that I had eyes in the back of my head and they were looking at Clarice, sending her a message about stuck-up French-speaking goody-goodies with fancy names and airs. I didn't turn around, though. I was determined to get off on the right foot in fifth grade.

But how I longed to speak French in order to impress Miss Casey.

IT TURNED OUT THAT I didn't need to impress Miss Casey. She was already impressed with all of us. Leastwise, that was how it seemed. By the end of the day, when I hopped off the school bus and ran to greet Gran, who was shelling late peas on the porch, I called to her, "Gran! Gran! Miss Casey is the best teacher in the world!"

Gran took both of my hands in hers. "I'm glad school is off to a good start, Adele," she said.

Now Adele, that's my mama's name. So I almost said, "*Adele?!* Gran, I'm Belle Teal." But something made me stop. Instead I said, "Yeah, it's off to a good start. I even like tonight's homework. We have to write a one-page autobiography. So's Miss Casey can get to know us better. And you know what? Miss Casey, *she's* going to write *her* autobiography for us. So's we can get to know her better. Did you ever hear of such a thing?"

Gran allowed as how she hadn't. Then she said vaguely, "You better go round up Lyman now, honey."

Lyman is my mama's brother. He's been dead since before the thermometer broke and got stuck on sixty.

THAT NIGHT I STAYED AWAKE in my bed until past midnight, watching the moonlight move slowly around the room, waiting for Mama to come home from a waitressing job. I knew she would peek in at me on her way to bed, and when she did, I said, "Mama?"

"Belle Teal? You still awake? Is everything okay?"

"Mama, today Gran called me Adele. And then she told me to round up Lyman for dinner."

I tried to read Mama's expression in the moonlight. She looked thoughtful and tired. And vaguely frightened. "Well, honey, she's getting older. Sometimes older people are forgetful. We have to be patient with Gran."

"But Mama, how could she forget my *name*? That's different than forgetting where you put the dish towel. And if she asked me to round up Lyman, then she thought he was still alive. And she thought he was a kid again. That's just not normal."

I thought Mama was going to remind me that it isn't nice to classify people as normal or not normal. But instead she said, "You're right. It wouldn't be normal for a younger person. But Gran is almost seventy and she's getting hazy. We might have to do some of her remembering for her now."

And that was all Mama would say on the subject. She smoothed my hair and kissed me good night.

ANYWAY, AFTER THAT GOOD START AT SCHOOL, things with Miss Casey just got better and better. I had been afraid Miss Casey would favor HRH Vanessa, because of Vanessa's fancy clothes and her being new and all. But Miss Casey treated everybody the same. Once, when I came to school wearing another one of my busting-apart shifts (but one I hadn't worn before), Miss Casey even told me I looked pretty. And she graded fair and gave us interesting homework and never embarrassed anybody publicly and generally smelled of Lilacque perfume (pronounced lee-lock, according to Vanessa).

I wondered if I could marry Miss Casey.

In fourth grade the autumn seemed to creep along, like somebody tiptoeing through a house so as to sneak up on something. But in fifth grade with Miss Casey, the fall just sped by in a blur and before I knew it, it was time for Thanksgiving, time for Gran and me to make our fruitcakes, time to plan our class Christmas program. The day I almost missed the bus (again), the day Gran forgot where she was born, well, that was the day we were finally going to begin working on our program. Clarice and me, we had been waiting for this day from the very second Miss Casey had said, "Boys and girls, our class has been asked to put on a Christmas pageant this year, which is quite an honor. I believe we will plan an entire program around the event. We will write our own Christmas poetry and read our poems after the pageant. Then we will serve refreshments to our guests. I would like each of you to bring in something that you have made at home, preferably from a cherished family recipe."

Well. I knew just what I would bring in. Fruitcake, homemade by Gran and me.

ON THAT MEMORABLE DAY, Clarice and me rushed into school and sat all perfect at our desks, even before the bell rang. Even before Miss Casey arrived. We hoped desperately that the planning of the program would begin the moment our morning business was accomplished. And sure enough, it did.

"Girls and boys," Miss Casey began, and I marveled at how she didn't always say "Boys and girls," that she remembered to put the girls first sometimes. "Have you given any thought to your cherished family recipes?"

"Yes!" we chorused.

"Wonderful. Why don't I make a list on the board so that we can all see our menu?" Miss Casey picked up a piece of chalk, a long new one, and turned to Dell Haney in one of the end seats of the front row. "Dell?" she said. "Let's begin with you."

"Well, my mama, she makes molasses cake," Dell said shyly.

"That's just fine," Miss Casey replied. And she wrote DELL - MOLASSES CAKE on the board. She turned to the girl behind Dell. "Mae?"

"Peach pie, with our own preserved peaches," said Mae proudly.

Miss Casey added peach pie to the list.

As the list grew longer, my mouth began to water. We were going to have a Christmas *feast* after the program—cakes and pies and cookies, black-eyed peas and fried chicken and biscuits. When Miss Casey got around to Vanessa, Vanessa stood up beside her chair and said, all hoity-toity, "I will be bringing my mama's fancy Noel lace cookies. They are French, I believe." Then she sat down again.

LACE COOKIES was added to the board.

Next it was Clarice's turn. "Vanilla fudge," she said.

And finally my turn. "My gran and I are going to make our fruitcake," I said.

I heard a faint snicker from somewhere behind me. Fruitcake *does* have a funny name and an unfortunate reputation: everyone claims they don't like it, but that they are delivered at least one every Christmas without fail, and no one will eat it. However, I knew for a fact that none of my classmates, excepting Clarice, had ever tasted anything like my gran's recipe. It's been in our family for decades. Plus, over the years Gran has perfected it. She has made so many changes on that dirty, sticky, flour-covered recipe card that the writing is hard to read. But every year Gran deciphers it. And every year the fruitcake gets a little better. It's expensive to make, and Mama and Gran and I never have enough money to go around, but we always manage to buy the ingredients to bake a very large quantity of fruitcakes. They are our special Christmas gifts for people. *Our* fruitcake is not a joke.

I ignored the snicker and said, "I guarantee it will be the best fruitcake you will ever eat."

"I'm sure it will be," said Miss Casey kindly as she turned to write on the board.

When the list was complete, Miss Casey switched herself to the next task, the one every single person in my class had been waiting for. "And now," she said, "I will assign the parts for the pageant."

Right at this point, HRH Vanessa's hand shot up. "Oh, Miss Casey," she said, "aren't we going to try out for the parts?"

"Well, there are no speaking roles," Miss Casey replied. "Except for the narrator. So there is no reason to try out. I have given this a lot of thought, and I have made the following choices."

Now there were twenty-three kids in my class, so in order to accommodate all of us Miss Casey had added a lot of extra shepherds, a scene with townspeople, and a whole barnful of animals. She started off with the main characters, and the very first one was the narrator. Guess what. Clarice had been given the part of the narrator. She is a very good reader and speaker, so that made sense. The next role was Joseph, which went to Dell. And next was Mary, which went to me.

Well.

You could have heard a pin drop. I knew that everyone, including me, had assumed that the role would go to Vanessa. And frankly, I wanted to be a rooster, because I had collected a lot of colorful feathers I could use on my costume. But no, Miss Casey, she had clearly pronounced *my* name after she said "Mary."

So there was a tiny little scuffle in the air of the classroom, but Miss Casey made like she didn't hear it and just continued on. She didn't say Vanessa's name until she got started with the list of shepherds. When she finally finished, she looked around at all of us and beamed. "Rehearsals will begin on the Monday after Thanksgiving," she said. "We'll talk about your costumes then too."

I tried not to explode. I was that proud. I couldn't wait to get home to tell Gran and Mama. I was going to be Mary in our Christmas pageant. It was an honor. I decided I could be a rooster any old time. Maybe for Halloween in sixth grade. The feathers would keep.

THANKSGIVING WAS A PLEASURE that year. Cousin Emery and Cousin Carrie and Cousin Samuel and Cousin March and Cousin Tic came over from Penny County. Me and Mama did all the cooking the day before. Mama had arranged for a day off, and her and I, we worked in the kitchen together for hours. We listened to the radio and didn't say much, but every now and then we would grin at each other out of the pure joy of preparing our feast. Gran backed out from helping us, saying it was going to be all she could do to make the fruitcakes the next day, they were taking up her whole mind. Well, Mama and me did a pretty good job with the feast. Even Cousin Tic said so, and he being fourteen which is just the worst age of all for a boy, that was some compliment.

After our guests had left and we had cleaned up, Mama and Gran and me sat by the fire for a while. I imagined I was in two places at once—on the braided rug in our parlor with Mewy in my lap and dreams of Christmas and pageants and fruitcakes in my head; and curled up in the rocker on our porch in the chilly air, watching the smoke from our fire curl out of the chimney. Sitting there dreaming with Mama and Gran, that was one of the nicest moments of the entire autumn.

THE NEXT DAY GRAN AND ME, we started on the fruitcakes before the sun came up. In fact, Gran was already in the kitchen when I stumbled out of bed. In spite of the quantity of food I'd eaten the day before, I was hungry, and I had my mind set on a big breakfast before we got to work. But one look at Gran silenced my stomach. She was up early all right, but she was just sitting at the table, staring at nothing. Before her lay the recipe card. Otherwise, the table was empty.

"Gran," I said, "we better get going. Where's all the ingredients?"

"Well, I don't know," Gran replied vaguely.

"What do you mean, you don't know?" I ran into the pantry where Gran had been collecting things. Soon I was setting out walnuts and raisins and currants and citron and candied cherries, flour and brown sugar and butter, bourbon and spices. So many spices—nutmeg and cinnamon and cloves. Seven in all, including the salt. Then thirty eggs. Thirty. We were going to make twenty-four pounds of fruitcake. And for that we needed exactly thirty eggs.

By the time our ingredients were lined up in front of us, Gran looked a little more like Gran. She helped me set out the baking tins and wax paper and cheesecloth.

And then we got to work. I couldn't read that ancient and dirty recipe card at all. It was so worn it felt like fabric. But Gran, she seemed to be in control, and she took charge of things. My world came into focus again. I followed Gran's directions, and we chopped and sifted and mixed and stirred and poured. Mama was at work, so Gran and me were on our own. Outside, the day slipped around us, weak morning sun and strong noon sun and fading afternoon light. It was suppertime and full dark before Gran proclaimed us finished. Two eggs were left over, we had run out of fruit and had to skimp on it toward the end, and we had used up an awful lot of bourbon, much more than usual, it seemed. So things hadn't come out as even as in previous years. But Gran and I congratulated ourselves on our good work, and our house smelled wonderful, like Christmas, and I thought of serving our fruitcake to my classmates. I pictured HRH Vanessa licking her lips, eating two pieces, unable to help herself. I decided that if she did that I would be very graciouslike and compliment her on her mother's French lace cookies.

WHEN SCHOOL GOT GOING AGAIN after our Thanksgiving break, we tackled our Christmas program. We spent some time on it nearly every day. Mostly we worked on the pageant. We wrote the lines Clarice would speak and planned our costumes. Although I was honored to be playing Mary, I was disappointed in her costume. It was right plain compared to that rooster costume I'd been turning over in my mind. The only plainer costumes were the shepherds', although Joseph's was none too grand. But the animals' costumes and especially the angel Gabriel's costume, now they were something else.

I comforted myself by watching the look on Vanessa's face every time we reported to Miss Casey the progress we were making with our costumes. HRH Vanessa still couldn't believe she had to play a shepherd. At least twice a week she asked if Miss Casey couldn't make a casting change, and each time Miss Casey patiently explained that her mind was made up. At which point I could count on Vanessa sending some little dig my way.

"I guess you don't have to look very far to find *your* costume, do you, Belle Teal?" she said once. "You dress like Mary anyway."

Another day she said, "I hope you don't trip over your robe. Mary's robe is awfully long. It would be a shame to fall on your face in front of the whole audience."

"Your robe is almost as long," I pointed out.

"But not quite as. My mother will hem it perfectly," Vanessa replied crisply.

BY THE SECOND WEEK IN DECEMBER we were hard at work on our Christmas poems. Miss Casey said they could be as long or as short as we liked, that they didn't necessarily have to rhyme, and that they could be on any Christmasy subject at all. She also said that each of us was going to have to read our poem aloud. No exceptions.

Well, that was fine by me. I had decided to write a poem called "The Pig's Christmas."

Vanessa was writing about heaven and some darn character she'd made up called Little Angel. I tried not to let her see any part of my poem. I knew that the combination of fruitcake, pigs, and my general appearance coupled with her having to play a shepherd could be dangerous. I hoped to stay pretty much out of her way until the day of the Christmas program.

IT WAS ONE SNOWY NIGHT exactly a week before Christmas Eve when Gran walked into our cozy parlor wearing nothing but that thin nightie of hers, looked at the Christmas tree glowing in a corner of the room, and said, "My land, the fruitcakes!"

The fruitcakes? What about the fruitcakes? If something had happened to them I was doomed. Our fruitcakes had to be stored in bourbon-soaked cheesecloth for weeks before they were ready. And the Christmas program was in just a few days. I didn't want to contribute anything else to our feast, not after the fuss I'd made over the fruitcakes.

I leaped to my feet, dumping Mewy from my lap. "What? What happened to the fruitcakes, Gran?"

"Why, we forgot to make them," she replied.

I stared at her. "We did not. We made them the day after Thanksgiving. Just like always."

Gran frowned. Then her eyes, they just sort of faded out on me, like her soul had disappeared.

I glanced at Mama, and she shook her head at me very slightly, as if to say, "Let it go, Belle Teal."

So I did. Even though I had to fight a strong urge to drag Gran to our storage room where the tins of fruitcakes were lined up under a drafty window. Later that night, when Mama came into my room to tuck me in, before I could even say one word, she took me in her arms and whispered, "Patience, Belle Teal," in my ear.

ON THE MORNING OF THE PAGEANT I couldn't find the sash to Mary's robe. Or the hood Mama and I had stayed up late one night working on while we listened to Christmas carols on the radio. By the time I had located them I was about to miss the bus.

"The fruitcakes!" I cried. "I haven't packed them up yet."

"Don't worry, honey," said Gran. "Your mama and I will bring them this afternoon. You won't need them until after the pageant, will you?"

"No," I replied nervously. I didn't trust Gran an inch. But I didn't want to embarrass her by letting on. So a few minutes later I ran onto the school bus, my costume in one hand, and the fingers of my other hand crossed tightly.

"Where's the fruitcakes?" was the first thing Clarice directed my way as I slid into our seat.

I made a face. "I was late. Gran said she and Mama would bring them to the program this afternoon. Mama got the whole afternoon off work."

Clarice raised her eyebrows at me. I thought she was going to say something about how maybe it wasn't wise to trust Gran with such a task. Instead she said, "I wonder what Her Royal Highness is planning."

I glanced at the front of the bus. HRH Vanessa was sitting there with her legs crossed, very prissy. That was when I realized she hadn't said a word to me as I boarded the bus. I thought that today of all days she would have found some unkind something to say. About my role in the pageant or fruitcakes or pigs. We'd had a poem rehearsal the day before, and when I had started in on "The Pig's Christmas" Vanessa had whispered to Mae, "Oh, a poem about Belle Teal." I thought Vanessa was going to explode from trying to hold in her laughter over her own joke. Now I realized I had waltzed right by her and she had barely even looked at me.

A little pocket of fear opened up in my stomach.

THAT MORNING MISS CASEY, she tried to get us to concentrate on our studies, but of course we couldn't. At last she decided that one final pageant rehearsal might count as some sort of English lesson. So we gathered up our costumes and headed for the all-purpose room. A few minutes later, our costumes in place, I found myself standing next to Vanessa. I was about to edge on over to Clarice, but then I thought that if I really wanted to sidestep trouble that afternoon, it wouldn't kill me to be nice to Vanessa for once.

"Your mom hemmed your costume perfect," I told her, "just like you said she would."

Vanessa nodded, then turned away.

I told myself that Vanessa didn't matter, that I was not going to let her ruin this day for me. I turned my attention to hoping that Gran had remembered to tell Mama that they were supposed to bring the fruitcakes to school.

AT LUNCHTIME IT BEGAN TO SNOW. My worry grew. But at two o'clock our parents and grandparents and guests began to arrive, despite the weather. They sat in a special section of folding chairs in the all-purpose room. Then the other students at Coker Creek filed in and took their seats. Presently the entire room was full. Me and Clarice stood behind the curtain at the end of the room. There was no stage, but that curtain was something else. Real professional. Clarice and I peeked around it. The room was noisier than a hundred school buses. Everyone was talking and laughing and shouting. The adults were calling "Merry Christmas!" and "Christmas gift!" to one another. The kids were talking about Santa and presents and church and choir practice.

"Okay, girls and boys," Miss Casey said quietly to me and my classmates. "It's time to begin."

The lights in the auditorium dimmed down. On the other side of the curtain the room grew quiet. Dell and I, we arranged ourselves with Mae, who was playing our donkey. And Clarice stepped in front of the curtain. She began to tell the story of the nativity. Our pageant had begun.

I didn't trip on my robe. At just the right moment I lifted Clarice's old Tiny Tears doll, who was supposed to be our Baby Jesus, out of the manger. I even managed to smile at the audience when the pageant was over and Miss Casey was running down the list of who played who. Despite HRH Vanessa, I had not shamed myself. I shot a triumphant look at her, and she looked away.

The Christmas poems were to come next. My classmates and me had just enough time to get shed of our costumes before the reading began. Miss Casey directed us to stand before the curtain in groups of five and take turns reading. Vanessa, she was in my group, which I considered a great misfortune. And she got to read before me. Another misfortune. I thought that at the very least, if I got to read before Vanessa did, then she wouldn't be able to control her laughter over "The Pig's Christmas" and no one would be able to understand her poem, which she ended up calling "God's Little Angel."

But Vanessa read first, I read right after her, and she just gazed down at her hands during my reading. I don't think she was even listening to me.

Vanessa and her strange behavior were all I could think about while Miss Casey wound up our program and directed our guests into the cafeteria where our Christmas feast would be laid out. At the first opportunity, I whispered to Clarice, "What in the world is going on with Vanessa? She's being way too—too—"

Nice wasn't the word I was searching for, but Clarice knew what I meant.

Clarice shook her head. "I don't know," she said suspiciously.

We hurried into the cafeteria and the first thing I did was search the crowd for Mama and Gran. There they were. Then I scanned the tables for our fruitcakes. And there they were.

I heaved a huge sigh of relief.

The next few minutes, well, they were taken up with finding our own personal guests and showing them where to get plates and forks and so on. I gave Gran and Mama a tour of the food. The fudge and biscuits and pies and chicken. Enough food for several feasts. "And those," I said at last, "are the French lace cookies that Vanessa's mother made."

I looked around for Vanessa and saw her standing with a tall man and a little boy, her daddy and brother, I guessed.

"Come on. Let's get plates," I said.

It was at that point that I noticed a small commotion over at the dessert table. This one lady, her hand to her mouth, which was all pursedlike, was pointing to something and saying, "Why, there's enough liquor in those to . . . Well, a person could become inebriated."

"What's 'inebriated'?" I asked Mama.

She didn't have a chance to answer.

Another lady said, "Don't let any of the children near them."

I pushed my way to the table. Whatever they were talking about, I wanted one.

"Clarice, Clarice, what is it?" I whispered loudly.

Clarice, who had been watching the commotion at close range, said, "Belle Teal, it's your fruitcakes. Do you put liquor in them?"

I felt the ground wobble beneath my feet. "They soak in bourbon," I replied.

"How much?"

I was about to say, "Not that much," when I remembered the day after Thanksgiving, and how the ingredients hadn't come out even like usual. I felt my face begin to flush.

The fruitcakes were whisked off the table and carried out of the cafeteria.

"Belle Teal?" I heard Mama's voice behind me, and knew somehow that Gran was with her.

I whirled around, ready to give Gran what for. But Gran's face stopped me. Her soul was gone again, her eyes vacant.

Well, that's no excuse, I thought, and was about to say something anyway, when Gran up and said to Mama, "Honey? Better round up Lyman now."

I shot arrows at Gran and Mama with my eyes, then turned and stalked away. I bumped directly into Vanessa.

Before she could say a word, I blurted out, "Okay, go ahead and laugh, Your Highness." And I realized I had never called her Your Highness to her face before.

Vanessa, she just stood there. Her eyes looked bright and wet. I couldn't help myself. I barged on ahead.

"You know you're dying to laugh at me. You've been waiting for this moment since September. So go ahead. Say the fruitcakes were a dumb idea and nobody likes them anyway. Say my pig poem is stupid and only someone like me would write about a pig. Say my clothes are raggedy. Say I'm a mess. Say my gran is a stupid old mountain lady and my mom is poor white trash. Say they're nothing compared to *your* mother. And her wonderful French lace cookies. Go ahead, Vanessa."

Vanessa, she just began to cry.

"See? You don't like it very much when I finally say something back to you, do you?"

Vanessa shook her head.

"Well, go on. Introduce me to your mother. Show her off to me so I can see how wonderful and perfect she is."

"I can't," whispered Vanessa.

"Why not?"

"Because she's dead."

Thank the good lord that just at that very moment I felt a hand on my shoulder and there was Miss Casey. All she said to me was "Vanessa's mother died this summer, Belle Teal. Vanessa is having a difficult time right now." And she led Vanessa to her father.

I don't know when Miss Casey had found out that particular piece of information. I realized there was a lot I didn't know. Like what goes on underneath people's outer skins. Or what was going on in my gran's brain. Or whether the little angel was supposed to be Vanessa's dead mother.

All I wanted to do was leave. Which I did as soon as I possibly could. Mama and Gran and me, we walked out of school into the snow and the gray light of winter, the empty fruitcake tins in a bag carried by Mama. I waited for a wave of awful feelings to wash over me. Disgrace. Fear for Gran. Shame for the things I'd said to Vanessa and for the look I'd given Mama and Gran. Instead I slipped one hand into Mama's and the other into Gran's, and realized one thing: Gran's strength had long ago flowed into Mama and into me. We could take care of each other, and we could take care of Gran. I could survive anything. For the moment, I concentrated on feeling only the strength of this family of women, my family.

MARGARET MITCHELL '22

Margaret Mitchell came to Smith in 1918 from Atlanta, where she was the daughter of an attorney and an active suffragette. She was forced to return home after only one year to care for her father and brother after her mother's death from the flu epidemic of 1919, but she soon went to work as a reporter for the Atlanta Journal. In 1926 her husband, John Marsh, persuaded her to begin work on her story of the Old South. It took the author ten years to tell what she regarded as the story of Atlanta, what readers abroad regarded as a panoramic fictional history of the tumult and suffering caused by the Civil War and Reconstruction, and what American readers everywhere think of as the story of Scarlett O'Hara. The famous film, made in 1939, brought Margaret Mitchell unimagined riches and numerous awards, but fame did not stop her from active support of the war effort throughout World War II. Although she continued to write, she never attempted another major work. "Being the author of Gone with the Wind," she joked, "is a full-time job and most days it is an overtime job filling engagements and meeting visitors." She died tragically in 1949 after being struck by a car as she crossed the street with her husband one evening on the way to a movie.

Margaret Mitchell Marsh received the Pulitzer Prize in 1937 for Gone with the Wind (1936), and over fifty years later it remains one of the best known American novels. The romantic plot follows the loves of Scarlett O'Hara, daughter of an Irish immigrant and owner of Tara, a large plantation. When Scarlett's love for Ashley Wilkes is frustrated by his marriage to the gentle Melanie Hamilton, Scarlett spitefully marries Melanie's brother Charles, who dies in the war. In the struggle to survive, Scarlett marries Frank Kennedy, her sister's fiancé, and with his money and her own unscrupulous determination, establishes a lumber business in Atlanta. Frank is killed avenging an insult to her, and Scarlett marries the war profiteer, Rhett Butler, who attracts her by qualities similar to her own. Her selfishness and continuing infatuation for Ashley destroy Rhett's love, however, and he deserts her. When Melanie dies, and Ashley rejects Scarlett, she realizes too late that Rhett is the one man she has ever really loved. The following selection is the memorable last chapter of Gone with the Wind.

Tomorrow at Tara

FROM *Gone with the Wind*

THE FRONT DOOR WAS SLIGHTLY AJAR and she trotted, breathless, into the hall and paused for a moment under the rainbow prisms of the chandelier. For all its brightness the house was very still, not with the serene stillness of sleep but with a watchful, tired silence that was faintly ominous. She saw at a glance that Rhett was not in the parlor or the library and her heart sank. Suppose he should be out—out with Belle or wherever it was he spent the many evenings when he did not appear at the supper table? She had not bargained on this.

She had started up the steps in search of him when she saw that the door of the dining room was closed. Her heart contracted a little with shame at the sight of that closed door, remembering the many nights of this last summer when Rhett had sat there alone, drinking until he was sodden and Pork came to urge him to bed. That had been her fault but she'd change it all. Everything was to be different from now on—but, please God, don't let him be too drunk tonight. If he's too drunk he won't believe me and he'll laugh at me and that will break my heart.

She quietly opened the dining-room door a crack and peered in. He was seated before the table, slumped in his chair, and a full decanter stood before him with the stopper in place, the glass unused. Thank God, he was sober! She pulled open the door, holding herself back from running to him. But when he looked up at her, something in his gaze stopped her dead on the threshold, stilled the words on her lips.

He looked at her steadily with dark eyes that were heavy with fatigue and there was no leaping light in them. Though her hair was tumbling about her shoulders, her bosom heaving breathlessly and her skirts mud splattered to the knees, his face did not change with surprise or question or his lips twist with mockery. He was sunken in his chair, his suit wrinkling untidily against his thickening waist, every line of him proclaiming the ruin of a fine body and the coarsening of a strong face. Drink and dissipation had done their work on the coin-clean profile and now it was no longer the head of a young pagan prince on new-minted gold but a decadent, tired Caesar on copper debased by long usage. He looked up at her as she stood there, hand on heart, looked quietly, almost in a kindly way, that frightened her.

"Come and sit down," he said. "She is dead?"

She nodded and advanced hesitantly toward him, uncertainty taking form in her mind at this new expression on his face. Without rising, he pushed back a chair with his foot and she sank into it. She wished he had not spoken of Melanie so soon. She did not want to talk of her now, to re-live the agony of the last hour. There was all the rest of her life in which to speak of Melanie. But it seemed to her now, driven by a fierce desire to cry: "I love you," that there was only this night, this hour, in which to tell Rhett what was in her mind. But there was something in his face that stopped her and she was suddenly ashamed to speak of love when Melanie was hardly cold.

"Well, God rest her," he said heavily. "She was the only completely kind person I ever knew."

"Oh, Rhett!" she cried miserably, for his words brought up too vividly all the kind things

Melanie had ever done for her. "Why didn't you come in with me? It was dreadful—and I needed you so!"

"I couldn't have borne it," he said simply and for a moment he was silent. Then he spoke with an effort and said, softly: "A very great lady."

His somber gaze went past her and in his eyes was the same look she had seen in the light of the flames the night Atlanta fell, when he told her he was going off with the retreating army—the surprise of a man who knows himself utterly, yet discovers in himself unexpected loyalties and emotions and feels a faint self-ridicule at the discovery.

His moody eyes went over her shoulder as though he saw Melanie silently passing through the room to the door. In the look of farewell on his face there was no sorrow, no pain, only a speculative wonder at himself, only a poignant stirring of emotions dead since boyhood, as he said again: "A very great lady."

Scarlett shivered and the glow went from her heart, the fine warmth, the splendor which had sent her home on winged feet. She half-grasped what was in Rhett's mind as he said farewell to the only person in the world he respected and she was desolate again with a terrible sense of loss that was no longer personal. She could not wholly understand or analyze what he was feeling, but it seemed almost as if she too had been brushed by whispering skirts, touching her softly in a last caress. She was seeing through Rhett's eyes the passing, not of a woman but of a legend—the gentle, self-effacing but steel-spined women on whom the South had built its house in war and to whose proud and loving arms it had returned in defeat.

His eyes came back to her and his voice changed. Now it was light and cool.

"So she's dead. That makes it nice for you, doesn't it?"

"Oh, how can you say such things," she cried, stung, the quick tears coming to her eyes. "You know how I loved her!"

"No, I can't say I did. Most unexpected and it's to your credit, considering your passion for white trash, that you could appreciate her at last."

"How can you talk so? Of course I appreciated her! You didn't. You didn't know her like I did! It isn't in you to understand her—how good she was—"

"Indeed? Perhaps not."

"She thought of everybody except herself—why, her last words were about you."

There was a flash of genuine feeling in his eyes as he turned to her.

"What did she say?"

"Oh, not now, Rhett."

"Tell me."

His voice was cool but the hand he put on her wrist hurt. She did not want to tell, this was not the way she had intended to lead up to the subject of her love but his hand was urgent.

"She said—she said—'Be kind to Captain Butler. He loves you so much.'"

He stared at her and dropped her wrist. His eyelids went down, leaving his face dark and blank. Suddenly he rose and going to the window, he drew the curtains and looked out intently as if there were something to see outside except blinding mist.

"Did she say anything else?" he questioned, not turning his head.

"She asked me to take care of little Beau and I said I would, like he was my own boy."

"What else?"

"She said—Ashley—she asked me to look after Ashley, too."

He was silent for a moment and then he laughed softly.

"It's convenient to have the first wife's permission, isn't it?"

"What do you mean?"

He turned and even in her confusion she was surprised that there was no mockery in his face. Nor was there any more interest in it than in the face of a man watching the last act of a none-too-amusing comedy.

"I think my meaning's plain enough. Miss Melly is dead. You certainly have all the evidence you want to divorce me and you haven't enough reputation left for a divorce to hurt you. And you haven't any religion left, so the Church won't matter. Then—Ashley and dreams come true with the blessings of Miss Melly."

"Divorce?" she cried. "No! No!" Incoherent for a moment she leaped to her feet and running to him caught his arm. "Oh, you're all wrong! Terribly wrong. I don't want a divorce—I—" She stopped for she could find no other words.

H E PUT HIS HAND UNDER HER CHIN, quietly turned her face up to the light and looked for an intent moment into her eyes. She looked up at him, her heart in her eyes, her lips quivering as she tried to speak. But she could marshal no words because she was trying to find in his face some answering emotions, some leaping light of hope, of joy. Surely he must know, now! But the smooth dark blankness which had baffled her so often was all that her frantic, searching eyes could find. He dropped her chin and, turning, walked back to his chair and sprawled tiredly again, his chin on his breast, his eyes looking up at her from under black brows in an impersonal speculative way.

She followed him back to his chair, her hands twisting, and stood before him.

"You are wrong," she began again, finding words. "Rhett, tonight, when I knew, I ran every step of the way home to tell you. Oh, darling, I—"

"You are tired," he said, still watching her. "You'd better go to bed."

"But I must tell you!"

"Scarlett," he said heavily, "I don't want to hear—anything."

"But you don't know what I'm going to say!"

"My pet, it's written plainly on your face. Something, someone has made you realize that the unfortunate Mr. Wilkes is too large a mouthful of Dead Sea fruit for even you to chew. And that same something has suddenly set my charms before you in a new and attractive light," he sighed slightly. "And it's no use to talk about it."

She drew a sharp surprised breath. Of course, he had always read her easily. Heretofore she had resented it but now, after the first shock at her own transparency, her heart rose with gladness and relief. He knew, he understood and her task was miraculously made easy. No use to talk about it! Of course he was bitter at her long neglect, of course he was mistrustful of her sudden turnabout. She would have to woo him with kindness, convince him with a rich out-pouring of love, and what a pleasure it would be to do it!

"Darling, I'm going to tell you everything," she said, putting her hands on the arm of his chair and leaning down to him. "I've been so wrong, such a stupid fool—"

"Scarlett, don't go on with this. Don't be humble before me. I can't bear it. Leave us some dignity, some reticence to remember out of our marriage. Spare us this last."

She straightened up abruptly. Spare us this last? What did he mean by "this last"? Last? This was their first, their beginning.

"But I will tell you," she began rapidly, as if fearing his hand upon her mouth, silencing her.

"Oh, Rhett, I love you so, darling! I must have loved you for years and I was such a fool I didn't know it. Rhett, you must believe me!"

He looked at her, standing before him, for a moment, a long look that went to the back of her mind. She saw there was belief in his eyes but little interest. Oh, was he going to be mean, at this of all times? To torment her, pay her back in her own coin?

"Oh, I believe you," he said at last. "But what of Ashley Wilkes?"

"Ashley!" she said, and made an impatient gesture. "I—I don't believe I've cared anything about him for ages. It was—well, a sort of habit I hung onto from when I was a little girl. Rhett, I'd never even thought I cared about him if I'd ever known what he was really like. He's such a helpless, poor-spirited creature, for all his prattle about truth and honor and—"

"No," said Rhett. "If you must see him as he really is, see him straight. He's only a gentleman caught in a world he doesn't belong in, trying to make a poor best of it by the rules of the world that's gone."

"Oh, Rhett, don't let's talk of him! What does he matter now? Aren't you glad to know—I mean, now that I—"

A S HIS TIRED EYES MET HERS, she broke off in embarrassment, shy as a girl with her first beau. If he'd only make it easier for her! If only he would hold out his arms, so she could crawl thankfully into his lap and lay her head on his chest. Her lips on his could tell him better than all her stumbling words. But as she looked at him, she realized that he was not holding her off just to be mean. He looked drained and as though nothing she had said was of any moment.

"Glad?" he said. "Once I would have thanked God, fasting, to hear you say all this. But, now, it doesn't matter."

"Doesn't matter? What are you talking about? Of course, it matters! Rhett, you do care, don't you? You must care. Melly said you did."

"Well, she was right, as far as she knew. But, Scarlett, did it ever occur to you that even the most deathless love could wear out?"

She looked at him speechless, her mouth a round O.

"Mine wore out," he went on, "against Ashley Wilkes and your insane obstinacy that makes you hold on like a bulldog to anything you think you want. . . . Mine wore out."

"But love can't wear out!"

"Yours for Ashley did."

"But I never really loved Ashley!"

"Then, you certainly gave a good imitation of it—up till tonight. Scarlett, I'm not upbraiding you, accusing you, reproaching you. That time has passed. So spare me your defenses and your explanations. If you can manage to listen to me for a few minutes without interrupting, I can explain what I mean. Though God knows, I see no need for explanations. The truth's so plain."

She sat down, the harsh gas light falling on her white bewildered face. She looked into the eyes she knew so well—and knew so little—listened to his quiet voice saying words which at first meant nothing. This was the first time he had ever talked to her in this manner, as one human being to another, talked as other people talked, without flippancy, mockery or riddles.

"Did it ever occur to you that I loved you as much as a man can love a woman? Loved you for years before I finally got you? During the war I'd go away and try to forget you, but I couldn't and I always had to come back. After the war I risked arrest, just to come back and find you. I cared so much I believe I would have killed Frank Kennedy if he hadn't died when he did. I loved you but I couldn't let you know it. You're so brutal to those who love you, Scarlett. You take their love and hold it over their heads like a whip."

Out of it all only the fact that he loved her meant anything. At the faint echo of passion in his voice, pleasure and excitement crept back into her. She sat, hardly breathing, listening, waiting.

"I knew you didn't love me when I married you. I knew about Ashley, you see. But, fool that I was, I thought I could make you care. Laugh, if you like, but I wanted to take care of you, to pet you, to give you everything you wanted. I wanted to marry you and protect you and give you a free rein in anything that would make you happy—just as I did Bonnie. You'd had such a struggle, Scarlett. No one knew better than I what you'd gone through and I wanted you to stop fighting and let me fight for you. I wanted you to play, like a child—for you were a child, a brave, frightened, bullheaded child. I think you are still a child. No one but a child could be so headstrong and so insensitive."

HIS VOICE WAS CALM and tired but there was something in the quality of it that raised a ghost of memory in Scarlett. She had heard a voice like this once before and at some other crisis of her life. Where had it been? The voice of a man facing himself and his world without feeling, without flinching, without hope.

Why—why—it had been Ashley in the wintry, windswept orchard at Tara, talking of life and shadow shows with a tired calmness that had more finality in its timbre than any desperate bitterness could have revealed. Even as Ashley's voice then had turned her cold with dread of things she could not understand, so now Rhett's voice made her heart sink. His voice, his manner, more than the content of his words, disturbed her, made her realize that her pleasurable excitement of a few moments ago had been untimely. Something was wrong, badly wrong. What it was she did not know but she listened desperately, her eyes on his brown face, hoping to hear words that would dissipate her fears.

"It was so obvious that we were meant for each other. So obvious that I was the only man of your acquaintance who could love you after knowing you as you really are—hard and greedy and unscrupulous, like me. I loved you and I took the chance. I thought Ashley would fade out of your mind. But," he shrugged, "I tried everything I knew and nothing worked. And I loved you so, Scarlett. If you had only let me, I could have loved you as gently and as tenderly as ever a man loved a woman. But I couldn't let you know, for I knew you'd think me weak and try to use my love against me. And always—always there was Ashley. It drove me crazy. I couldn't sit across the table from you every night, knowing you wished Ashley was sitting there in my place. And I couldn't hold you in my arms at night and know that—well, it doesn't matter now. I wonder, now, why it hurt. That's what drove me to Belle. There is a certain swinish comfort in being with a woman who loves you utterly and respects you for being a fine gentleman—even if she is an illiterate whore. It soothed my vanity. You've never been very soothing, my dear."

"Oh, Rhett . . ." she began, miserable at the very mention of Belle's name, but he waved her to silence and went on.

"And then, that night when I carried you upstairs—I thought—I hoped—I hoped so much I was afraid to face you the next morning, for fear I'd been mistaken and you didn't love me. I was so afraid you'd laugh at me I went off and got drunk. And when I came back, I was shaking in my boots and if you had come even halfway to meet me, had given me some sign, I think I'd have kissed your feet. But you didn't."

"Oh, but Rhett, I did want you then but you were so nasty! I did want you! I think—yes, that must have been when I first knew I cared about you. Ashley—I never was happy about Ashley after that, but you were so nasty that I—"

"Oh, well," he said. "It seems we've been at cross purposes, doesn't it? But it doesn't matter now. I'm only telling you, so you won't ever wonder about it all. When you were sick and it was all my fault, I stood outside your door, hoping you'd call for me, but you didn't, and then I knew what a fool I'd been and that it was all over."

He stopped and looked through her and beyond her, even as Ashley had often done, seeing something she could not see. And she could only stare speechless at his brooding face.

"But then, there was Bonnie and I saw that everything wasn't over, after all. I liked to think that Bonnie was you, a little girl again, before the war and poverty had done things to you. She was so like you, so willful, so brave and gay and full of high spirits, and I could pet her and spoil her—just as I wanted to pet you. But she wasn't like you—she loved me. It was a blessing that I could take the love you didn't want and give it to her. . . . When she went, she took everything."

SUDDENLY SHE WAS SORRY FOR HIM, sorry with a completeness that wiped out her own grief and her fear of what his words might mean. It was the first time in her life she had been sorry for anyone without feeling contemptuous as well, because it was the first time she had ever approached understanding any other human being. And she could understand his shrewd caginess, so like her own, his obstinate pride that kept him from admitting his love for fear of a rebuff.

"Ah, darling," she said coming forward, hoping he would put out his arms and draw her to his knees. "Darling, I'm so sorry but I'll make it all up to you! We can be so happy, now that we know the truth and—Rhett—look at me, Rhett! There—there can be other babies—not like Bonnie but—"

"Thank you, no," said Rhett, as if he were refusing a piece of bread. "I'll not risk my heart a third time."

"Rhett, don't say such things! Oh, what can I say to make you understand? I've told you how sorry I am—"

"My darling, you're such a child. You think that by saying, 'I'm sorry,' all the errors and hurts of years past can be remedied, obliterated from the mind, all poison drawn from old wounds. . . . Take my handkerchief, Scarlett. Never, at any crisis of your life, have I known you to have a handkerchief."

She took the handkerchief, blew her nose and sat down. It was obvious that he was not going to take her in his arms. It was beginning to be obvious that all his talk about loving her meant nothing. It was a tale of a time long past, and he was looking at it as though it had never happened to him. And that was frightening. He looked at her in an almost kindly way, speculation in his eyes.

"How old are you, my dear? You never would tell me."

"Twenty-eight," she answered dully, muffled in the handkerchief.

"That's not a vast age. It's a young age to have gained the whole world and lost your own soul, isn't it? Don't look frightened. I'm not referring to hell fire to come for your affair with Ashley. I'm merely speaking metaphorically. Ever since I've known you, you've wanted two things. Ashley and to be rich enough to tell the world to go to hell. Well, you are rich enough and you've spoken sharply to the world and you've got Ashley, if you want him. But all that doesn't seem to be enough now."

She was frightened but not at the thought of hell fire. She was thinking: "But Rhett is my soul and I'm losing him. And if I lose him, nothing else matters! No, not friends or money or—or anything. If only I had him I wouldn't even mind being poor again. No, I wouldn't mind being cold again or even hungry. But he can't mean—Oh, he can't!"

She wiped her eyes and said desperately:

"Rhett, if you once loved me so much, there must be something left for me."

"Out of it all I find only two things that remain and they are the two things you hate the most—pity and an odd feeling of kindness."

Pity! Kindness! "Oh, my God," she thought despairingly. Anything but pity and kindness. Whenever she felt these two emotions for anyone, they went hand in hand with contempt. Was he contemptuous of her too? Anything would be preferable to that. Even the cynical coolness of the war days, the drunken madness that drove him the night he carried her up the stairs, his hard fingers bruising her body, or the barbed drawling words that she now realized had covered a bitter love. Anything except this impersonal kindness that was written so plainly in his face.

"Then—then you mean I've ruined it all—that you don't love me any more?"

"That's right."

"But," she said stubbornly, like a child who still feels that to state a desire is to gain that desire, "but I love you!"

"That's your misfortune."

She looked up quickly to see if there was a jeer behind those words but there was none. He was simply stating a fact. But it was a fact she still would not believe—could not believe. She looked at him with slanting eyes that burned with a desperate obstinacy and the sudden hard line of jaw that sprang out through her soft cheek was Gerald's jaw.

"Don't be a fool, Rhett. I can make—"

He flung up a hand in mock horror and his black brows went up in the old sardonic crescents.

"Don't look so determined, Scarlett! You frighten me. I see you are contemplating the transfer of your tempestuous affections from Ashley to me and I fear for my liberty and my peace of mind. No, Scarlett, I will not be pursued as the luckless Ashley was pursued. Besides, I am going away."

Her jaw trembled before she clenched her teeth to steady it. Go away? No, anything but that! How could life go on without him? Everyone had gone from her, everyone who mattered except Rhett. He couldn't go. But how could she stop him? She was powerless against his cool mind, his disinterested words.

"I am going away. I intended to tell you when you came home from Marietta."

"You are deserting me?"

"Don't be the neglected, dramatic wife, Scarlett. The rôle isn't becoming. I take it, then, you do not want a divorce or even a separation? Well, then, I'll come back often enough to keep gossip down."

"Damn gossip!" she said fiercely. "It's you I want. Take me with you!"

"No," he said, and there was finality in his voice. For a moment she was on the verge of an outburst of childish wild tears. She could have thrown herself on the floor, cursed and screamed and drummed her heels. But some remnant of pride, of common sense stiffened her. She thought, if I did, he'd only laugh, or just look at me. I mustn't bawl; I mustn't beg. I mustn't do anything to risk his contempt. He must respect me even—even if he doesn't love me.

She lifted her chin and managed to ask quietly:

"Where will you go?"

There was a faint gleam of admiration in his eyes as he answered.

"Perhaps to England—or to Paris. Perhaps to Charleston to try to make peace with my people."

"But you hate them! I've heard you laugh at them so often and—"

He shrugged.

"I still laugh—but I've reached the end of roaming, Scarlett. I'm forty-five—the age when a man begins to value some of the things he's thrown away so lightly in youth, the clannishness of families, honor and security, roots that go deep—Oh, no! I'm not recanting, I'm not regretting anything I've ever done. I've had a hell of a good time—such a hell of a good time that it's begun to pall and now I want something different. No, I never intend to change more than my spots. But I want the outer semblance of the things I used to know, the utter boredom of respectability—other people's respectability, my pet, not my own—the calm dignity life can have when it's lived by gentle folks, the genial grace of days that are gone. When I lived those days I didn't realize the slow charm of them—"

AGAIN SCARLETT WAS BACK IN THE WINDY ORCHARD OF TARA and there was the same look in Rhett's eyes that had been in Ashley's eyes that day. Ashley's words were as clear in her ears as though he and not Rhett were speaking. Fragments of words came back to her and she quoted parrotlike: "A glamor to it—a perfection, a symmetry like Grecian art."

Rhett said sharply: "Why did you say that? That's what I meant."

"It was something that—that Ashley said once, about the old days."

He shrugged and the light went out of his eyes.

"Always Ashley," he said and was silent for a moment.

"Scarlett, when you are forty-five, perhaps you will know what I'm talking about and then perhaps you, too, will be tired of imitation gentry and shoddy manners and cheap emotions. But I doubt it. I think you'll always be more attracted by glister than by gold. Anyway, I can't wait that long to see. And I have no desire to wait. It just doesn't interest me. I'm going to hunt in old towns and old countries where some of the old times must still linger. I'm that sentimental. Atlanta's too raw for me, too new."

"Stop," she said suddenly. She had hardly heard anything he had said. Certainly her mind had not taken it in. But she knew she could no longer endure with any fortitude the sound of his voice when there was no love in it.

He paused and looked at her quizzically.

"Well, you get my meaning, don't you?" he questioned, rising to his feet.

She threw out her hands to him, palms up, in the age-old gesture of appeal and her heart, again, was in her face.

"No," she cried. "All I know is that you do not love me and you are going away! Oh, my darling, if you go, what shall I do?"

For a moment he hesitated as if debating whether a kind lie were kinder in the long run than the truth. Then he shrugged.

"Scarlett, I was never one to patiently pick up broken fragments and glue them together and tell myself that the mended whole was as good as new. What is broken is broken—and I'd rather remember it as it was at its best than mend it and see the broken places as long as I lived. Perhaps, if I were younger—" he sighed. "But I'm too old to believe in such sentimentalities as clean slates and starting all over. I'm too old to shoulder the burden of constant lies that go with living in polite disillusionment. I couldn't live with you and lie to you and I certainly couldn't lie to myself. I can't even lie to you now. I wish I could care what you do or where you go, but I can't."

He drew a short breath and said lightly but softly:

"My dear, I don't give a damn."

SHE SILENTLY WATCHED HIM GO up the stairs, feeling that she would strangle at the pain in her throat. With the sound of his feet dying away in the upper hall was dying the last thing in the world that mattered. She knew now that there was no appeal of emotion or reason which would turn that cool brain from its verdict. She knew now that he had meant every word he said, lightly though some of them had been spoken. She knew because she sensed in him something strong, unyielding, implacable—all the qualities she had looked for in Ashley and never found.

She had never understood either of the men she had loved and so she had lost them both. Now, she had a fumbling knowledge that, had she ever understood Ashley, she would never have loved him; had she ever understood Rhett, she would never have lost him. She wondered forlornly if she had ever really understood anyone in the world.

There was a merciful dullness in her mind now, a dullness that she knew from long experience would soon give way to sharp pain, even as severed tissues, shocked by the surgeon's knife, have a brief instant of insensibility before their agony begins.

"I won't think of it now," she thought grimly, summoning up her old charm. "I'll go crazy if I think about losing him now. I'll think of it tomorrow."

"But," cried her heart, casting aside the charm and beginning to ache, "I can't let him go! There must be some way!"

"I won't think of it now," she said again, aloud, trying to push her misery to the back of her mind, trying to find some bulwark against the rising tide of pain. "I'll—why, I'll go home to Tara tomorrow," and her spirits lifted faintly.

She had gone back to Tara once in fear and defeat and she had emerged from its sheltering walls strong and armed for victory. What she had done once, somehow—please God, she could do again! How, she did not know. She did not want to think of that now. All she wanted was a breathing space in which to hurt, a quiet place to lick her wounds, a haven in which to plan her campaign. She thought of Tara and it was as if a gentle cool hand were stealing over her heart. She could see the white house gleaming welcome to her through the reddening autumn leaves, feel the quiet hush of the country twilight coming down over her like a benediction, feel the dews falling on the acres of green bushes starred with fleecy white, see the raw color of the red earth and the dismal dark beauty of the pines on the rolling hills.

She felt vaguely comforted, strengthened by the picture, and some of her hurt and frantic regret was pushed from the top of her mind. She stood for a moment remembering small things, the avenue of dark cedars leading to Tara, the banks of cape jessamine bushes, vivid green against the white walls, the fluttering white curtains. And Mammy would be there. Suddenly she wanted Mammy desperately, as she had wanted her when she was a little girl, wanted the broad bosom on which to lay her head, the gnarled black hand on her hair. Mammy, the last link with the old days.

With the spirit of her people who would not know defeat, even when it stared them in the face, she raised her chin. She could get Rhett back. She knew she could. There had never been a man she couldn't get, once she set her mind upon him.

"I'll think of it all tomorrow, at Tara. I can stand it then. Tomorrow, I'll think of some way to get him back. After all, tomorrow is another day."

HARRIET DOERR '31

*arriet Huntington Doerr, born in Pasadena, CA, in 1910, began her college
education at Smith in 1927 and completed it fifty years later at Stanford
University. She loved the food for mind and body at Smith. "Best food I ever ate
at any college; I gained about fifteen pounds the first semester, and worked to lose
it the second. But I never lost the love of history studied first at Smith." Between
her Smith and Stanford education, Harriet Doerr married an engineer, raised two
children, and lived in Mexico for varying periods over fifteen years. After her
husband's death, she completed her undergraduate degree, still majoring in history, and started a new career in writing. At Smith she would have been called an
Ada Comstock Scholar, Smith's program for students of nontraditional age, for
she graduated from Stanford at the age of sixty-seven.*

*Her first novel Stones for Ibarra won the American Book Award in 1984,
the 1985 National Book Award for First Fiction, the Bay Area Book Reviewers
Award, the Godal Medal of the Commonwealth Club of California, and the
American Academy of Arts and Letters Harold D. Vursell Award. It was adapted
for television in 1988 as a Hallmark Hall of Fame production starring Glenn
Close and Keith Carradine as Sara and Richard Everton, fictionalized versions
of Harriet Doerr and her husband who left a comfortable life in northern California to settle in a remote Mexican village.* Consider This, Señora *(1993) is
also set in Mexico, where landscape and culture merge into unique visions for
other expatriates, all fictional but based on Harriet Doerr's own friends and ac-
quaintances. Four North Americans settle in Amapolas, Mexico, and transform it and themselves into something more beautiful than before.*

The selection here is from her third volume, Tiger in the Grass: Stories
and Other Inventions *(1995). "The Local Train" is an early story, with the
precision and polish of the later novels; it anticipates* Stones for Ibarra *in its
memorable composite of the light, smells, and sounds of Mexico and the unquestioning faith of its people.*

The Local Train

FROM *The Tiger in the Grass: Stories and Other Inventions*

"IT WAS GOD'S WILL," said Trinidad. "Otherwise I might have taken the Wednesday train or the Friday train from Libertad to Obregón, when I could buy flannel, buttons, and yarn at less cost. Because I was sixteen and foolish, señora, I was not ready for the baby I had been carrying for almost seven months."

Trinidad sat with Sara Everton under the widening shade of an ash tree, on a pine bench that was as upright as a church pew. The two women faced a walled garden, where limp vines and seared lilies drooped in the heat of the April afternoon. The uncompromising sun still paralyzed the air and baked the earth, although its rays slanted almost horizontally from the west.

Dust from the road had powdered Trinidad's flat black slippers. She carried ten small eggs in a wire basket. When Sara asked the price, Trinidad said, "Whatever you wish to pay."

Sara Everton realized that the eggs were the product of hens who scratched a living from straw, weeds, and piles of trash, and paid slightly more than the amount asked for a dozen large ones in the city supermarket.

From the bench the two women looked over the adobe wall, past the plowed field, the dry arroyo, and the village, with its three church towers and two domes, and across the broad empty plain to the mesas that closed the eastern horizon.

Sara inquired about Trinidad's children.

"Señora, I have ten," her guest told her. "Three dead and seven living."

Unlike almost everyone else in Ibarra, Trinidad had not been born in this town. Only a year ago, she had come here to live with her sister. The two widows raised chickens and embroidered coarse cotton tablecloths in cross-stitch designs of harsh colors: heliotrope, hot pink, and saffron yellow. Trinidad's hair, which showed no gray and was still as thick as ever, was pulled straight back into a knot, her skin was smooth over high flat cheekbones, her unwavering glance was directed from eyes where wisdom had been acquired without loss of innocence.

"Was the infant of whom you speak the first of your children?" Sara asked.

"Yes, señora, the first of them all, and a son, and the only one among them who was to be granted a miracle."

A silence followed. The tree shadow edged out, like a pond spilling, over the parched soil.

Then Trinidad said, "I think you know the state of Michoacán, where I was born and lived all my life, in the village of Libertad, until I came here, to these dry hills, to be with my sister."

At these words Sara Everton saw the state of Michoacán rise like a mirage from the clods of the field before her. As in the finale of a silent movie, when there appears behind the credits a vision of improbable rewards: a humble cottage almost buried in roses or a wire cage from whose open door two doves soar out of sight—like these illusory heavens, there now floated up before her the image of wet green meadows, red furrows of fertile earth, steep slopes of extinct volcanoes serrated from crater to ground with ledges of ripening corn, low white houses almost crushed by their tile roofs. She heard the rush of water in ditches and canals and was not surprised when a lake materialized, drowning the famished plots of land, the baseball field, the cemetery and the naves of the churches. Within an hour there would be rain that would silver the surface of the lake as well as the leaves of the eight olive trees that lined the road.

Sara cast off her trance. "Yes, I know Michoacán," she said, and asked Trinidad what had happened to her firstborn.

"The distance is so short, señora," Trinidad said, "just fifty kilometers from Libertad to Obregón. Only one hour by the local train, and it stops often on the way. I traveled alone because my husband was to meet me at the end of the line, in the market town where he had gone the day before to sell a calf. In that short distance, in that single hour, it happened."

Trinidad sat very still, her hands folded in her lap. "I thought the train would leave late, as usual, so I almost missed it. I had to run the last hundred meters, with the conductor waving from the step and the heads in the open windows leaning out to watch me, to see if the conductor would wait or not. I managed to pull myself up into the vestibule just as the train started to move. You know these trains, señora, only two second-class cars, one freight car, and the engine. I looked in both cars, and the wooden seats, each one intended for three people, seemed to be taken, and many of them by more than three passengers. So I was prepared to stand, no harm done, I thought, being young and strong, when the conductor showed me to the one place that was left, a seat on the aisle."

Now Trinidad went on without pausing. "Across from me was a family of seven, all eating tacos from the mother's string bag, except the baby, who was at her breast. In front of me near the window was an old man who fell asleep, and beside him an old woman who became ill from the motion and continuously coughed in her *rebozo*. Directly in front of me was a woman with a boy of three, who stood looking at me over the back of the seat. The woman bought him an orange crush and then another to keep him happy. When he started to whimper she spanked him, and the two orange crushes that had gone in and through him by then burst out below and ran in little streams onto my shoes from the seat where he stood.

"Next to me was a very quiet, very ugly girl. She had pale eyes with no lashes, and a long face. Perhaps she was quiet because she was ugly. She was with a man who sat next to the window. His mouth was twisted by a scar that slanted from his cheekbone to his chin. He was drunk and angry. I think he was trying to make the girl say yes, to admit something, but she only shook her head without speaking. Once he shook her shoulder hard enough to make her teeth rattle, and once he slapped her cheek so hard she cried. Twice the conductor came to warn this man, saying that he would put him off at the next stop if the disturbance continued. Then the man would look out the open window with his lips moving, one hand clenched to his knee and the other in his pocket, and we would have a moment's peace.

"But he always returned to the argument, angrier than before, until at last, when there were only ten minutes of the trip left, the girl spoke, still not looking at him. 'Then kill me,' she said. And when he heard these words, out of his pocket came his hand, holding a knife that looked as if it lived there. He switched it open and stabbed her in the chest, in the neck, in whatever part of her he encountered, while she struggled and screamed, until the conductor came running and, with the help of three young men who were passengers, disarmed this man and took him away, his arms bound to his sides with rope."

Now Trinidad looked at Sara. "And the plain girl, with her pale eyes wide open and blood pouring from her mouth like coffee from the pot, lay dead with her head on my shoulder and her blood running down to my knees, soaking through my shawl and my apron and my dress and my garments beneath. Soaking through my skin until it reached my unborn child and he swam in her blood.

"So great was my fright, señora, that I could not utter a word and no tears came. Two men carried off the girl, and when we arrived in Obregón a few minutes later, there stood my husband, fixed to the platform, thinking that the people from the train who helped me walk to him were bringing him an expiring wife.

"And so it was that my first son, Florencio, whom we call Lencho, was born five weeks before full term, and we feared he might bear some mark of the shock he and I had suffered. But, señora, he was a perfect baby, unmarked, unscarred. Only later we began to notice that when I dropped the cover of a pan, Lencho did not start and when I called to him by name he did not turn. So after a few months we realized that Lencho was deaf and a little later came to know that he couldn't talk.

"Then I gave birth to more children, a year and a half apart, and we continued to farm our small plot of land in Libertad. Lencho was very intelligent. He watched our mouths and learned to understand some of the things we said. Of course, he could not go to school with the others. Instead, he helped his father plant corn and *chiles* in the spring, and every morning he took the cow to graze.

"And so nine years passed in that part of Michoacán, which is my *tierra*, my true home. One day my husband's cousin came, who had not been in Libertad since he left to study at preparatory school and college, and then the university, where he was trained to be a doctor. He looked at Lencho and made him open his mouth.

"Then he told me I must take the boy to a specialist in San Luis Potosí, which is five hundred kilometers north of Libertad. The cousin said to waste no time. So I borrowed the money for the bus fare, promising young chickens and fresh cow's milk in return. Two days after we arrived in San Luis the specialist operated on Lencho's throat. The surgery lasted three hours, and afterwards, when Lencho was in his bed again, as white and quiet as a corpse, I thought: They have brought him back to this room to die.

"But when he woke up an hour later he turned his head toward a step or a voice. He started making sounds, and in the next weeks and months the sounds became words."

Trinidad looked at the American woman. "Now I have told you how the Virgin protected Lencho," she said.

Sara nodded. She said, "Yes."

Trinidad, standing to leave in the gathering dusk, told Sara how soon after Lencho's cure the whole family traveled across two states of Mexico to thank the Virgin of San Juan de los Lagos, who is responsible for miracles of this sort. From the bus station they crossed to the church, where they waited for two hours in the courtyard, on their knees among the kneeling crowd, until it was their turn to enter. When they finally reached the altar, Trinidad lit a candle for Lencho to place among the hundreds already lighted there, and each child had a flower to add to the others that lay in heaps and sheaves at the Virgin's feet.

"She might have walked away on flowers, señora," said Trinidad.

By the time she went off with the empty egg basket, the shadow of the ash tree had climbed the eastern wall. Its branches scarcely stirred. The birds that inhabited it might already have settled in for the night.

Sara lingered there, staring across the darkening valley to the hills lying in full sun beyond. She closed her eyes and listened. For a few seconds no door slammed, no dog barked, no child called. It was so still she could hear the turn of a leaf, the fold of a wing.

SYLVIA PLATH '55

*S*ylvia Plath came to Smith College from Wellesley, MA, in 1950. She returned to the College as an instructor in the English Department for the academic year 1957/58 following two years as a Fulbright Fellow in Cambridge, England, where she met and married Ted Hughes on Bloomsday, 16 June 1956. Only two of Path's works were published in her lifetime: The Colossus (1960), a volume of poetry, and The Bell Jar (1963), a novel pseudonymously published and now newly reissued in London, that fictionalizes her guest editorship of the college issue of Mademoiselle in August 1953 and the attempted suicide that delayed her graduation from Smith. At the time of her death, 11 February 1963, she was preparing for publication a second collection of poems that her husband reordered and published as Ariel in 1965. Winter Trees (1972), from which "Purdah" is drawn, was also prepared by Ted Hughes. His collection of eighty-eight poems about Sylvia Plath, Birthday Letters (1998), published on the thirty-fifth anniversary of her death and only months before he died of cancer, records their mutual poetic promise, their love and failed marriage, and their impassioned poetic rivalry.

The letters printed here are from the Mortimer Rare Book at Smith College, as are many working drafts of her poetry. The letter to artist and friend Enid Mark '54 was written while Sylvia Plath was still an undergraduate at Smith. "To Elly," a recently acquired letter written to actress, writer, and friend Elinor Friedman Klein '56 in April 1957, reveals a vibrant woman— funny, generous, and loving—finishing her Cambridge degree, planning to return to Smith to teach, and making her own place as poet. The four poems mentioned in the letter are "Ella Mason and Her Eleven Cats," "The Snowman on the Moor," "Sow," and "On the Difficulty of Conjuring Up a Dryad"—all published in Poetry in July 1957. The poem "Purdah" composed in October 1962, ends with the unloosing of "the lioness" of her strong poetic voice that shatters "the chandelier / Of air," a shattering depicted by Enid Mark in the image that follows.

Letters and Poems

Wednesday afternoon
[26 January 1955]

DEAR ENID...
It was a delight to hear from you. I am, to answer your question, the sort who can somehow always pick up a friendship that was very dear, no matter how long the time, nor how wide the space in between. I am sure that if I went to Africa for ten years, I would come back naively expecting to pick up right where I left off, and hoping that everyone else would feel that way too. At any rate, it seems most natural to be talking on paper to you again, and the new name is strange and wonderful, too.

Life here at Smith has been incredibly rich this year. I am becoming a fatalist and think that somehow this postponed senior year was necessary for me to grow more slowly in time, like cider needing years in the dark to become mellow. At any rate, all avenues of life are full and miraculous. I found myself writing a thesis on "The Magic Mirror: A Study of the Double in Two of Dostoevsky's Novels" with young, brilliant, delightful Mr. George Gibian, and being fascinated by my topic till the end, and reading all about mirror images, shadow legends, everything from ETA Hoffman's fairy tales to Freud!

To top it off, by accident (being assigned an interview) I took Mr. Kazin's writing course also first semester, with the delight of his asking me in, long interviews every two weeks, and a final joy of his sharing a pizza and coffee with me at the Little Italy one rainy iceglazed December afternoon. I turned out a lot for him, mostly rough sketches, which have all been rejected by *The New Yorker*. However, one which I rewrote with a "plot" (very unusual for me) and a frothy sense of humor (more unusual) was looked at with interest by the *Ladies Home Journal*. They asked me to rewrite it and send it back, and now I am undergoing that excruciating wait, dying for the mail in terror and desire every day, telling myself sternly that they are taking all this time to write a very nice detailed letter of rejection! Cross your fingers!

I'd really love to see some of your stories, Enid. Just for the joy of reading them; I'm so deep in rejections that I am hardly equipped to criticize! I too, hope to write for *Seventeen* someday. But they are very demanding . . .

Next semester is the usual review unit, continued Shakespeare with Miss Dunn, intermediate German, Mr. Kazin's famed American Lit. course which everyone in the college seems to be taking, and a lovely private special studies unit with Mr. Fisher (whom I'm just getting to know) which He suggested: The Theory and Practice of Poetics. I have to turn in a "batch" of poems every week and a long critical essay that looks from here like another thesis. At any rate, the prospect is enchanting, and I do think the poems are coming better . . .

Gordon, the Amherst graduate, now an ensign in the Navy, is in Cuba at present, but I had a very good Christmas vacation in Wellesley with him . . . our times coincided exactly. I have, however, put off all thought of marrying him to a very indefinite future, for a multitude of reasons, primary among them, the precarious uncertainty of our future growth and activity. It is fine if a man is older, more mature, has crystallized out a bit, but even though Gordon is 25, he is amazingly young yet (or I am amazingly old) and I am Machiavellian enough to want to grow to the fullest . . .

New York has been most hospitable lately, with that charming young French boy, Richard Sassoon. This past week, in celebration of completed thesis and exams was a round of plays ("The Dybbuk") movies ("Gate of Hell" and "Temptation of Saint Joan" at the Museum of Modern Art) and French restaurants like the Cafe St. Denis and Le Gourmet. Now, at last, I think I can bear cold water and brown bread, hotdogs and coffee for two months with joy, so glutted am I on escargots and huitres!

Do write, send stories, and I hope I may perhaps say hello to you and your wonderful husband in person sometime spring vacation, if all goes well.

Love, Sylvia

Purdah

Jade—
Stone of the side,
The agonized

Side of a green Adam, I
Smile, cross-legged,
Enigmatical,

Shifting my clarities.
So valuable!
How the sun polishes this shoulder!

And should
The moon, my
Indefatigable cousin

Rise, with her cancerous pallors,
Dragging trees—
Little bushy polyps,

Little nets,
My visibilities hide.
I gleam like a mirror.

At this facet the bridegroom arrives.
Lord of the mirrors!
It is himself he guides

In among these silk
Screens, these rustling appurtenances.
I breathe, and the mouth

Veil stirs its curtain.
My eye
Veil is

A concatenation of rainbows.
I am his.
Even in his

Absence, I
Revolve in my
Sheath of impossibles,

Priceless and quiet
Among these parakeets, macaws!
O chatterers

Attendants of the eyelash!
I shall unloose
One feather, like the peacock.

Attendants of the lip!
I shall unloose
One note

Shattering
The chandelier
Of air that all day plies

Its crystals,
A million ignorants.
Attendants!

Attendants!
And at his next step
I shall unloose

I shall unloose—
From the small jeweled
Doll he guards like a heart—

The lioness,
The shriek in the bath,
The cloak of holes.

Tuesday, April 9, 1957

Dear dear elly. . .
It seems all I do these days is sit in bramble patches like Eyore, imagining the lovely decks of the Queen Elizabeth & the shiny little cottage at Hidden Acres with [its] shiny little icebox & shiny little stove where my blessed mother has got Ted & me stowed away for 7 weeks on the Cape: because we didn't have a white wedding, with giant organs. I feel all itch to get home & Ted is, thank god, dying to leave England & come along. We dock at Pier 92 on June 25th. We are gritting our teeth, me studying for these monolith behemoth exams covering 2000 years of tragedy, morality, etc. etc. in 5 days of 6 hours a day writing. I tried to get leave to hire a stenographer, being as my pen-hand is as useful to me now as the vermiform appendix. But no.

The main difference, when you will see us (apart from my hair being 2 inches longer) is that Ted is very famous. Only a select few know how famous. It is like this.

We received a telegram (or rather Ted did, I am vicarious) recently to the effect that Ted's first book of poems "The Hawk in the Rain" has won the Anglo-American contest sponsored by the New York City Poetry Society & judged (hold your hat) by W. H. Auden, Stephen Spender, & Marianne Moore: *Harper's* is publishing the book this August & the Poetry Center man (who sounds lovely—he just had a baby boy, or his wife did) says everyone who's read the book is "raving," hopes success won't spoil Rock Hunter, etc. Our First Publishing Party. The fusty headed British editors are just waking up to the fact that their only hope, the Light of future British poetry, is sailing away to greener pastures, if that is metaphorically possible.

And me: I am peculiarly happy with a job teaching freshman English at yes, Smith. I'll have plenty of time to write & must admit that I'm really excited at the prospect: near NYC, Boston, publishers, editors & I do love the English faculty. Ted will try to get a part-time job when we arrive, because People like interviews.

He is very ready to shake hands with Russ Morrow, I think.

Some wealthy backer of *Time* & *Life* is flying a chartered planeful of debutantes over here for May Balls in June: could you stow away?

All the knots we were in last August, with the absurd & inhuman prospect of me living incognito at Newnham have melted. I am home. At home. Eating peanuts & making my own good coffee au creme. Pots au feu.

I wish you would be an actress. Full time. Saw a picture of actress in *Camino Real* which just opened in London & wanted it to be you. You have Got It. I wish you would be one. Is it true, how lovely, charming, that one Jody B. is engaged by Columbia pictures.

Poetry Chicago has just accepted 4 very long poems from each of us to come out about June or July: they're very symmetrical: one for you, one for you, and one for Peter Geekie.

Mother is throwing a little backyard reception Saturday afternoon, June 29th & you will be formally invited but both of us want very much for you to come. Please do. We want to see you soon, so write anyway until we can.

Much love from us both. . .
Sylvia

ART
PORTFOLIO

ENID MARK '54

*E*nid Mark maintains her studio in Wallingford, PA, though she was born and raised in New York, where she attended the High School of Music and Art. After Smith, where she did honors work in English, she married and moved to suburban Philadelphia, receiving further training in Printmaking at West Chester University in Pennsylvania. She taught and directed the program for gifted students in her local school district before working full time at her lithographs, etchings, and silkscreen prints which have been widely exhibited throughout the United States and abroad. Among her awards are Purchase Prizes from the Delaware Art Museum, the University of Delaware, and American Color Print Society Awards.

She turned to producing her own illustrated limited editions at the suggestion of Ruth Mortimer, the late curator of the Rare Book Room at Smith, which holds many of Enid Mark's publications. The first book to bear the imprint of the ELM Press was The Bewildering Thread (1986), poems selected by Ruth Mortimer and Sarah Black, lithographs by Enid Mark. Other books include Promises (1982) with lithographs based on photographs taken in Israel, and her newest book is Precessional (1998), a collaboration with MacArthur Award-winning poet Eleanor Wilner.

The print here of shattering glass is the fifth image in a series of increasingly larger images in About Sylvia (1996), a collection of lithographs and poems about Sylvia Plath '55, friend and classmate of Enid Mark. This image is opposite Anne Sexton's poem, "Wanting to Die," with its haunting lines: "But suicides have a special language./ Like carpenters they want to know which tools./ They never ask why build." One of Sylvia Plath's letters to Enid Mark appears in the Plath selection, where "Purdah" quietly endorses the image.

Among the many permanent collections in which her work is included are the National Gallery of Art, Washington, DC; the Getty Center for the History of Art and Humanities, Los Angeles; the Philadelphia Museum of Art; and the rare book collections at Smith, Harvard, Yale, the New York Public Library, the British Museum, the Victoria and Albert Museum, the National Library of Canada, the Israel Museum, and the Library of Congress.

Enid Mark '54
Shattering Glass
Lithograph, 9" x 5 1/2"
from *About Sylvia* 1996

BARBARA COONEY '38

*B*arbara Cooney Porter came to Smith from Brooklyn and she now keeps a studio and home on the Damariscotta River in Maine. After growing up on Long Island and spending childhood summers with her family in Maine, she studied studio art and art history at Smith. After Smith, Barbara Cooney studied at the Art Students League in New York, showing her portfolio to publishers charged with the responsibility of engaging illustrators.

Shortly after graduation, she published her first book, Ake and His World (1940) by the Swedish poet Bertil Malmberg. A year later, she published King of Wreck Island (1941), a book she wrote and illustrated. She was on her way to success, but took time out to serve in the Women's Army Corps during World War II and to raise four children who became as independent as their mother, who climbed Mount Olympus to see as Zeus saw, and who went to Appalachia to meet author Gloria M. Houston and see the setting of The Year of the Perfect Christmas Tree: An Appalachian Tale (1988).

"Of all the books I have done," she says, "Miss Rumphius (1982), Island Boy (1988), and Hattie and the Wild Waves (1990), are the closest to my heart. These three are as near as I ever will come to an autobiography." Like Miss Rumphius, Barbara Cooney has traveled the world, settled down by the sea, and tried to make the world more beautiful. Also like Miss Rumphius, she loves the lupines that bloom in early summer in Maine, her acknowledged "heaven on earth," the state that named her "State Treasure" in 1996 and established the Lupine Award in 1989 to honor outstanding children's books by state residents. Not surprisingly, Miss Rumphius was named a New York Times Best Book of the Year and received the American Book Award for the Best Picture Book for Children. These honors echo others. She has illustrated over one hundred books for children, winning two Caldecott Medals for Chanticleer and the Fox (1959), which she adapted and illustrated, and Ox-Cart Man (1979) by Donald Hall.

In 1976, Barbara Cooney was given the Smith College Medal for her many achievements to date, and more have followed. Pictured here is her illustration from When the Sky Is Like Lace (1975).

Barbara Cooney '38
from *When the Sky Is Like Lace* (1975) by Elinor Lander Horwitz
Watercolor and Prismacolor on paper, 10 1/2″ x 12″
Kerlan Collection, University of Minnesota Libraries

MARCIA GYGLI KING '53

Marcia Gygli King was born in Cleveland, OH, and after majoring in English at Smith, went to the University of Texas at San Antonio for her MFA with further study at the Corcoran School of Art in Washington, DC. Her training was classical, drawing from the model, copying the master, but she has always drawn with authority. She draws extensively outdoors, often traveling to areas where sea and land merge, using her drawings to capture not only the surface but the inner sense of a place.

Marcia Gygli King's method is unusual. After working out a composition in drawings, she prepares the canvas with underpainting of dark green. Then she paints the composition on immense sheets of hard plastic, and using a technique similar to monoprinting, transfers the painted image onto the prepared canvas. The transferred image has peaked areas of paint and slight blurs in edges that are not possible in a conventional directly painted image. She then goes back over the painting with brushes and paints directly on the canvas, adding punctuation and articulated brushstrokes on the surface. Frames are integral parts of each painting, designed to complement each composition; their extravagant forms often physically dominate the painted images. Like sculptures rather than paintings, the frame often extends into the viewer's space, in some works leaving the canvas as an ancillary member. This blurring of the distinction between media, between painting and sculpture, frame and canvas, frame and furniture, is a signature feature of King's art. Mel McCombie says King's work "fuses grand and low modes." Her most recent work, "The Botanical Series," is of enormous flowers, six to seven feet high, and the frames are not part of the pictures.

Her work is part of the permanent collections at the Guggenheim Museum, Brooklyn Museum, and Kouros Gallery in New York; Herbert F. Johnson Museum at Cornell; Cleveland Museum of Art; Guild Hall Museum, East Hampton, NY; Newark Museum, NJ; National Museum for Women in the Arts; and Robert College, Istanbul, Turkey. She is the subject of four documentary videos and has had solo exhibits throughout Texas, New York, North Carolina, California, and Washington, DC. She has also received an MTA Grant for Creative Stations for the Jay Street-Borough Hall Station in Brooklyn.

Marcia Gygli King '53
The Nichol's Barn—Sagaponack, L.I., 1991-1992
Oil on canvas, 6'5"H x 7'5"L x 6"D
Collection of Jean Rosner

GRACE KNOWLTON '54

*G*race *Knowlton's formal training beyond her Smith degree includes a master's degree in art and education awarded in 1981 by the Teachers College at Columbia University, New York. Her growth as a sculptor, photographer, and installation artist, however, has been largely the result of innovative personal experimentation as she combines media or creates her own way of working with materials to suit her purposes. She has worked extensively with platinum/palladium photographs, to which she has often added collage elements or modified with the addition of paint. The photographic images are often minimalist—thematic series of culverts, pilings, pipes, and her own sculpture—which she embellishes by hand. Her photographic work also includes lightboxes and screens to which she applies her images, enlarged from negatives directly onto the photographic film and then worked by hand with drawing.*

Knowlton is perhaps best known for her signature spherical sculptures that first began with clay vessels that she "closed" on the potter's wheel. The clay spheres or "balls" were gradually enlarged, first as she coiled the clay into molds and then as she cast the forms in concrete. She experimented with steel as a result of her work with Spanish sculptor Martin Chirino and later turned to other, more tractable, metals. The three sculptures from the Brooklin Series (named for Brooklin, Maine), are pictured here as they appear in situ on the lawn behind Neilson Library at Smith. Under the trees and gathered in association on the grass, they resemble immoveable boulders but unlike their counterparts in nature (for which they are often mistaken) they are made of thin skins of copper sheets welded together and then patinated. Her more recent sculptures have incorporated brightly colored strips of metal wrapped to form spheres.

Grace Knowlton's work has been included in numerous solo and group exhibitions, including Layers and Traces: An Imprecise Search for Angels *at the Smith College Museum in 1992, which included an outdoor installation of the Brooklin Series, an exhibition of Knowlton's photographs, and a collaborative fresco installation with Daniel Bozhkov.*

Grace Knowlton '54
Three Forms from the *Brooklin Series,* 1991
Part purchase with a gift of funds from Members of the Class of 1954
and part gift from the artist (Grace Farrar Knowlton '54).

CONNIE COHEN '55

*F*rom the Greek island of Paros in the Aegean, where Connie Pollack Cohen set up a studio and worked several weeks each year from 1980-82, comes the series of paintings and photographs from which "Blue Door" is chosen. The Greek paintings were exhibited at Gallery Madison 90 and the photographs at Ward Nasse Gallery, both solo exhibits in 1984 in New York. "The brilliant light, Cycladic architecture and color-filled villages on Paros make it a fertile field for artistic exploration," she says. "I've tried to capture some of its magic." Her success is clear in the light and shadow on weathered stone and whitewashed walls of the visual poetry here.

Born in Philadelphia, Connie Cohen came to Smith from New York City where she has lived since 1941. After graduating from Smith with an art history major, Connie continued to paint and photograph while engaged in social work, for over thirty years as a founder and president of The Friends of PS 169, the Robert F. Kennedy School, serving emotionally handicapped inner-city children.

International travel has inspired many paintings and photographic series, starting with three months in France on the Experiment in International Living followed by the Smith junior year program in Aix-en-Provence and Paris. Later trips to Japan, Italy, Portugal, Scotland, England, Mexico, and Haiti have resulted in artistic work and exhibits. In 1989 she was invited to exhibit in the Spaso House Gallery of the U.S. Ambassador's Residence in Moscow, and her paintings have also been shown at the Galleria Comunale in Assisi, Italy. In 1995 her paintings of Mallorca were exhibited at The Images Gallery in New York. In these a translucent ground allows the linen canvas to create color, texture, and tone for the image.

Cohen feels strongly that drawing is the foundation on which all paintings are based, so she returns to it regularly. She has taught drawing in New York and in Scottsdale where in recent years she has spent ever more time in a second home. The unique light and landscape of the Desert Southwest figures prominently in her current work. Painter, photographer, and sculptor, Connie Cohen now has work in numerous private and corporate collections in the United States and Europe.

Connie Cohen '55
Blue Door, Paros, Greece, 1985
Oil painting on Belgian linen, 36″ x 50″

SUSAN HILLER '61

*A*fter graduating from Smith College, Susan Hiller pursued graduate studies in anthropology. Then, abandoning an academic career, she moved to France where she studied art before settling in London, where she has lived since the early seventies. Now acknowledged as a major influence on the course of contemporary British art, her early work was informed by Minimalism and conceptualism and consisted of investigative works involving groups of people as well as paintings, books, and performance events. An important early work was Dream Mapping (1974), a collaborative piece for seven dreamers, exhibited at the Los Angeles Museum of Contemporary Art in "Out of Actions: Between Performance and the Object 1949-79."

Since the 1970s, Susan Hiller has made use of cultural artifacts as starting points, extending the archaeological definition to include artists' materials and formats. Her more public works from the 1980s onwards have been conceived with the participation of the viewer as an integral element. Many of Hiller's installations and her photographic, video, audio, and painted works involve the spectator in an exploration of dreams, fantasy, and the realm of the irrational and uncanny. A recent work in cyberspace, Dream Screens (1998), continues her commitment to innovation and exploration.

Susan Hiller's work has been internationally acclaimed and widely exhibited, particularly in Europe and the United Kingdom. Her 1996 mid-career retrospective at the Tate Gallery included works such as the video installation Belshazzar's Feast (1983-84), from the collection of the Tate Gallery, and the museological assemblage from the Freud Museum (1992-96), featured in the exhibition "The Muse in the Museum" at the Museum of Modern Art, New York, in 1999. There is an extensive bibliography on Susan Hiller's work, including the recent book Thinking about Art: Conversations with Susan Hiller.

The photograph reproduced here is a detail from the artist's series The Secrets of Sunset Beach (1987-88). Hiller created these images by projecting slides of her own "automatic scripts" on the walls of a small beach house she occupied during a teaching visit to Los Angeles, and then photographing the palimpsest of natural and artificial light falling mysteriously across the furnishings of the room. As the writer Susan Butler has observed, these photographs are "poised at a juncture of observation and imagination, waking and dreaming."

Susan Hiller '61
The Secrets of Sunset Beach (detail), 1987
Hand-printed R-type photograph, 22″ x 18 1/8″

MARTHA ARMSTRONG '62

Martha Armstrong's "Fall Construction" is one of many paintings of the same Vermont scene; the others are appropriately titled "Windy Morning," "Summer—Late Afternoon," and "Late Summer." The bold lines in sweeping diagonals contrast with the vertical trees, constructed by opposition, bringing the background into the foreground, projecting a picture plane with a logic distinct from its original yet indebted to it. Painting landscapes requires remembering the facts but translating them into an illusion more memorable because more lasting. As she puts it in her classes and catalogues, "What you're trying to do in painting is make the marks, forms and colors bear all the weight of reality and feeling. I get at this best painting outside—the studio without walls."

Martha Armstrong went from Smith to the Rhode Island School of Design to earn an MS in 1963, an education punctuated by summers at the Cincinnati Art Academy, where lessons in technique allowed her to find her own voice, now recognized in what Alexi Worth, New York art critic, defines as "zigzagging impulsive shapes" and "plunging fish-eye perspectives." She practices her art now in Hatfield, MA, but she has series of Vermont, France, California, and Kansas, too, bodies of work that testify to her own movement. She has taught and lectured in and around Philadelphia, Michigan, New York, Indiana, Chicago, Maryland, Rhode Island, New Hampshire, Virginia, and at Smith, where she taught from 1990-97.

Her prizes include the Schnaeder Prize from the Woodmere Art Gallery in Philadelphia, and the Camargo Foundation Grant for work in Cassis, France, as well as awards from juried exhibitions throughout Pennsylvania, New York, and New England. Recent solo exhibits include those at the Spheris Gallery in Walpole, NH; Mulligan-Shanosky Gallery in San Francisco; and Walter Wickiser Gallery in New York.

Her husband Alan, once an environmental lawyer, is now a writer, and Martha Armstrong is illustrating his new book, The Dogs' Stories. Together they have two grown children.

Martha Armstrong '62
Fall Construction, Martha, 1997
Oil on canvas, 48" x 60"
The Asheville Art Museum, NC

PATRICIA TOBACCO
FORRESTER '62

*P*atricia Tobacco Forrester is a native of Northampton, MA, and has resided in Washington, DC, since 1981. Forrester went on to Yale for her MFA (1965) and earned a Guggenheim Foundation Fellowship in Printmaking (1967). She paints from life. "No preliminary drawing, no photographs are ever involved," she writes. "I sit on the ground using a cardboard box to lift my paper and tilt it slightly toward me." In other words, like Monet, Forrester is a plein-air painter who works directly in nature rather than in the studio. Yet while her luxuriant watercolor paintings are a direct response to nature, they are not slavish imitations of nature. She uses startling contrasts like tropical blossoms in a winter scene, inserting a surreal element into naturalness. Traveling to exotic places, she sets her easel wherever she finds her subject—the islands of Hawaii, the River Valley of Santo Domingo, the rain forests of Jamaica.

"The subject of my work is always growth: how trees and plants bulge and stretch and open." Brilliantly colored, larger-than-life flowering forms—lotus blossoms, hibiscus, birds of paradise—are arrayed in their natural habitat against contorted tree forms, verdant undergrowth, and distant river valleys. "By bleeding color into color I hope to make an analogy with how natural forces affect each other."

Her first solo exhibition was held in 1968 in the San Francisco Museum of Art, and since then her work has been presented in over forty one-person shows in virtually every region of the United States, from New York to Honolulu. She was elected to membership in the National Academy of Design in 1992. Forrester's large-scale watercolors have received acclaim from critics across the country. In 1981, The New York Times notes that she "has brought a fresh eye and an accomplished technique to this work," in addition to "a certain tender feeling that lives on easy terms with her rigorous sense of pictorial form." Her work can be found in the collections of the Art Institute of Chicago, the Brooklyn Museum, the Corcoran Gallery in Washington, DC, the National Museum for Women in the Arts, and the British Museum in London, among other museums and collections.

Patricia Tobacco Forrester '62
Fully Ripe, 1989
Watercolor on paper, 40″ x 60″

SANDY SKOGLUND '68

*S*culptor, photographer, and installation artist Sandy Skoglund began as a painter and filmmaker during graduate study at the University of Iowa, where she received her MFA in 1972. After moving to New York, she created conceptual and process works; her first experiments with photography were serial images of New England motel cottages made in 1974, during a time when she was actively exploring performance art as well. As she moved away from conceptual art, Skoglund retained an interest in repetition and seriality, apparent in the brightly patterned Food Still Life series of 1978, which parodies the perfection of commercial advertising photography. The following year, Skoglund made the first of her sculptural tableaux and the installation photographs based on them, the work for which she is best known. These installations developed into more complex assemblages that included her own sculpture, for example, the fluorescent green cats prowling a gray apartment interior in Radioactive Cats (1980), perhaps her most famous image. She began to preserve the sculptural installations, which are often shown with their associated photograph, as related, but independent works of art.

The installation photograph shown at the right, Walking on Eggshells, was included in the artist's mid-career retrospective, Reality Under Siege, organized by the Smith College Museum of Art and touring nationally from 1998 through 1999. It was one of three new works commissioned for the exhibition, including the room-sized installation (sans models) and the lithograph Babies at Paradise Pond (1996), based on a photograph of Smith College students and baby sculptures (from the installation Maybe Babies). Walking on Eggshells began with an idea of eggs arranged as cobblestones (the floor of the installation), and came to include snakes and rabbits as animals associated with eggs, and then expanded as a socio-cultural exploration of snake and rabbit images through the ages, which appear on the wall tiles of the tableau. Skoglund chose to deploy her animal sculptures in a domestic setting she had not yet used: the private space of a bathroom, which she has rendered in cast-paper sculptures of the relevant appliances and fixtures. This stunning, and obsessive, visual tour de force, was completed with the act of crushing a path through the eggshells.

Sandy Skoglund's work is internationally heralded and has been shown throughout the United States and Europe. She is represented in many major museum and private collections.

Sandy Skoglund '68
Walking on Eggshells, 1997
Room-sized installation
Cibachrome print by the artist, 47 3/8" x 60"

JANE GOLDMAN '73

*J*ane Goldman came to Smith from Dallas and went on to the University of Wisconsin for her MFA (1978). She is the co-owner and director of Mixit Print Studio, an intaglio printmaking studio in Somerville, MA. She describes herself as a lyrical realist image maker, working from a combination of free association and direct observation. Her philosophy of art comes from Philostrates, writing about contemporary Greek painting in the third century: "Everything has a color of its own, including . . . the air that envelops all things."

Goldman's media include watercolor, oil, intaglio, lithography, relief, screenprint, and terrazzo. She designed a public art installation for the Massachusetts Port Authority at Boston's Logan International Airport. A 45,000 square-foot terrazzo floor on the theme of a New England aquatic journey, this commission will be completed in 1999. Phase II will be completed in 2001. One of her drawings, marked by poetic specificity, and an installation photograph, serene in spirit while complex in composition, are shown here.

Since 1975, Goldman's work has been exhibited widely in the United States and abroad. She has received grants from the Massachusetts Council on the Arts, MacDowell Colony, Yaddo, and the Virginia Center for the Creative Arts. She has received resident fellowships from the Ballinglen Arts Foundation in Ballycastle, Ireland; the Oberpfalzer Künsterhous in Schwandorf, Germany; and the Cité des Arts in Paris. She has had solo exhibitions at private galleries in New York, Boston, Dallas, Madison, Seattle, and Washington, DC. Her work is included in the permanent collection of the Bibliothéque Nationale (Paris), Brooklyn Museum, Boston Museum of Fine Arts, Fogg Art Museum, Cleveland Museum of Art, Detroit Institute of Arts, Library of Congress, and many other public and private collections.

A nationally recognized printmaker, Goldman has made prints at the invitation of numerous presses, including Peregrine Press in Dallas, Stewart & Stewart Screenprint Publishers in Bloomfield Hills, MI, and the Littleton Press in North Carolina. She has taught at Massachusetts College of Art, UCLA, Rice University, Hartford Art School, and the Wellesley College Greenhouse. The proficiency of her printmaking technique is as remarkable as her content, and her Logan installation makes the art an integral part of the architecture.

Jane Goldman '73
Atlantic Journey, 1999
Preparatory sketch Terrazzo floor design, Logan International Airport

PAMELA SEE '73

*I*llustrator, actress, and gardener, Pamela See lives now in Florence, MA, having come as a high school student to the Northampton School for Girls, where she found stability after a mobile childhood as the daughter of a marine. She stayed to go to Smith, where she majored in biology with a firm concentration in botany. In a special studies in botany and art, she drew an herbarium, based on "Autumnal Tints," an essay by Thoreau, that is part of the permanent exhibit in the Clark Science Center. Her senior art project was a design of gloves she found on the campus through the winter months, a project still recalled fondly. Her studies complemented her family's gardening history, which she later extended by an acclaimed garden plot of Shirley poppies, larkspur, and coneflowers—all winter annuals—that amazed and delighted the Northampton community. She is a faithful friend to the botanic garden at the College, illustrating brochures like "Celebrating a Century," designed for the centennial in 1995.

Meticulous exactitude characterizes all her work, as seen here in Anethum graveolens, "Wild Dill." This drawing in pen and ink is part of an herb series of thirteen commissioned by the Mortimer Rare Book Room for The Frame or Forme of a Garden of Delight and Pleasure (1984) in memory of Katherine Lancaster Krieghbaum '38. An earlier series of twelve botanical drawings, Weeds of Northampton (1980), printed by the Catawba Press, is smaller in scale but equally impressive in design and execution.

Her first illustrations were for Stone Wells and Sugar Maples (1976) by Marjorie Holland and C. John Burke, now E.D. Simonds Professor in Life Sciences. For Professor Charles Redington at Springfield Technical College, she has illustrated Plants in Wetlands (1994) and Animals in Towns and Cities (1999), part of a series.

When she is not drawing, Pamela See is acting. In 1974, fresh out of Smith, she co-founded the No Theater in Northampton which now has international acclaim as an avant-garde collaborative repertory group of writers, producers, and actors. More recently she accepted a position in New York with The Wooster Group, an off-Broadway company now enjoying twenty-five years of success. And she gardens with skill and avidity when home.

Pamela See '73
Wild Dill, 1984
Pen and ink on paper, 16 1/4" x 24"
Mortimer Rare Book Room, Smith College

LESLEY DILL '75 MAT

*B*eginning in February 1998, four billboard-sized black-and-white prints by Lesley Dill appeared in and around Tampa, FL, to bring art to the public. Her signature combinations of photographic images and excerpts from the poetry of Emily Dickinson are the result of a decade of juxtapositions of image and word. "Words evoke images and images evoke words," she says in explanation of her relief sculptures, adding that art and language should reveal bit by bit as a person does.

Dill grew up in rural Maine, where American folk art influenced her earliest work. After receiving her undergraduate degree cum laude with a major in English from Trinity College in Hartford (1972), Lesley came to Smith for an MAT in art before going to the Maryland Institute of Art in Baltimore for her MFA (1980).

The gown at right makes visual the point of Dickinson's poem 1440:

> The healed Heart shows its shallow scar
> With confidential moan—
> Not mended by Mortality
> Are Fabrics truly torn—
> To go its convalescent way
> So shameless is to see
> More genuine were Perfidy
> Than such Fidelity.

Dill makes a statement of strength within vulnerability that was unthinkable a decade ago. The American Transcendental tradition and the Hindu and Buddhist sculpture of India are strong influences on much of her work. Profoundly American in their earnest self-exposure, her works move again Neo-Conceptualism and slacker joke art. She works with wood, copper, and paper to transform a concept to a visual statement.

Her work has been widely exhibited in major museums throughout the country and in many foreign countries and is now part of the collections of major museums throughout the United States. Her workshops and her performances approach legend for students and viewers alike. Lesley Dill is represented by the George Adams Gallery in New York.

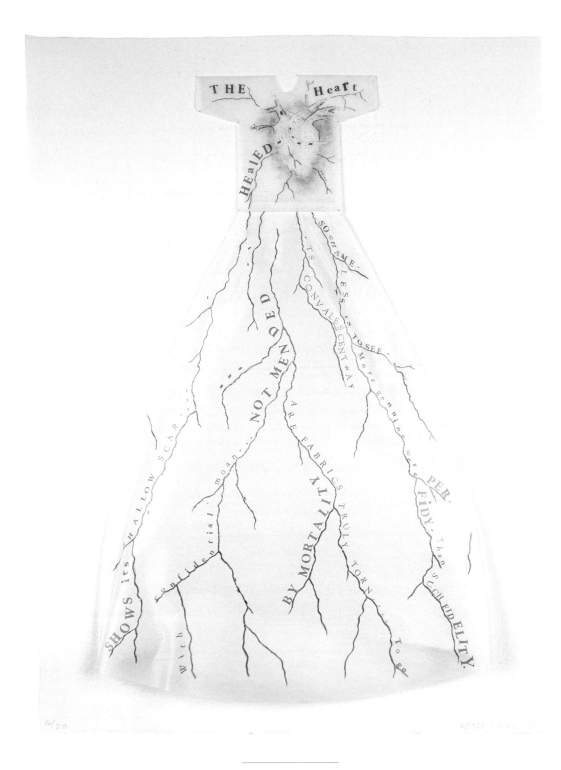

Lesley Dill, MAT '75
The Poetic Body: Poem Dress of Circulation, 1992
Lithograph, letterpress, and collage on Japanese silk tissue mounted on paper
Overall dress: 16″ x 10 1/8″; mount 18″ x 13 ″
Smith College Museum of Art
Gift of Rita Rich Fraad (Rita Rich, '37) and Janice Carlson Oresman (Janice Carlson, '55)

ELIZABETH POLS '75

*E*lizabeth Pols grew up in a large family in Maine, the daughter of a professor of philosophy at Bowdoin College. It was in Maine that she developed a passion for the natural world, and nature remains one of the most constant subjects of her art. Sabbatical years with her family in Italy were also a formative influence on her artistic interests, though she had no formal training until she came to Smith in 1971. After her first year there, she joined her family for a sabbatical in Tuscany, where she studied at Villa Schifanoia, a graduate school of art and music in the hills above Florence. Pols says her artistic imagery coalesced during that year in Italy. After Smith, Pols earned an MFA in printmaking at the University of Massachusetts. A job in graphic design, taken to support herself in graduate school, evolved into a satisfying career. She is now art director and associate editor of the magazines UMass and Synergy at the University of Massachusetts Amherst. She also designs exhibition catalogues and posters for a number of New England museums. She is the designer of this book, Smith Voices: Selected Works by Smith College Alumnae; her aesthetic sensitivity and her knowledge of design have enriched every page of this volume.

As a complement to her work in design, Pols maintains an active career in editorial illustration; much of that work is focused on precise renderings of the animal world. Capitalizing on her new interest in children's books, she is working on a series of bas-relief paintings illustrating a story by Rudyard Kipling. She is a member of the Western Massachusetts Illustrators Guild and participates in its annual group shows.

After her start in predominantly monochromatic graphic arts, Pols now works in watercolor, oil, and mixed media. The 1997 oil pictured here, "La Fiorentina," pays visual homage to the artist's mother who is shown in the full Tuscan sun on the Ponte Vecchio in Florence. Not seen in the image is the artist herself, at that time a small child at her mother's side. Elizabeth Pols, now close to the age of her mother in the painting, lives in the hills of western Massachusetts with her husband and son.

Elizabeth Pols '75
La Fiorentina, 1997
Oil on canvas, 19" x 23"

EMILY EVELETH '83

*E*mily Eveleth came to Smith from Farmington, CT, where she was born and raised. After graduating cum laude from Smith, she went on to the Massachusetts College of Art, where she received the Painting and Drawing Department Achievement Award in 1986. She was awarded a Massachusetts Artist's Foundation Fellowship in 1989, an NEA/New England Foundation for the Arts Fellowship Award in Painting in 1994, an Art Matters Inc. Fellowship in 1995, and a French Government Grant for the Artist Residency Program in Rochefort-en-Terre, France in 1996.

Emily Eveleth's signature paintings, represented by "Lemon Creme," are a series of paintings of doughnuts. Humor is sometimes the point, but the paintings are more than delectable. Two jelly doughnuts atop one another in "R & K," are surprisingly sensual. In "Proscenium/Sentience" two jelly doughnuts a foot apart seem to be gabbing. In "Shy," a timid pastry peeks over the edge of a platter. The paintings are serious, she says; "it's the subject that's inherently silly." Her brushwork enlivens the edible subject with what can only be called personality. Ed McCormack of *Artspeak* says her paintings are "beautifully, almost reverently limned in a manner that highlights the genuine sensual qualities of the humble baked goods, rather than turning them into hipper-than-thou jokes about the gooey vulgarity of consumerism."

Another series includes back views of heads, which have the same texture and anonymity as her majestic jelly doughnuts. And like the doughnuts, they're funny because Eveleth paints them so seriously, as portraits with no need of the face. In addition to these series, Eveleth returns to her artistic roots periodically by painting spare but lovely landscapes of fields and countrysides, usually on a very small scale.

Eveleth is represented by the Danese Gallery in New York and the Howard Yezerski Gallery in Boston. She has had solo shows at the Allan Stone Gallery, New York; Harcus Gallery, Boston; the Danforth Museum of Art in Framingham, MA; Smith College; and Eastern Connecticut State University. She has shown in group exhibits at various New England museums, and she is represented in a number of corporate collections including Morgan Stanley, Fidelity, Wellington Management, and Bank of Boston, among others.

Emily Eveleth '83
Lemon Creme, 1991
Oil on canvas, 52″ x 58″

NICOLE DE LISLE '87

Nicole de Lisle was born and raised in the town of Ashburnham, MA. She came to Smith in 1983 to major in studio art, especially printmaking. At Smith Nicole was the art editor for The New Current literary magazine, and she designed and illustrated several College programs and publications. She also edited the Virginia Woolf manuscript, "The Patron and the Crocus" in the Mortimer Rare Book Room, a testament to her literary interest.

Following graduation, she completed the Radcliffe Publishing Course, concentrating in book and magazine design, before participating in the Smithsonian Resident Associates Program. Once in Washington she worked in the graphics department of The National Geographic Society, and she designed and edited the 1990 Traveler's Guide to Museum Exhibitions in Canada and the United States for Museum Guide Publications, Inc. The years working in graphic design sharpened her aesthetic sense, but after four years she returned to her first love of fine art by joining San Diego's Brighton Press, where she worked with master printers to create hand-printed books featuring original prints by contemporary artists.

Nicole received her MFA from the University of Pennsylvania, focusing on painting, sculpture, and installation, in addition to printmaking. Included among her exhibitions was Places from the Center, a show featuring solo and collaborative installations by five women artists. In 1994 she received the coveted Vermont Studio Center Scholarship for summer study. The following year she was commissioned by the Dean to create a work for Sheldon Hackney, who retired from the presidency of the University of Pennsylvania to direct the National Endowment for the Humanities.

Nicole de Lisle has taught at Chestnut Hill College in Philadelphia, Montgomery County Community College, and the University of Pennsylvania. She now lives and keeps a studio near Boston, where she has been working on a series of paintings that includes "Milk Bowl," exhibited here for the first time. "Art is really about the intensity of tenderness," according to May Sarton, and this work attests to the presence in the artist's life of her two young children, Vanessa Claire and Logan Alexander.

Nicole de Lisle '87
Milk Bowl, 1998
Gouache, 8″ x 12″

SOON EE NGOH '91

*S*oon Ee Ngoh grew up in Petaling Jaya near Kuala Lumpur in Malaysia and was educated under the British education system in which art was regarded as a field of little importance and was rarely given any serious consideration by teachers or the general public. Only at Smith did she finally have the freedom to explore her potential as an artist. During her undergraduate years she concentrated in printmaking, preferring woodcut to lithography. After graduation, she returned to Malaysia for eighteen months to teach art courses in an American program at a private college. In the fall of 1994, she returned to the United States to develop her work in the MFA program at the University of Massachusetts Amherst, where she graduated in 1998.

She names the Baroque artist Caravaggio as the strongest influence in her own work. "I saw slides of his work in Art 100 and fell in love with his quality of light and his dynamic, theatrical composition." In her own early work, Ngoh arranged the objects to create diagonals in the composition to provide movement. Soon Ee Ngoh's work has evolved from a formal context to one that is more philosophical in nature. In her current still lifes, her favorite form, objects (nuts, shells, keys) are portrayed as personal metaphors to address such issues as mortality, relationships, obligations, and responsibilities of adulthood. Each object may represent more than one metaphor, as in the seashell, a metaphor for memory, childhood, and the sanctity of the home. While the formal elements are still integral to the work, they are used to enhance the metaphorical narrative within the work while bringing a particular meaning to her technical virtuosity.

Her self-portraits are influenced by Käthe Kollwitz whose retrospective seized Soon Ee Ngoh's imagination in 1992. Shown here is a self-portrait in melancholy mood, reflective of her response to her mother's imminent death. This work was the first piece in her thesis show in the spring of 1998. Soon Ee Ngoh now teaches as an assistant professor of art at Mississippi State University.

Soon Ee Ngoh '91
Without, 1995
Intaglio print on copper, 7" x 6"

ISOLDE STEIN '93

*I*so Stein was born in Germany, where she was raised, educated, and lived until 1957, when she immigrated to the United States. She worked in business for several years, moving from Volkswagen Export Division to managing the office of a fashion designer and on to writing the first comprehensive motor guide for Germany. In New York she studied painting with Sam Feinstein, concentrating on abstract impressionism. At SUNY Purchase she studied filmmaking and did independent film work before taking drawing and other courses at Manhattanville College. She married a psychiatrist, had three sons, and now lives in Amherst, MA, having moved to Western Massachusetts from Rye, NY, in 1975.

As her children grew up, she taught creative art to early elementary school children in Mamaroneck, NY, and to gifted children in Amherst, and she produced educational films for the Center for Preventive Psychiatry in White Plains. When Smith made known its Ada Comstock Scholars Program for students of nontraditional age, Iso Stein was among the first to apply. Course by course she acquired her degree while her sons gradually began their own college careers. For two years (1985-87) she served as co-president (with Carole S. Fickert '87) of the Adas, establishing their place in the full academic and social life of the College. She still exerts her leadership in helping to facilitate the 1998 Ada Comstock Scholars Alumnae Art Exhibit. Stein earned her own place academically, graduating with high honors in studio art, presenting a thesis series of eleven landscape paintings in oil.

Iso Stein's studio art major allowed her several opportunities for exhibiting her work on campus, and her contacts in the broader community brought her invitations to share her work locally. She had a solo exhibit at the Eclipse in Boston in 1994 and at the Northampton Cooperative Bank in Amherst in 1995. Since graduation, Stein has worked in oil, watercolor, and collage, using her home studio with its views of the New England landscape for the former and her keen sense of design for the latter. The collage here is "Art Deco," a structured compilation of images balancing lines and curves to present a mood as well as an artistic period. Her work is in private collections in the United States, the Netherlands, and Germany.

Isolde M. Stein '93
Art Deco, 1993
Collage, works on paper, 11″ x 9 1/2″

JENNIFER TOTH '94

*H*aving grown up in Minneapolis hearing about the benefits of women's colleges from her mother Susan Allen Toth '61, Jennifer Toth entered Smith in 1990. She spent her sophomore year at Carleton College near her home in Minneapolis, however, to confirm her decision that Smith was where she should be. Art was not the major she expected to have, but when, after her first painting class, Martha Armstrong '62 nominated Toth for the prestigious Norfolk Scholarship at Yale, she decided to pursue as a major what had been an avocation. For two summers she attended the Chautauqua Art Institute to study under former Smith professor Stanley Lewis. With magna cum laude and a Phi Beta Kappa key for comfort, Jennifer Toth entered Yale for the MFA, following Janet Fish '60, Patricia Tobacco Forrester '62, and Elizabeth Meyersohn '80, Smith artists who preceded her to Yale. In time, Toth came to appreciate her own uniqueness and her unusual sensibility to the picture plane. But she remembers well crying in frustration at the difficulty of realizing her vision. "At the same it was exhilarating and fascinating to be struggling so hard. How could I make that log go back in space? Why does this painting look so flat?"

Yale challenged Toth, who was not prepared to commit to a personal subject matter, having learned from painters who believed in painting itself as a subject matter. So she took two years off before finishing her second year. She attended The New York Studio School and lived in New York City. She traveled to India for three months, an experience to be reflected in her later work, before accepting a full scholarship to return to The New York Studio School. In her second year there she completed the self-portrait here, "Selves with Red Umbrellas."

When she returned to Yale, she began a series of nude self-portraits in poses taken from Indian sculpture. She began to incorporate her dog, making dog-women worlds which have both humor and some unease. At her final critique, she displayed three of these paintings, each twelve feet long and eight high. After winning a prize at graduation for excellence in painting, she traveled to Greenland for a month. Now she teaches basic drawing at Smith and works as an artist in the schools in New York City.

Jennifer Toth '94
Selves with Red Umbrellas, 1997
Oil on canvas, 50″ x 50″

GAIL OTIS '95

*L*ike many Ada Comstock Scholars, the program for students beyond traditional age, Gail Otis took a somewhat circuitous route to Smith. She grew up
on Long Island and went to the University of Denver to become a psychology
major. What she discovered in Colorado was that she loved animals more than
people. She became a certified veterinary technician, working for veterinarians for
fifteen years. Her longest service was in animal orthopedic surgery in the Comparative
Medicine Department at Yale Medical School. She met and married her husband at
Yale, remarking that a Golden Retriever on intravenous fluid brought them together.

She spent two years as a full-time potter before coming to Smith in 1990 to
complete her undergraduate degree. She had always had an interest in photography, but at Smith it became her passion. The power of the camera helped her to see
worlds within worlds, as though discovering a visual language. She focused first on
The American Rodeo: A Study in Motion, the series that became her honors
thesis, one piece of which is represented here. Her work required considerable research
and travel to the West and Southwest during peak rodeo season. Her knowledge of
horses from her veterinarian years helped her to get into the circle of cowboys for the
best photographic opportunities. Then she did a series on New England fairs, especially bizarre entertainment options. Her new work concentrates on bodies in stress
and distress at fitness centers and on the culture and images of motorcycles and
motocyclists. The subjects she chooses are in areas that intrigue her. "The final images I
select are often inconsistent with whatever preconceptions I may have had." Photography is for Gail Otis an evolutionary process, a constant discovering of her own voice.

Gail Otis's photographs have won awards in juried shows throughout New
England and the Southwest. She even has a piece in the Cowgirl Hall of Fame in
Santa Fe, NM. After Smith, she went on for further training to the Massachusetts
College of Art for a year before accepting an internship with John Marcy in plati-
num and fine art printing and now holds a position with Stephen Petegorsky, photographer. Between photographic missions, she teaches art at the Police Academy in
New Haven, CT, where she trains officers to feel by exercising their eyes and where
she works with new officers to raise the self-esteem of inner-city youth. But photography is never far from her mind.

Gail Otis '95
Waiting, 1994
Cibachrome photograph, 16″ x 20″

ISABEL CASE BORGATTA '43

After attending Smith College, Isabel Case Borgatta went on to further study at the Yale University School of the Fine Arts, where she received a BFA degree in 1944. At the New School and the Art Students League in New York, she studied with the Spanish immigré artist Jose de Creeft. Like de Creeft, who championed direct carving in stone, Borgatta has worked in slate, marble, granite, alabaster, and serpentine, creating her sculptures by carving into rock without first making preliminary drawings and often without a completely formulated idea of how the finished work will appear. In this way, Borgatta's subjects, primarily female figures with a mythic or primordial quality, emerge from raw stone. Writing in 1987, critic Mark Van Doren described Borgatta's remarkable affinity for her materials, which are "surprised...into expression" by her technique.

Isabel Case Borgatta has cited a variety of influences on her work from Classical western art, to the arts of Southeast Asia and Pre-Columbian art. Seraph, reproduced at the right, recalls the emblematic angels of New England gravestones, specifically those of the cemetery in the town of Sleepy Hollow, where the artist's family lived. The seraph, itself a distillation of angelic form as a bodiless being with wings, is here conceived in the artist's hallmark style of rough textures (the wings and hair) contrasted with smooth passages of stone (the seraph's face, with its crisply cut features and rounded cheeks and forehead). Seraph is an example of Borgatta's smaller-scale sculpture, although some of her carved figures are as large as six feet in height. In the early 1960s, the artist also experimented with the greater freedom of large-scale fabric or textile-based figurative sculptures.

Isabel Borgatta's sculptures are included in a number of private and public collections. Her work has been shown widely in group exhibitions at the Pennsylvania Academy of Fine Arts, the Whitney Museum, and the Brooklyn Museum, at college and university museums, and other national and international venues. A founding member of Women in the Arts and the Women's Caucus for the Arts, Borgatta has received numerous awards during her long and distinguished career, including the Ettl Award from the National Society of Sculptors in 1996, the first time this honor was given to a woman.

Isabel Case Borgatta '43
Seraph, 1990
Marble, 30"L x 12"H x 12"D

SOPHY BURNHAM '58

*S*ophy Doub Burnham grew up in Maryland. After receiving her cum laude degree in art history from Smith, she became an assistant curator at the Smithsonian. She married a newspaper reporter from Harvard and had two daughters. While raising her family Sophy Burnham became a free-lance writer, earning awards for her honesty in perceiving ironies. She then undertook extensive research on the art world for her first book The Art Crowd (1973), a detailed exposé of the corruption and control of the contemporary art market. The book revolutionized the way people look at art, whether in museums, catalogues, or reviews. It earned its author a position as editor for David McKay, the publisher.

Her next books, Buccaneer (1977) and The Dogwalker (1979), were written for children as were some radio plays on NPR, but The Threat to Licensed Nuclear Facilities (1975) and The Landed Gentry in America (1978) returned her to social commentary. So prolific was she through the 1980s that she can claim more than a hundred essays and articles in Esquire, The New York Times Magazine, New York, Town & Country, New Woman, Vogue, McCall's, Saturday Review, and other national magazines. Her topics range from environmental concerns to pornography, bee-keeping to divorce, money to Machu Picchu. Little did she know that her next two books would precipitate a veritable flood of books, movies, and television stories on angels and otherwordly encounters.

A Book of Angels (1990) and Angel Letters (1991) shared the same bestseller list for months. While they were being translated into twenty languages, Burnham kept writing in the same vein: Revelations (1992), a novel about a minister who finds God a reality; The President's Angel (1993), a novel based on fact; and The Ecstatic Journey: Walking the Mystical Path in Everyday Life (1997), a meditation on mysticism in theory and in practice. For one who did not grow up believing in miracles or angels, Sophy Burnham provides convincing testimony to her own and others' transformations by inexplicable forces, improbable coincidences, and angelic encounters. Here she describes one of her own angelic encounters from A Book of Angels.

Visits from Angels

FROM *A Book of Angels*

STRANGE THINGS HAPPEN IN THIS WORLD. I don't pretend to understand them, but I put them down in case other people have had such experiences and want to know they're not alone.

WILLIAM BLAKE SAW ANGELS IN THE TREES. He was merely a ten-year-old boy who one day looked up and saw angels and afterward could not stop drawing them and writing his ecstatic poetry in homage of them . . . Jacob wrestled with an angel . . . And an angel came to Abraham . . . and Joseph Smith founded the Mormon Church after a meeting with the angel Moroni . . . And today a little child will see an angel, or an angel will unexpectedly swoop in to save an adult's life, as happened once with me.

It seems extraordinary: I cannot forget it. Once an angel saved my life. I saw him the way you see the words on this page: the colors, the magnificent leap of my heart on seeing him—*Home!* cried my soul as he scooped me out of the path of death. But I'm not sure he was more miraculous than the Jamaican charlady who entered my mother's hospital room at exactly the right moment to bring me an insight a few days before my mother died. We are told that angels appear as voices, dreams, signs, visions. They carry messages. The mystery is why they appear at all, much less in one form or another, changing their spots with such engaging charm.

Of course, some people insist that angels don't exist, never having seen one. And other people ask why they appear only to certain humans, though others still say that angels come to everyone. The question to ask is: Who will recognize them when they come?

> Be not afraid to have strangers in your house,
> for some thereby have entertained angels unawares.
> —Heb. 13:2

It is said that angels come as thoughts, as visions, as dreams, as animals, as the light on the water or in clouds and rainbows, and as people too. Are they walking on this earth as people in disguise? Or do they appear for that one moment and vanish into ether again? Or is it really us, mere humans, who for a moment are picked up by the hand of God and made to speak unwittingly the words another needs to hear, or to hold out a lifeline to another soul?

Once a man on the highway saw me pull over in my faltering car and stopped to help. This was on the New England Thruway, on my way from New York to Cape Cod. It was eight o'clock on a Saturday night in a slashing rain. My car kept stalling out at 60 miles-an-hour, which was the safe high speed. The motor would die and my pace sink to 25 miles-per-hour, while I stabbed on my warning blinkers, wondering if I'd be slammed from behind. A man stopped his pickup, seeing me helpless at the side of the road, and accompanied my failing car in his truck for miles and miles out of his way, his flashers protecting me. That wonderful man spent six hours trailing me (imagine!), six hours of his time to ensure that I limped safely to my destination. I tried to find him later in

New London, to thank him, but either I misplaced the address or he had left by then.

For each moment of horror in the world we find these acts of goodness, by the hands of angels. Here is how another stranger helped my reconciliation with my mother when she lay dying. My Jamaican angel, a charlady, come to give me back my life.

M Y MOTHER WAS A GREAT LADY, small and muscular, endlessly active. She would haul the Gravely tractor around the lawn, then slap together a salami and tomato and lettuce and cheese sandwich on Wonder bread with imitation mayonnaise. She would eat two of these for lunch, standing at the kitchen counter, drinking several cups of coffee, as if sitting were a waste of time. Then off again to play a round of golf or rake up leaves or meet a friend in town or run to market or the bank. She was always moving, yet her favorite words to me were, "Relax! You're so jittery. Just sit down. You don't have anything to do here now but sit."

Which would set my teeth on edge, because the babies (her grandchildren) needed feeding or changing or something to divert them, and she was always picking, pecking at my skin.

And at her own. All her life she suffered from eczema. She was in constant pain and never talked about it.

In 1973 my husband, David, and I moved back to Washington from New York, and at that time I began an effort to mend my relationship with my mother. It took several years. She had had one bout with breast cancer and half her side had been lopped away. An Amazon removing her breast in order to draw her archer's bow would not have shown more disdain for her body than my mother did. After breast cancer she got lung cancer and had a piece of lung removed. That made her stop smoking, though she continued to sit in the study with my father, who lit one cigarette after another in the stuffy room, while the fire belched out clouds of smoke (the chimney held swallow nests which my mother decided would be too expensive to remove). At the end of her life my mother was so unhappy, stricken with grief by my father's stroke and her incapacity to help, embittered at the cruel trick fate had played, that her pain and anger often came tearing out at me, barbed and cutting.

"Oh, *journalists*," she snorted. Both David and I were encompassed in that term. "*New York!* You're all so provincial."

Sometimes she would turn on my writing. One book in particular she loathed. She never explained its offense, but for several years she could hardly look at me without recalling it: "What an *awful* book." She said it again and again. "I was just ashamed reading that. Ashamed. I don't know how you can hold up your head in public, knowing you've written that."

"Well, what exactly didn't you like?"

"The whole thing. You can only hope it doesn't sell."

It would be a lie to say it didn't hurt. Once I fled the house before her assaults. But I also wanted a reconciliation.

One day in June, 1978, she telephoned to say that she felt a little under the weather and had gone to bed. The doctor diagnosed it as walking pneumonia. Also she had slipped in the bathtub and hit her ribs, so she had a terrible pain in her side. My brother and his wife and David and I talked in whispers in the kitchen, as if she could overhear from upstairs. The sight of our mother lying down was still new to us. In forty years we'd hardly ever seen her sick, and then suddenly she'd had the two battles with cancer. We worried the pneumonia might be serious.

A month later she was in the hospital. I moved to Baltimore to be nearby. Every day I drove to see her in the hospital, and every day she bickered and quarreled with me. Reporters at *The New York Times* had gone on strike: my husband was out of work, our financial situation precarious. I had taken a job as a consultant to a federal agency and was keeping my sanity and reducing my grief with bouts of intense hard work.

My mother picked and picked at me. Why didn't I relax? Just sit in the garden? Take it easy and do nothing for a while? Did I *always* have to work? What was wrong with me? Intermittently she would worry about our finances: Were we all right? Could David find another job? But usually her attention focused on the fact that mine was divided. Looking back I see the quarrels were partly my fault. I didn't comprehend her fear. Why didn't I tell her I was scared for her—and for myself?

One day in the hospital she lit into me again. Peck-peck. Nothing I could do was right. I sank deeper in my chair, desolate: what was I doing there, when all she did was tongue-lash me? At this moment a broad-faced black woman came in to mop the floors of this cramped hospital room, hardly big enough to fit a bed, a chair, a chest of drawers. My mother was sitting straight up against her pillows. She wore a nightgown with a little bedjacket over it. Her hair, freed from its customary bun, lay thin and loose on the pillow. Beside the bed stood an enormous oxygen tank with a plastic tube running to her nose, and this she had removed and waved in one hand like a pasha with his hookah as she shot off her charges at me, complaining about the way I dressed and my pathetic efforts to write, scorning my present assignments on urban affairs as trivial and pointless. Not even the entry of the hospital attendant quieted my mother's tirade.

I hunched in my chair, hurt and angry, wondering if I should simply get up and leave. Here was my mother, dying: there were things we should be saying to each other, not nagging, picking, at me so.

"I grudge you the mother-talk." The Jamaican charwoman stopped her mopping. My mother and I both looked up startled. Neither of us had understood her lilting Island accent. But a trill of recognition ran through me.

"What?" I sat up straight.

"I grudge you the mother-talk," she repeated, looking from one to the other of us, smiling with a broad, gold smile. "My own mother died when I was twelve," she sang, "and I've had no one in all these years to give me mother-talk. It is so nice to hear."

My mother looked embarrassed. I sat up even straighter, hit by joy. *Of course!* She was cuffing the cub, was all. I had not understood. It took only a few moments for that beautiful dark-skinned woman to finish with the floor—three swishes of her mop and she had done. She left, but she left us in a different state.

I did not consider her an angel at the time, but marveled at the synchronicity of the encounter, this woman walking in to explain my mother's behavior and walking out again. From that moment our relationship took a turn.

We began to talk on another level. We could approach the topic of death, say how much we cared for each other.

A week later she was dead.

DREAMS AND IMAGES. This is a difficult section to write, for now we are out of the path of ghosts and angels and demons and saints and into sheer perception. Or is perception angels too? Saint Gregory said, "In this visible world, all dispositions are executed through invisible creatures." Are our senses guided by angelic thought? The important thing to note is that all these things represent ways of receiving information that transcend the routine levels—analysis, reasoning, logic—which we are taught to trust. These means of receiving information are not open to us all the time, and some people have more access to these routes than others; whether by practice or by accident they become conduits, somehow, through which the information may be passed. It is my belief that the information is passed through an electrical energy and that this energy has something to do with love and also with the suspension, even momentarily, of doubt.

I believe it is like a river, a flowing that we hook into at times to receive transcendent information. We do not know where it is coming from, but we know how it comes—surrounded by light, crashing over us with total conviction—that it is different from our egotistical thoughts, from mere desire, or the tug of fear. It must always be tested against reality, but when it has passed the tests, you must always act upon it, even if other people say it cannot be true.

Western peoples in the last century have given angels and demons new meaning, remythologized into a trinity of superego, ego, and id. But I have seen light pouring off the hands and skin of people. This may seem odd, given what I have written of the darkness of the human soul. Once I had an operation. I was two weeks in Massachusetts General Hospital in Boston, and when I was recovering, I had an epiphany. I have often wondered if it was induced by drugs, but in that case would not everyone have such moments in a hospital? I saw with extraordinary clarity. I marveled at it: *This is the way artists see,* I thought, humbled by the miracle of a towel rack, the fold of a sheet. A tree outside the window, the children playing football on the grass reduced me to tears. I was reading Dostoevsky's *The Brothers Karamazov* at the time and could take in only a few paragraphs without putting it down, it so affected me. One day standing at the window, looking at sky and clouds, I was smitten by the order of the universe. I could hear the singing of the planets, the low, deep roar of stones and rocks. I understood . . . everything—things that today I don't even have the language to pose questions about, and the beauty of this order was so sharp that tears coursed down my cheeks. And more extraordinary, when I looked out the window, the leaves and trees and grass were flashing with an inner light. I saw light shining from the skin of people, pouring off the hands and faces both of nurses and of fellow patients. (All but one! One patient pacing the hospital corridor for exercise was shrouded in a black, deep cloud: I recoiled, repelled.) The others, however, were haloed with light. Back in Washington in my own garden, I bent in worship at this radiance pouring from the leaves and grass, from every living thing. "Look. Look at the light," I would say. And then realized that other people didn't see it flaming off the vines "like shining from shook foil." For two weeks I could see the earth flaring with this living light, and then it began to fade away. I felt myself losing the capacity to see. I thought, *I would give my soul to keep on seeing that;* and then I realized that I'd just been given it. This was before I saw my mother's ghost.

Only rarely since then have I seen light shining like that off the skin of people. Once I was in Costa Rica. I was waiting in the shabby airport in San Jose, waiting as all travelers in airports wait; and this time there was no excuse of drugs (as in the hospital), and neither can I trace the event to alcohol or even to fatigue. I sat down, and suddenly I saw ordinary people flaring with light— Indian women with their babies, students, tourists, American businessmen, soldiers, and diplomats. Light poured off their faces, shoulders, hands—wherever they showed bare skin. I sat in that grungy, plastic, South American airport and trembled at the sight, and the tears ran slowly down my cheeks in humility and gratitude. I put on my sunglasses so that no one would see. I was shaking at the *goodness* of people, at the beauty of these luminous beings shining with light.

Once David had a stay in Georgetown Hospital. Mr. Johnson, the man in the bed next to his, was dying of cancer. Soon after he returned home, David was reading in bed. He looked up from his book.

"I think I'll go visit Mr. Johnson today," he said; and at that moment a shock of light passed over him, streaming from his skin.

Who was it who said, "Beauty is reality seen with the eyes of love"?

Since then I have been witness only one other time to this phenomenon—although I have glimpsed it in a veiled or shadowy way, a passing, fleeting, quickening of light flaring in another person and dying down again. It is the light of love.

JOYCE POOLE '79

*J*oyce Poole '79 grew up as much in Malawi and Kenya as in Washington, DC. She came to Smith in 1974 and extended her Smith career by a year to study elephants with Cynthia Moss '62 in Amboseli National Park in Kenya. She wrote a highest honors thesis on sexual patterns of bull elephants and presented her prize-winning paper to the American Society of Mammalogists. After more observation and data collection in Kenya, she took time to complete her doctoral dissertation in animal behavior at Cambridge University. Her research expanded to include the social structure of the Amboseli elephants, the patterns of musth, ecological variation and reproductive patterns, dominance and aggression, and mate competition. So eager was she to return to Africa that she wrote her dissertation in a record time of nine and a half months, earning her degree in 1982. With funding from the Guggenheim Foundation, she spent several months at Princeton refining her methods for determining vocalization patterns, low-level vibrations that humans cannot hear. Her sucess was later featured in Natural History magazine. She received a Smith College Medal in 1996 for her work helping to save endangered elephants in Africa, including the international campaign to ban the sale of ivory.

When working as the coordinator of the Elephant Program for the Kenya Wildlife Service under Richard Leakey, Joyce Poole had to come to "an uneasy truce" with her new political voice, though even then the voice of the behavioral biologist can be heard. The various voices of Joyce Poole now include that of mother, and her daughter Amber Selengei speaks the last words of the book, echoing those the mother speaks in praise of Africa at the beginning, "'It is so beautiful!'"

Reprinted here is a chapter from the middle of Coming of Age with Elephants: A Memoir (1996) on how Joyce Poole determined that elephants have not only self-awareness but also language, not only social patterns but also emotions. In it we see an animal behaviorist at work gathering data, analyzing it, and drawing inferences from emerging patterns.

Elephant Thinking

FROM *Coming of Age with Elephants: A Memoir*

> They move finished and complete, gifted with extension of the senses we have lost or
> never attained, living by voices we shall never hear.
> —Henry Beston, *The Outermost House*, 1928

THE DEVELOPMENT OF CONSCIOUSNESS, language, compassion, and a sense of self are seen as true signs of humanity. The roots of these attributes, which evolved over several millions of years, can be found in our ape relatives, the chimpanzees. But what of other nonhuman species? Do some of the vocalizations used by elephants, for example, suggest that they are communicating with more than just signals, that they have a rudimentary form of language with syntax? Does some of their behavior indicate they have a sense of humor, a sense of death, a sense of self? And if elephants have a sense of self, how do they see themselves in relation to the rest of the natural world? These are difficult questions for which we do not yet have answers. But because elephants are complex social mammals, and because they often appear to act in ways that imply that they sometimes think and feel consciously and are self-aware, it is worthwhile examining the evidence.

One window into the way in which elephants think and feel is to assess what we know about their vocal communication. Our studies of elephant communication are still at a very early stage, and some of our interpretations of elephant sounds may well prove to be wrong. Only additional time watching elephants and recording, analyzing, and playing back elephant calls will correct our mistakes and allow us to clarify the many questions that remain.

One of the more fascinating vocalizations that elephants use is a low-frequency sound that we have called the "Let's go" rumble. When the matriarch of a family decides to stop feeding, for example, and move to the swamp, she usually flaps and slides her ears loudly against her body in what Cynthia and I have called a flap slide and then walks off. Other family members just have to pay attention and follow if they want to remain with the group. But when another adult female or younger family member wants to go somewhere else, she typically stands on the edge of the group, facing in the direction that she wants to go, often with one leg lifted and swinging back and forth, as if intending to take a step, and gives a soft, relatively unmodulated low-frequency rumble. If there is no reaction on the part of her family, she will wait several minutes and repeat this rumble over and over until the rest of the family either follows her lead or she goes off on her own. I think it would be fair to say that the Let's go rumble expresses an elephant's thoughts to the others: "I want to go in this direction, let's go together." Would it be accurate to say, then, that the Let's go rumble is a word? Sue Savage-Rumbaugh, who has studied the question of language in chimpanzees, has written that to qualify as a word, a communicative signal must have the following four attributes: (1) it must be an arbitrary symbol that stands for some object, activity, or relationship; (2) it must contain stored knowledge; (3) it must be used intentionally to convey this knowledge; and (4) recipients must be able to decode and respond appropriately to the symbols. I believe that the Let's go rumble meets all four criteria.

A related vocalization, or series of vocalizations, is one that I have called discussion rumbles. Elephants use those during times when they appear to be having a discussion, usually a disagreement, about the plan for the day's activities. A typical situation would be when some elephants in the family appear to want to pursue one goal, such as go to the swamp (and repeatedly move off and return), while the others seem to prefer to do something else (and move off in the other direction or stand facing in the opposite direction). The apparently debating rumbles (and there may prove to be several different types) go back and forth between the individuals, sometimes for twenty minutes or more, very much in the cadences of a human conversation, but in slow motion. Are the elephants actually conveying anything in a manner akin to that of using strings of words with syntax? Is one elephant actually sending a message as sophisticated as "I want to go to the swamp because I am hungry and thirsty," while another responds, "I don't want to go to the swamp because I have a small baby that I cannot take into the swamp," for example? Although in some cases elephants can become quite agitated by the lack of accord in their group, I have also watched them use a similar but slightly different sounding series of rumbles in a nonconflict situation, to apparently "chatter away" to another individual. Could it be that the so-called discussion rumbles contain subtle differences in syntax and that by using such syntax, the elephants are able to convey a variety of different thoughts and feelings to one another?

The attack rumble, which I have heard on only a very few occasions, is another vocalization that, like the "Let's go" rumble, appears to function like a word. When a group of elephants feels threatened, it may do one of three things: turn and flee, bunch up in a circular defensive posture, or cluster in a pyramidal shape, with the largest females in the center front, and attack *en masse*. Apparently the matriarch usually takes the lead in deciding how to react. We have long assumed that when elephants flee, they are sometimes responding to an infrasonic alarm call given by a group member, but we have yet to record any sound that fits this description. In an offensive situation, however, elephants do exchange a very loud series of rumbles, quite unlike any others, which I have heard on several occasions when I have been under attack by a group. A large adult female, possibly the matriarch, initiates the rumbling, to which others respond by returning the rumble and clustering together, heads high and often touching, into a pyramidal formation. The rumbling reaches a crescendo, until suddenly the entire group, including tiny babies, attacks. It is as if the elephants are exhorting one another, "Let's attack! Are you ready?" and then, perhaps, at some subtle change in the calls, "Attack now!"

Somewhat similar to the attack rumble is another call that I refer to as the coalition rumble, though we may find that these two vocalizations differ only in intensity. Related females use the coalition rumble to chase off annoying young males, an unrelated female, or another family group. Because a female on her own cannot drive away more than one elephant or any larger than herself, she elicits the assistance of another female or females in her family. Prior to the attack the elephants rumble, with their heads high and together, and also may clank their tusks against one another.

A baby or juvenile will use a distinct call when it is lost. The search for its family starts with a low-frequency rumble, quite different from any other rumble, and as the lost elephant becomes more and more frantic, its call becomes louder and louder, until after a time it ends with a scream. I have often lain in bed at night listening to the calls of a frightened calf, followed by the rumble of an adult, and finally by the sounds of the calf running off in that direction rumbling, trumpeting, and screaming.

Juveniles and adult females use two vocalizations that may develop from the lost call: the contact call and the contact answer. Females who are separated from their families use these two calls at varying sound-pressure levels to relocate their relatives or just to keep in contact with animals that are nearby but may be out of sight. Calling elephants are usually, but not always, answered by members of their family. Preliminary results from recent playbacks of recordings by Karen McComb, who is studying elephant communication in Amboseli, have suggested that the elephants who do answer tend to be more closely bonded to the caller than those who do not answer. My own observations suggest that the contact call may be more complex than that. I once observed an adult female call several times in the space of an hour and be answered first by another adult female in the group, then by her eldest daughter, and later by her youngest calf. I have watched a female separated from her family by a distance of two kilometers be answered by various different members of her family at different times but also by a nonfamily, nonbond group member. To the human ear, one contact call sounds much like another, except for variations in intensity, but with time we may very well find that there are other subtle differences between contact calls, and that a female may be able to call specific individuals. I am not suggesting that elephants call each other by name, but I do think that there may be subtly different sounds for "my mother," "my sister," "my eldest daughter," and so on.

AS A BEHAVIORAL ECOLOGIST, I have been trained to view nonhuman animals as behaving in ways that don't necessarily involve any conscious thinking and that their decisions have been simply genetically programmed through the course of natural or sexual selection. But in the course of watching elephants, I have always had a sense that they often do think about what they are doing, the choices they have, and the decisions that they are making. For example, when a young musth male is threatened by a high-ranking musth male, his usual response is to drop out of musth immediately. He lowers his head, and urine dribbling can cease in a matter of seconds. Many biologists would explain this phenomenon simply by arguing that males who behave in manner X live to produce more surviving offspring than males who behave in manner Y, and thus the trait for behaving in manner X is passed on to future generations. Thus, male elephants today automatically behave the way they do because they have been programmed through the successful behavior of their ancestors to do so. Although I rely on such explanations myself, as I have gotten to know elephants better I have been more and more convinced that they do think, sometimes consciously, about the particular situations in which they find themselves. In the case of the young musth male, I believe that he may actually consider his options: to keep dribbling, stand with head high, and be attacked, or to cease dribbling, stand with head low, and be tolerated. In other words, the male may in fact have some *conscious* control over the amount of urine he dribbles. With dominance rank between males changing on a daily basis, a male needs to be able to adjust his behavior accordingly. From past experience he knows the characteristics of his rival's body size, fighting ability, and how that rival normally ranks relative to him, but if his rival is in musth he also needs to assess whether he is in full musth and what sort of condition he is in. All of this information must be assimilated on a daily basis and gauged relative to his own condition. Can so complex an assessment be carried out without thinking? And I wonder whether the more parsimonious explanation wouldn't be that they think.

Teaching, which has been assumed to be a uniquely human attribute, is one behavior we have observed in elephants. For example, young females coming into estrus for the first time do not seem to understand what they are supposed to do. They tend to flee from all males, rather than standing close to the highest-ranking musth male and running only from young, nonmusth males, as older females have learned to do. On numerous occasions Cynthia and I have watched a mother apparently teaching her daughter how to behave, leading her directly to a musth male and then standing with her, initiating the movements she should go through. This behavior can sometimes make it difficult to determine which of the two females is actually in estrus.

I also have always felt that elephants have a sense of themselves *as* elephants, that they see themselves as different from other species. Elephants seem to have categories in which they classify other animals. They have a particular dislike for species that are either predators or scavengers, even if those animals are not a threat to elephants or are scavengers that are not feeding on an elephant carcass. For example, if an elephant comes across a group of jackals and vultures feeding on a zebra carcass, typically it chases them off or at least shakes its head in what I would characterize as annoyance. It is as if elephants do not like the sight of blood or have a particular aversion for carnivores.

Elephants also show their dislike for animals that run around in an apparently chaotic fashion. They have a particular distaste for wildebeest during the rut, and at times they will leave what they are doing to chase a wildebeest in apparent irritation. I have found a number of rabbits and birds flattened by elephants, and Cynthia watched an elephant step on a yellow-necked spurfowl that jumped up directly under the elephant's chin, causing it to be startled. Elephant chasing and sometimes killing of "irritating" animals is different from their chasing of "despicable" animals. Whereas they generally ignore other herbivores unless they are behaving in an unacceptable fashion, they typically react to carnivores by chasing or by simply shaking their heads or flicking their trunks in their direction.

People tend to assume that if animals do have any thoughts, then they are probably confined to representing real objects and events. But elephants often interact with what I call imaginary enemies. In the cool of the evening one often finds young elephants off by themselves on the edge of a group, beating up bushes and running through the long grass as if on the attack. The elephant charges through the grass head down, picking up bits of vegetation, sticks, and branches, and tossing them in the air as it comes to an abrupt stop and, with head and tusks high, stares through wide eyes at some imaginary enemy. It then turns around and charges at the enemy in the opposite direction and around in circles. If elephants are assumed not to have the capacity for thought, are not able to remember or anticipate objects and events, then we must conclude that these young elephants are merely genetically programmed to behave in this absurd way. Personally, I believe that they are, in human terms, acting out some fantasy. As I think of my own experiences, as my thoughts have moved from fantasy back to reality, there is always a moment of self-awareness, a jolt of catching myself in the act of being someone else, somewhere else, or doing something I know that I couldn't. If we acknowledge that elephants have fantasies and an imagination, it suggests that they, too, may have comparable moments of self-awareness.

NANCY DAVIS REAGAN '43

*W*hen *Nancy Davis arrived at Smith College from Chicago, she already
knew that her main interest lay in the theater. During her years at Smith
she acted in several plays, including* Susan and God, So Wonderful in White,
and The Factory Follies, *a wartime morale booster directed by Hallie Flanagan,
creator of the college's theater department; she also performed with the Bander-log
acting troupe, a comedy group established in 1941. After graduation she appeared
professionally in plays such as* Ramshackle Inn *and* Lute Song *on Broadway.
She made her television debut in 1947 with the Kraft Television Theater, and in
1949 she became a contracted actress with MGM. Her first film for the studio was*
Shadow on the Wall, *in which, according to* Variety, *she gave "a standout
performance . . . . [this] actress is a definite comer." Nancy Davis's films include*
East Side, West Side *(1950),* The Next Voice You Hear *(1950),*
Donovan's Brain *(1953), and* Hellcats of the Navy *(1957). In 1952 she
married fellow actor Ronald Reagan and raised two children, Patricia and
Ronald, along with two stepchildren, Maureen and Michael.*

*By the time her husband became President of the United States in 1980, the
new First Lady had long been working for the public interest. When they lived in
California, Nancy Reagan visited wounded Vietnam Veterans and hosted returning prisoners of war in her home. She visited schools for handicapped children and
helped promote a program that matched these children with foster-grandparents. In
1977 she was named Woman of the Year for her volunteer efforts. During her eight
years as First Lady, Nancy Reagan focused much of her attention on the issue of
drug and alcohol abuse and became an honorary chairperson of the Just Say No
Foundation. Her leadership brought the drug and alcohol problem to the top of the
national agenda.*

Nancy Davis Reagan's writings include To Love a Child *(1982) and* My
Turn: the Memoirs of Nancy Reagan *(1989). The following excerpt from*
My Turn *chronicles some of the challenges she met with dignity and humor dur-
ing the Reagans' first years in the White House.*

Nothing Prepares You

FROM *My Turn: The Memoirs of Nancy Reagan*

WHEN WE ARRIVED IN WASHINGTON, in January of 1981, I honestly thought I understood the demands and pressures of being the first lady. I had been married almost thirty years to a well-known actor and television personality, and I had been a movie actress myself. I wasn't a newcomer to politics either, having spent eight years as first lady of California—the largest state in the nation and the most media-conscious place on earth. While I knew that Washington was different, I thought I was prepared for living in the public eye.

But I found out the hard way that nothing—*nothing*—prepares you for being first lady.

In those first few months, as controversy after controversy swirled around me, I often thought of what Helen Thomas, the veteran UPI reporter, had said to me shortly after the election. We were sitting together on the campaign plane, discussing the possibility that Ronnie would be elected, when Helen mentioned the enormous pressures on the first lady. I nodded and said, "I'm sure you're right, but there will always be a part of me that is private, that's mine."

"You may think so," Helen said. "But you have no idea what it's really like. I don't see how you *can* know until you get there."

Well, it didn't take me long to find out what Helen meant.

From the moment I walked into the White House it was as if I had no privacy at all. Everything I did or said, whether as first lady, wife, or mother, was instantly open to criticism—to interpretation, speculation, second-guessing. My clothes. My friends. My taste in decorating. My relationship with our children. The way I looked at my husband! My entire *life* was suddenly fair game for comment by the press and the public alike.

BUT THE FIRST BIG CONTROVERSY was over the renovation of the White House. I have always been a nester, and my first priority in any new house has always been to get that house in order. I like to be organized, and I also like to provide a warm, restful, and welcoming home for my husband. I always did, but it seemed especially important now that Ronnie was president. And I think it made a big difference to him, whether he knew it or not.

I knew the White House needed work, but it wasn't until we moved in that I began to realize how *much* work was actually required—especially in the private living quarters. Some of the bedrooms on the third floor hadn't been painted in fifteen or twenty years! The floors hadn't been touched in ages. There were cracks in the walls. The long, wide Center Hall, which runs the entire length of the second floor, was virtually empty.

When I realized the magnitude of the job that faced me, I was overwhelmed. After all, this wasn't just *our* house; it was the White House. We would be living here for four years, or perhaps eight, but the White House belongs to *all* Americans. It's supposed to be something we're proud of, but I was dismayed by how shabby it was when we first moved in.

WHILE I HAD NO DESIRE to turn the White House into an imperial palace, I did want to reclaim some of the stature and dignity of the building. I've always felt that the White House should represent this country at its best. To me, this was so obvious that I never dreamed that I would be criticized for my efforts. If anything, I expected to be applauded.

Nor did it ever occur to me to think in terms of a public-relations campaign. I just went ahead with the restoration without thinking about public opinion. I hadn't yet realized that my actions might provoke anger or controversy. Perhaps somebody on my staff should have, but they were just as inexperienced in these matters as I was.

Whenever a new family moves in, Congress appropriates fifty thousand dollars for renovations and upkeep. Ronnie and I decided not to accept this grant: For one thing, it wasn't nearly enough to make up for years of neglect. For another, we thought it would be better if the money came from private contributions, not from the taxpayers.

Our goal was to raise two hundred thousand dollars, but we soon raised more than four times that much. It was true, as all the papers reported, that some of our wealthier friends were very generous. But so were many other Americans who were excited to be a part of this historic project and who sent in smaller donations—twenty dollars, ten dollars, even one dollar. They didn't get their names in the paper, but I was grateful that they cared.

WITHOUT THE HELP OF TED GRABER, who had helped me decorate our home in Pacific Palisades, I don't think I could have done it. I love decorating, and I've never worked harder than I did during the first three weeks after the inauguration. Ronnie and I normally go to bed early, but sometimes, at night, it would suddenly occur to me that a lamp or a painting might go better in some other spot. At eleven o'clock, Ronnie would call out, "Honey, where are you? It's late. Come to bed!" I would be down the hall in the Yellow Oval Room, moving an end table or wrestling with a chair.

I didn't want to redo the White House in my own image, but I did want to restore it. Some of the White House treasures were tucked away and out of sight—for instance, the lovely Persian rug with semiprecious stones that had been hanging on the back of a door on the first floor, where nobody could see it. I moved it up to Ronnie's study, where it could be enjoyed, and hung it behind his desk.

Many other items were in storage, so together with Rex Scouten and Ted Graber, I drove out to the White House storage facility in Alexandria, Virginia, near National Airport, which consisted of a World War II warehouse and two Quonset huts, with no temperature control. It broke my heart to see hundreds of historic pieces from the White House, some of them over a century old, deteriorating and in urgent need of restoration.

When Ted and I began taking pieces out of storage, the people at the warehouse were delighted. "Take more, take more," they kept saying. "These things shouldn't be *here*." We selected dozens of chairs, desks, tables, and mirrors, had them restored, and moved them into the White House.

Because so much money had been raised, we were also able to refinish many of the mahogany doors and hardwood floors. We restored the marble walls on the State and ground floors, cleaned the floors with acid-etching, and cleaned all twenty-nine of the White House fireplaces.

We also took care of other problems in the residence that hadn't been touched since the Truman administration. Some of the original handmade plumbing fixtures for the bathrooms and kitchens had to be replaced with modern fixtures because those items hadn't been made in years, and it cost a small fortune to repair them. We embarked on a long list of mundane but essential improvements, including rewiring, replacing worn carpeting, repainting, and fixing the heating and air-conditioning.

The most dramatic and visible improvement was the newly renovated Center Hall. The walls were painted a light yellow to make it seem brighter, and we created several sitting areas by using items that had been in storage, including a reproduction Sheraton sofa and two bergère chairs, and a Chippendale-style bench, which was covered in rose fabric. To break up the long expanse, Ted inserted an eighteenth-century English octagonal writing desk that had been donated to the Kennedys by Jules Stein, the founder of MCA. When we came across it in storage, I recognized it, and I called Jules to tell him it was back in the White House. He was so pleased, and I was particularly glad I had made the call when I learned of his death shortly after.

I'll never forget the moment that made it all worthwhile. One evening, after most of the second floor had been finished, Ronnie and I were having dinner in the sitting area in the West Hall. We were served by one of the butlers, who had been there for thirty-seven years. As he was setting down the tray in front of me, he looked down the Center Hall, smiled, and said, "It's beginning to look like the White House again."

I felt as if I had just been awarded the Congressional Medal of Honor.

I T ISN'T OFTEN IN LIFE that one is lucky enough to enjoy a second beginning, but during one five-minute period in the spring of 1982, I was able to make a fresh start with the Washington press corps.

It happened at the annual Gridiron Dinner, which, as I soon learned, was one of the most important events in Washington. The Gridiron is a small, select club of sixty print journalists. Every spring they hold an elegant white-tie dinner, which is limited to six hundred invited guests. The program is always the same: Members of the press perform clever and (hopefully) funny skits that poke fun at both Democrats and Republicans. These skits are followed by two speakers—one from each party. The evening ends with a brief toast to the president—followed by his response.

For politicians and reporters in Washington, the Gridiron Dinner is the social event of the year. The guest list always includes the Speaker of the House, members of the Cabinet, top White House aides, justices of the Supreme Court, and leading members of Congress, along with a fair number of anchormen, publishers, columnists, diplomats, and other opinion leaders.

A FEW WEEKS BEFORE the 1982 dinner, Sheila Tate [Nancy Reagan's press secretary] realized that after the year I had just gone through, it was inevitable that the evening would include a skit about me. She thought it would be terrific if I appeared in that skit, in a surprise cameo role.

It turned out that the Gridiron members were planning to have somebody sing a song about me. Someone suggested that I should respond with a song of my own that would attack the press.

"Forget it," I told Sheila. "I'm not willing to attack the press. If I'm going to do this at all, I think I should make fun of myself."

"Are you willing to sing?" she asked.

"Sure."

"Dance?"

"Absolutely."

"Would you be willing to smash a plate that was painted to look like the new White House china?"

"Of course! But only if it's a surprise. I don't want anybody to know in advance—not even my husband!"

To help us prepare a suitable response to their skit about me, the Gridiron officers provided us with the lyrics to their song, in which a singer pretending to be Nancy Reagan sang new words to "Second-Hand Rose," an old Fanny Brice hit song from the 1920s that had recently enjoyed a revival. Their lyrics went like this:

Second-hand clothes.
I give my second-hand clothes
To museum collections and traveling shows.
They were oh so happy that they got 'em
Won't notice they were ragged at the bottom.
Goodbye, you old worn-out mess.
I never wear a frock more than once.
Calvin Klein, Adolfo, Ralph Lauren and Bill Blass.
Ronald Reagan's mama's going strictly First Class.
Rodeo Drive, I sure miss Rodeo Drive
In frumpy Washington.

Second-hand rings.
Donate those old used-up things.
Designers deduct 'em.
We're living like kings.
So what if Ronnie's cutting back on welfare.
I'd still wear a tiara in my coiffed hair.

Sheila then asked Landon Parvin, one of our best speech-writers, to work on a set of lyrics for my response. Meanwhile, we had to decide what I would wear. With the enthusiastic help of my staff, we put together a really ridiculous costume—it made me look like a bag lady on Halloween. I wore white pantaloons with blue butterflies, yellow rubber rainboots, a blue blouse with white dots, and over that a really ugly sleeveless red cotton print housedress. Over *that* I wore a blue print skirt pinned up on the side with a sequined butterfly, a long strand of fake pearls, a mangy boa, and a red straw hat with feathers and flowers. I was gorgeous!

During dinner (dressed properly, of course), I was so nervous that I couldn't eat a thing. Maybe, just maybe, it was because six hundred of the most influential people in America were about to see the first lady make a complete fool of herself.

But it was too late to back out. When the singer on stage was singing "Second-Hand Clothes," I turned to Ronnie and told him I had to go to the ladies' room. Sheila Tate, who was even more nervous than I was (if that's possible), was sitting between two newspaper publishers. "Oh, boy," one of them said. "Mrs. Reagan has just left the head table. I bet she's really ticked off."

Backstage, I got into my costume. One of the stage props was a big clothing rack, the kind you see in the stock room of a store. I hid behind the rack where nobody could see me, while the Gridiron skit poking fun at me went on. When the song was over, I parted the clothes and walked out.

I was greeted by a thunderous silence. For a few seconds, nobody realized who this woman was, or why she looked so ridiculous in those silly clothes. But when it sank in, the audience rose and gave me a standing ovation before I even opened my mouth. When the room was quiet again, I sang Landon's lyrics to "Second-Hand Rose":

> I'm wearing second-hand clothes
> Second-hand clothes
> They're quite the style
> In the spring fashion shows.
> Even my new trench coat with fur collar
> Ronnie bought for ten cents on the dollar.
>
> Second-hand gowns
> And old hand-me-downs
> The china is the only thing that's new.
> Even though they tell me that I'm no longer Queen,
> Did Ronnie have to buy me that new sewing machine?
> Second-hand clothes, second-hand clothes,
> I sure hope Ed Meese sews.

When I was finished, the audience responded with another standing ovation. Even better, they had laughed at all the right places, and I began to relax and enjoy myself. The only snag came at the very end, when I was supposed to smash the "china" plate on the stage. I threw it down, but it didn't break!

I was wondering what Ronnie's reaction would be to all of this, but when I got back to the table he was still laughing, so I knew he had thought it was all right.

I never dreamed that my appearance that night would be so influential. It was talked about for the rest of our years in Washington, almost as though it were an important political event—which in a way it was. This one song, together with my willingness to sing it, served as a signal to opinion-makers that maybe I wasn't the terrible, humorless woman they thought I was—regal, distant, disdainful. From that night on, my image began to change in Washington.

It had been a long time since I had received any favorable press, so I treasured the newspaper reviews of my performance. The Gridiron Dinner is supposed to be off-the-record, but I wasn't about to quibble when reports about it in the press were kind to me. FIRST LADY FLOORS 'EM WITH SONG AND DANCE, said the New York *Daily News*. SHE SINGS, SHE JOKES, SHE'S A HIT, said the *Los Angeles Herald Examiner*.

According to the *Washington Post*, "the sophisticated audience of journalists, politicians and their friends responded to her performance as though she had undergone a major change. A number of those image-makers left the ballroom saying that Nancy Reagan's song-and-dance number had transformed her image."

And the *New York Times* said: "President Nixon once played the piano and Betty Ford once danced, but the consensus was that no other First Lady had ever come so well prepared. . . . Socko!"

CYNTHIA VOIGT '63

*B*orn in Boston and raised in Connecticut, Cynthia Voigt attended women's schools for most of her education. After graduation from Smith, she worked as a secretary in a New York advertising firm for a few months, then married, and moved to Santa Fe where she took education courses in order to qualify as a teacher. Returning to the East, she taught English in Maryland, first in a public high school, then at private schools. After more than twenty years teaching almost every grade from second to twelfth, Cynthia Voigt left teaching to pursue a full-time writing career. Now she proudly describes herself as "a recovering English teacher and writer."

Her first book, Homecoming (1981), published seven years before she retired from teaching, earned a New York Times Outstanding Books citation and an American Book Award nomination, the first of many honors for the twenty-four books to follow. The American Library Association gave two books, Tell Me If the Lovers Are Losers (1982) and A Solitary Blue (1983), citations as Best Young Adult Books. Her most celebrated book, Dicey's Song (1982), won the Newbery Medal, an American Library Association Notable Book Citation, and an Honor Book Citation from the Boston Globe-Horn. For The Callender Papers (1983) came the Edgar Allan Poe Award for best juvenile mystery. For The Runner (1985), she won the Silver Pencil Award from Holland and the Deutscher Jugend Literatur Preis from Germany. The California Young Readers' Medal came for Izzy, Willy-Nilly (1990). She has been awarded the ALAN Award and the Ann V. Zarrow Award for the quality of all her work taken together. One of her favorite runner-up mentions is the Rattenfanger Literatur Preis, which is given by the city of Hamelin, and translates the Ratcatcher Prize. Voigt refers to her third, private career as the wife-and-mother one. A resident of Maine, she is the mother of two children.

Despite her many prizes, Voigt considers herself "someone who writes for people who like to read," whether early readers, adolescents or adults. Cynthia Voigt's thoughtful narrative style and complex characters come to life in "The Captain's Wife," a story published here for the first time.

The Captain's Wife

SHE SURPRISED HERSELF when she welcomed the old man's courtship. She had thought her life was full, and completed; she lacked nothing and she wanted no more than she quite comfortably already had. No other man had been able to lure her from her spinsterhood, but this old man, this Ahab, tempted her. He wasn't so old, only older by far than she, but she was young in years and young in life.

Perhaps she welcomed him that she might be the younger a widow.

Or perhaps because a whaling captain kept so long away from land and home. Thus as Mrs. Ahab she could have the freedoms of wife without relinquishing the freedoms of spinster.

Whatever her reason might have been—and there might well be many reasons to turn to marriage—and many of those might well have to do with love, a loving feeling—she did welcome Ahab, when the captain called upon her.

He courted her suddenly, without warning, and his courtship blew like a storm into her life. He had no fine manners for her drawing room. He brought her no baubles, no bonbons, and did not murmur besotments over her bent head. Instead he set before her—like flags planted on the empty beaches of a new continent—the energy of his mind and the energy of his body. Those energies were the best of him; those and his will to do lifelong battle in an unequal struggle against the seas and skies and winds and waters; his will to stand even before an immortal adversary; his will.

She met his energy with her own, and did not feel a need of posies, or poems, promenades to fiddle tunes or promenades along the sea front where all might see how she had brought Captain Ahab to courtship. He spoke to her about the deaths of kings and about his ship, how she brought in profits for her masters and earned livings for her crew. He spoke of strange stars that shone below the equatorial belt and he told her what the philosopher had taught his pupil, Alexander. She listened, and commented, and he was glad to hear her thoughts about what part cleanliness plays in prevention of the spread of sickness, and about the immortality of the human soul. The air between them filled with words carrying thoughts, like the flurry of letters between lovers.

He would make her no promise more than the bare vows, he said.

She asked for no more, she said. She did not say, Her old life now would seem to her flat, colorless and dispiritous. So she must wed him, or find another such man to wed her, or jump into the sea with a cannonball bound close up against her heart. She would wed him, she said.

There will be no marriage bed, he said.

He bore a scar down his face and she did not know how his body too might be scarred. She would wed him, she said.

There would be no Captain's Wife on board his ship, bringing the unease of the ill-luck of women to the crew, he said. She must endure without complaint his long absences. She must keep his house as if its master would return at any moment, he said. He would give her his name and his purse, and set her out on life's seas where his hand was at the helm, he said, if she would do him the honor of being his bride.

She would wed him, she said.

She could keep her house, he said. It would become his house and home.

She said, Yes, even knowing the hardnesses of the life he gave her over to.

She could keep her gardens and her good works, he said.

She said, Yes, even knowing the wilfullnesses of the man she was giving herself over to.

They were married, and he went about his business of outfitting and manning his ship, for the voyage. His new wife made her home over into his, and kept a fish chowder hot against his return, and kept the fires bright, and kept his shirts freshly starched and his humidor filled.

For she had her own vow, made to herself.

She had her own desire.

For a child.

A child in her womb, to be her labor and her labor's reward.

But first, she knew, she must secure the old man to her, with her energy, and good spirits, and intelligence, and unassuming nature. That done, she would come to his bed, with her candle and her nakedness. Then, unless what she had heard of men was false, he would give her his seed; his seed would make the child which was what her heart had grown to desire.

Boy or girl child, that mattered little. She had no preference between boy or girl.

Accustomed to the solitude of her garden, and its silences, life with the old man suited her. He praised her companionship first, then her cooking and cleaning, then her fondness for him and at last, as she contrived, her flesh. When it was the third night that she had come naked and candlelit into his chamber, he said, "Stay the night," when she rose to leave his bed. He held her arm tight in his strong hand. She acquiesced, as she would have even without his hand to hold her. She had traced his body's long scar with her fingers and heard him breathe hard with his pleasures. She had found herself, too, running in pleasure's traces.

When her captain was to sail, she went to the docks. He made formal farewell, the married captain leaving his wife behind. He was leaving her in the company of Bildads. "You'll have wife and child awaiting your return," she told him then. She watched his face, where the scar cut. "My mind never ran to a child," he said. "Your body did," she said. 'This is your will?" he asked. "And my desire, too," she said. 'Then God's grace on all three of us," he said, and turned to his ship.

She waited out the months and weeks and days, while her child grew within her. She weeded and planted in her gardens, growing flowers and food. She knitted and stitched, to clothe her child warm during the first years of its life. She read the Captain's volumes, Scripture, Shakespeare, Plato, nourishing her spirit and her mind. She told no one of her pregnancy, and then her belly told all.

The birthing was easy at first, like sea swells, and her bed was the big-keeled boat, riding the swells. The swells grew and the boat shrank, until she didn't know at the falling of each swell if she could survive another, and she shrieked like the crew of a doomed vessel.

The midwives moved around her bed, shadowy figures in the shadowy light, and she did not know if they waved her forward or if she pulled them along after her.

Until the bed was not a ship but a living creature, and she strapped upon its back. Unable to get free, and breathe. Her body was the creature she was bound to, and it dragged her down into a black and swirling, drowning pain.

She rolled her head from side to side to find help—as if there were benefit in companionship. Her thoughts watched on helplessly; until she caught them and dragged them down after her.

Until a sudden silence filled the room, and the cry of a living child floated on that deep, watery silence.

She breathed in the understanding—The size of it, beyond the cruelty of pain and the goodness of ease. The immortal of it, and she had been caught up in it, and still she lived. It seemed that something so dimensioned must crack the human frame and spirit when they joined into the same effort. How could it not? This birthing of a life.

The faces of the midwives came pink-cheeked out of the shadows, speaking now in their common language, placing the child into her arms. "This is a son."

SHE HELD HER FIRST BORN, as she hoped to hold all of her children at their births. Thoughts of how mighty are the forces of birth left her, carried out perhaps with the soiled sheets, slipped out in the bowl of bloody afterbirth; although there was a new knowledge now in the eyes she met in a mirror. Knowledge of what, she could not say—and her son needed feeding, needed cleaning, needed tenderness—except that the darkness of it was terror and the brightness of it was terror, and she carried the scars of it invisibly in her flesh.

He would be glad of a son, her old man. She waited for news of his return and the child grew, sturdy of limb and bold spirited. He had his father's heliotrope eyes.

They brought old Ahab home on their shoulders, one leg of ivory and one of flesh, and his eyes burned in his face. He had a fever without heat. He sometimes spoke angrily to her, sometimes wildly, and sometimes cajolingly, but he never called her by name and never touched his son—who stood now, on his own pink and ten-toed feet, and met the day merrily. The Captain refused to share his bed with her, that too. "I've only one good leg left to me—and that one's no use to you!" he cried, locking his door against her.

Sometimes he spoke to those who were not in the room—and he never left the house, not even though his ship was being already outfitted—and sometimes he sat in brooding silence, for day after long, dark day, thinking of the voyage. This was the voyage of revenge, although he did not say so openly. His eyes had looked on death and locked glances there. Whatever else he might name it, she knew that Captain Ahab was for death.

Let him go, then. She was not the wife for that journey. Let him go alone. He refused her, without being asked, as she would have refused him, had he asked her.

He spoke to those unseen presences. "Ye'll not have the boy," he muttered. "The boy'll not be the one to have you," he promised. "I'll be the one to have you, and pour your blood into the water."

Ahab sailed on Christmas Day, away from shore and home, and his wife watched from the high attic window, for he had forbidden her the dock. She watched the tall masts, and knew how blond and brave were the tiny figures moving in the ship's rigging, setting out the sails.

A season passed and the boy could walk alone; another season and he could chew on gingerbread he held in his own hands. Season after season until he could speak, to say his name and his wishes, until he could run and—in the growing, blooming seasons—work beside her in the garden.

A year passed from the time her old Captain had sailed from Nantucket harbor and out to the whaling grounds, and then another year, and a third. The boy had been a year and not much besides when he had seen his father for the last time, then he was two years, then three, four, and coming up on five.

The Captain's ship had not been seen, or reported. The time had stretched out long, until a

Captain's wife must start to wonder, "Am I widow now? How long have I been widowed, all unknowing? Strange world, where a woman cannot know her own bereavement, a child his own half-orphaning. Am I now? Will I ever again be? Wife?"

She wondered, and waited to hear, and watched her child grow into a boy—wrapped warm in a woolen coat, the boy rolled down the hillside, shrieking.

Until one May afternoon, she looked up from her gardening to see a man outlined against the bright sky. She rose and adjusted her neckerchief. She shook out her skirts as she went down the brick path, to greet him. Her heart beat fast.

He was bronzed by some fiercer sun than filled the New England sky, where storms blew fierce but sun fell weak. He was not much older than she and she counted herself a young woman.

Especially to be Old Ahab's widow, if that was what he had come to tell her.

He took off his hat, and his eyes were shadowed by death.

"You sailed with him," she said.

"How can you know that?"

"And now you come to tell me he is dead," she said.

Her son was at her side now.

"I have come to tell you the manner of his death," the young man said. "I have come to tell the way he found his death, what confluence of chance and fate and his own iron-crowned will made the maelstrom that sank him."

"It will have been a whale," she said.

"Madam," and his eyes glowed with the words that would make his story, "it was the White Whale."

She didn't know if she wished to hear. She knew the old tale of the Venetian daughter, and how dangerous it was to a maiden's heart to hear told the heroic deeds of men. But she was not a maiden; she was a propertied widow, with a child. Her son should know the story of his father's death and deeds. The Captain's wife hesitated, and held the sailor, lest he think of leaving before she had made up her mind, with a question. "And the ship?"

He shook his head, sorrowed.

"And all the fine men upon her?" she demanded now. What had her Captain done, taken death to sea with him? If so—as so it seemed—then this young man had—as she had herself—escaped Old Ahab's toils.

He opened his mouth, but no words came out. He nodded his head, and she saw that the sun on that other side of the world had gilded his hair. "I only am escaped, to tell thee," he whispered, like a man speaking to ghosts, or to God.

"Speak plain, man," she said, and broke the spell. "On land, what are you?"

He laughed to tell her "A schoolmaster, that humble trade."

"Then come in, schoolmaster, and tell us your story. We will give you dinner, too, if you will do us the honor of eating with Ahab's son, and widow."

He would, and gladly too, he said. She knew he would court her then, and she thought she would be won. "What is your name, schoolmaster?" she asked.

He was preceding her down the brick walk, between half-weeded flower beds. He stopped, squared his shoulders, turned to face her, seeming somehow taller and broader than when he first stood at her gate. He said, "Call me Ishmael."

"No," she said. "I will call you by your own, your man's, name," she said. She had a son, and property. She was for life. "What is your name?" she asked again, with sweet patience.

SUSAN SNIVELY '67

*S*usan Rumble Snively came to Smith from Kentucky and left magna cum laude. *Since receiving her PhD in English Literature at Boston University in 1976 with a dissertation on Sylvia Plath, she has published three volumes of poetry, and she continues to write and read her poems to large gatherings in search of her irreverent wit, emotional honesty, and clarity of poetic image. She sings almost as well as she writes, and the Da Camera Singers in the Pioneer Valley rely on her pitch and fidelity. During the academic year, Susan Snively is a Dean of Students and Writing Counselor at Amherst College, squiring students through papers and theses in all disciplines. She is often a leader of workshops on the writing of poetry at the Five Colleges and beyond. She has taught at Smith, Mount Holyoke, Simon's Rock, and Boston University. She makes her home in Amherst, MA, having recently moved into the second-oldest house in the village. The history of her house may be the subject of poems to come.*

She has received numerous fellowships including ones from the College English Association, Massachusetts Arts and Humanities, National Endowment for the Arts, Bread Loaf Fellowship, and an Arts Fellowship from the Massachusetts Arts and Humanities Foundation for her writing. Her poetry has appeared in such journals as The Kenyon Review, The Massachusetts Review, The Yale Review, The Georgia Review, Poetry, The American Scholar, Ploughshares, *and* Poetry East. *Her collections,* From This Distance *(1981),* Voices in the House *(1988), and* The Undertow *(1998) demonstrate her technical virtuosity in rhythm, rhyme, and stanza forms in poems ranging in subject from the personal to every form of artistic endeavor, including cooking.*

"Too Late" is reprinted from The Undertow, *and "The Flowers" and "Ultimatum" are published here for the first time.*

Too Late

It's too late to become a ballet dancer.
At nine, I could execute piqué turns
like a dervish, faster than the other girls.
My arms were supple as grass. But now
I get a little dizzy, trying a turn
or three in the kitchen when nobody's home.
Look what happened to poor Zelda Fitzgerald,
practicing arabesques to a scratchy record
of "Valencia." It only goes to show—
if age doesn't get you, bad taste will.

It's too late to become a famous actress.
I teach, therefore I act, especially reading
poetry aloud, hoping to move
someone to tears or fright, or to stop
their chewing gum and staring out the window.
But always I feel I may have gone too far.
A student praised me once, on a course survey,
"Ms. S—— can do so many interesting accents."

It's not likely I'll be a nuclear physicist,
although I was once overjoyed to learn
how small the nucleus is, hanging inside
its atom like a dust mote in a basilica.
I realize now that what I know of physics
is like a dust mote inside the whole round world,
and that what fascinated me at twelve
was disaster, always just about to happen.
My awe was a useful substitute for religion,
but not, alas, the real thing. Nor will I

become a singer, although I have sung
and occasionally receive a compliment
from someone who doesn't know much about singing.
High D is gone, taking high C with her,
and good old B-flat isn't what she should be.
Now and then, singing along with a tape,
I'll note a curious wobble, like cooked spaghetti,
underneath my usually bang-on pitch.
Oh, it's the car, the bumpy road, I'll think,
but no, it's something else. Neglect. Age.

There's still time to be a decent cook,
a glutton jeweled with the glaze of manners,
eager to please while pleasuring her mouth.
I used to say I'd rather write than eat,
but now I'm not so sure. To love a word,
"wine," for example, is to love the thing
itself, as well as the occasion—
voluptuous evening hour, sybarite friends—
that stirs it into shimmer, so that reflection
tastes the same as a life without regret.

The Flowers

Near the grocery store's fish counter
I met up with an older friend

the same age as my mother
and, as she was, youthful and funny.

When I helped her remember "smelts,"
she told me she'd just turned eighty

and I thrust into her basket
the flowers I thought were mine

though I hadn't paid for them yet.
Clearly my own mind was going,

and when I remembered what I'd done,
I tracked my friend through the store

to correct my stupid mistake.
I put my arms around her

because she is who she is,
and because I'd told her the sadness

that confused my day and my mind.
Now I am scared and grateful,

grateful for her patience,
her humorous eyes, the blue hat

that perfectly matched her scarf
and only reminded me later

of my mother's elegance
which she wore with spunky ease.

But I'm scared of what I needed
and that need's unmannerly craving

for the company of the dead
who keep turning up missing,

and for the living, whom I miss
as if they were also dead.

Ultimatum

On a line from Marvin Bell

Don't say you don't remember it.
I want to put your face up to memory

and startle you with its clear edge.
I want to put your face right in it.

It is a pity that I feel this way,
but I no longer pity myself

since I learned to look through the windows
of a house where I no longer live.

But it isn't the house that matters.
Heads turning together in the car

mowing the dry leaves,
the grain of the floor we painted,

bats in the trees, evenings
of cold sharp stars,

a joke rising above the candles
into the alcoholic air,

the morning I swept broken glass,
unable to speak:

Don't say you don't remember it.
I want to put your face right in it all.

Of the many words for healing,
I choose only the ones that seem true,

and so if certain scars open and bleed
like angry mouths,

I would rather see them do that
than become one of the forgetful.

I will look through the windows of the house
although they are invisible

and feel the power of this looking
(though in the darkness I wring my hands)

as if I am one of the dead
who are chosen to come back and watch

the living repeat the longings
and crimes and confusions of the past.

It is not what I see but what I know
that holds my sight inside the crystal

and makes my voice leap across the distance
that stretches so long between us:

Don't say you don't remember it.
Keep silent, if you would be at peace.

JANE YOLEN '60

Although Jane Yolen has worked as an editor, teacher, and workshop leader, her primary career is as a full-time professional writer. Born in New York City and now dividing her time between Hatfield, MA, and Scotland, Jane Yolen often alludes to "the old stories," because readers of all ages need the past to understand art and culture today. Conveying that understanding requires creative diversity, the hallmark of Jane Yolen's success.

After Smith, she worked in publishing for several years, learning the value of her own spare prose and her own imprint, since 1988, of Jane Yolen Books for Harcourt Brace Jovanovich. While in New York she studied poetry at Hunter College, and later, while raising her three children with her husband David Stemple, she received an MEd from the University of Massachusetts (1976).

Her first book for children, Pirates in Petticoats (1963), factually represents her research on female pirates. Her picture books include the Caldecott Award winner, Owl Moon (1987) and a Caldecott Honor Book, The Emperor and the Kite (1967). She has published a number of volumes of verse, including How Beastly!: A Menagerie of Nonsense Poems (1980), and Dinosaur Dances (1990). Prose poems best define All the Secrets in the World (1991) and Letting Swift River Go (1992), a true story of the flooding of four New England towns to create the Quabbin Reservoir. Her literary fairy tales include The Girl Who Cried Flowers and Other Tales (1974), winner of the Golden Kite Award from the Society of Children's Book Writers. Yolen's fantasy stories include the Pit Dragon Trilogy for young adult readers and the Commander Toad science fiction series for younger children. Small wonder that she was honored with the Kerlan Award in 1988 for the body of her work, characterized by a sense of wonder, fantasy, and psychological truth. One of her most recent works is Tea with an Old Dragon (1998), illustrated by Monica Vachula '73, about Sophia Smith, founder of Smith College.

A Smith Medalist and author of more than two hundred books, Jane Yolen "tells the story that needs to be told." Appearing here is "Sister Emily's Lightship," an imaginative rendering of Emily Dickinson's inspiration, winner of the 1997 Nebula Award for best short story, given by the Science Fiction and Fantasy Writers of America.

Sister Emily's Lightship

I DWELL IN POSSIBILITY. The pen scratched over the page, making graceful ellipses. She liked the look of the black on white as much as the words themselves. The words sang in her head far sweeter than they sang on the page. Once down, captured like a bird in a cage, the tunes seemed pedestrian, mere common rote. Still, it was as close as she would come to that Eternity, that Paradise that her mind and heart promised. *I dwell in Possibility.*

She stood and stretched, then touched her temples where the poem still throbbed. She could feel it sitting there, beating its wings against her head like that captive bird. Oh, to let the bird out to sing for a moment in the room before she caged it again in the black bars of the page.

Smoothing down the skirt of her white dress, she sat at the writing table once more, took up the pen, dipped it into the ink jar, and added a second line. *A fairer House than . . .* than what? Had she lost the word between standing and sitting? Words were not birds after all, but slippery as fish.

Then, suddenly, she felt it beating in her head. *Prose! A fairer House than Prose*—She let the black ink stretch across the page with the long dash that lent the last word that wonderful fall of tone. She preferred punctuating with the dash to the hard point, as brutal as a bullet. *I dwell in Possibility.*

She blotted the lines carefully before reading them aloud, her mouth forming each syllable perfectly as she had been taught so many years before at Miss Lyon's Mount Holyoke Female Seminary.

Cocking her head to one side, she considered the lines. *They will do*, she thought, as much praise as she ever allowed her own work, though she was generous to others. Then, straightening the paper and cleaning the nib of her pen, she tore up the false starts and deposited them in the basket.

She could, of course, write any time during the day if the lines came to mind. There was little enough that she had to do in the house. But she preferred night for her truest composition and perhaps that was why she was struggling so. *Then those homey tasks will take me on*, she told herself: supervising the gardening, baking Father's daily bread. Her poetry must never be put in the same category.

Standing, she smoothed down the white skirt again and tidied her hair—"like a chestnut bur," she'd once written imprudently to a friend. It was ever so much more faded now.

But pushing that thought aside, Emily went quickly out of the room as if leaving considerations of vanity behind. Besides the hothouse flowers, besides the bread, there was a cake to be made for tea. After Professor Seelye's lecture there would be guests and her tea cakes were expected.

THE TEA HAD BEEN ORDERLY, the cake a success, but Emily headed back upstairs soon after, for her eyes—always sensitive to the light—had begun to tear up. She felt a sick headache starting. Rather than impose her ailments on her guests, she slipped away. They would understand.

Carlo padded up the stairs behind her, so quiet for such a large dog. But how slow he had become these last months. Emily knew that Death would stop for him soon enough. Newfoundlands were not a long-lived breed usually, and he had been her own shaggy ally for the past fifteen years.

Slowing her pace, despite the stabbing behind her eyes, Emily let the old dog catch up. He shoved his rough head under her hand and the touch salved them both.

He curled up beside her bed and slept, as she did, in an afternoon made night and close by the window blinds.

I T WAS NIGHT IN TRUTH when Emily awoke, her head now wonderfully clear. Even the dreadful sleet in her eyes was gone.

She rose and threw on a dressing gown. She owed Loo a letter, and Samuel and Mary Bowles. But still the night called to her. Others might hate the night, hate the cold of November, huddling around their stoves in overheated houses. But November seemed to her the very Norway of the year.

She threw open first the curtains, then the blinds, almost certain of a sight of actual fjords. But though the Gibraltar lights made the village look almost foreign, it was not—she decided— foreign enough.

"That I had the strength for travel," she said aloud. Carlo answered her with a quick drum roll of tail.

Taking that as the length of his sympathy, she nodded at him, lit the already ensconced candle, and sat once again at the writing table. She read over the morning's lines:

> *I dwell in Possibility—*
> *A fairer House than Prose—*

It no longer had the freshness she remembered, and she sighed.

At the sound, Carlo came over to her and laid his rough head in her lap, as if trying to lend comfort.

"No comfort to be had, old man," she said to him. "I can no longer tell if the trouble is my wretched eyes, sometimes easy and sometimes sad. Or the dis-order of my mind. Or the slant of light on the page. Or the words themselves. Or something else altogether. Oh, my dear dog . . ." She leaned over and buried her face in his fur but did not weep for she despised private grief that could not be turned into a poem. Still the touch had a certain efficaciousness, and she stood and walked over to the window.

The Amherst night seemed to tremble in on itself. The street issued a false invitation, the maples standing sentinel between the house and the promise of road.

"Keeping me in?" she asked the dog, "or others out?" It was only her wretched eyes that forced her to stay at home so much and abed. Only her eyes, she was convinced. In fact she planned a trip into town at noon next when the very day would be laconic; if she could get some sleep and if the November light proved not too harsh.

She sat down again at the writing table and made a neat pile of the poems she was working on, then set them aside. Instead she would write a letter. To . . . to Elizabeth. "Dear Sister," she would start as always, even though their relationship was of the heart, not the blood. "I will tell her about the November light," she said to Carlo. "Though it is much the same in Springfield as here, I trust she will find my observations entertaining."

The pen scratched quickly across the page. *So much quicker*, she thought, *than when I am composing a poem.*

She was deep into the fourth paragraph, dashing "November always seemed to me the Norway . . ." when a sharp knock on the wall shattered her peace, and a strange insistent whine seemed to fill the room.

And the light. *Oh—the light!* Brighter even than day.

"Carlo!" she called the dog to her, and he came, crawling, trembling. So large a dog and such a larger fright. She fell on him as a drowning person falls on a life preserver. The light made her eyes weep pitchers. Her head began to ache. The house rocked.

And then—as quickly as it had come—it was gone: noise, light, all, all gone.

Carlo shook her off as easily as bath water, and she collapsed to the floor, unable to rise.

L AVINIA FOUND HER THERE on the floor in the morning, her dressing gown disordered and her hands over her eyes.

"Emily, my dear, my dear . . ." Lavinia cried, lifting her sister entirely by herself back onto the bed. "Is it the terror again?"

It was much worse than the night terrors, those unrational fears which had afflicted her for years. But Emily had not the strength to contradict. She lay on the bed hardly moving the entire day while Mother bathed her face and hands with aromatic spirits and Vinnie read to her. But she could not concentrate on what Vinnie read; neither the poetry of Mrs. Browning nor the prose of George Eliot soothed her. She whimpered and trembled, recalling vividly the fierceness of that midnight light. She feared she was, at last, going mad.

"Do not leave, do not leave," she begged first Vinnie, then Mother, then Austin, who had been called to the house in the early hours. Father alone had been left to his sleep. But they did go, to whisper together in the hall. She could not hear what they said but she could guess that they were discussing places to send her away. For a rest. For a cure. For—Ever—

S HE SLEPT, WAKED, SLEPT AGAIN. Once she asked for her writing tablet, but all she managed to write on it was the word light ten times in a column like some mad ledger. They took the tablet from her and refused to give it back.

The doctor came at nine, tall and saturnine, a new man from Northampton. Vinnie said later he looked more like an undertaker than a physician. He scolded Emily for rising at midnight and she was too exhausted to tell him that for her it was usual. Mother and Vinnie and Austin did not tell him for they did not know. No one knew that midnight was her favorite time of the clock. That often she walked in the garden at midnight and could distinguish, just by the smell, which flowers bloomed and bloomed well. That often she sat in the garden seat and gazed up at the great eight-sided cupola Father had built onto the house. His one moment of monumental playfulness. Or she sat at the solitary hour inside the cupola contemplating night through each of the windows in turn, gazing round at all the world that was hers.

"Stay in bed, Miss Dickinson," warned the doctor, his chapped hands delicately on hers. "Till we have you quite well again. Finish the tonic I am leaving with your mother for you. And then you must eschew the night and its vapors."

Vinnie imitated him quite cruelly after he left. "Oh, the vay-pures, the vay-pures!" she cried, hand to her forehead. Unaccountably, Carlo howled along with her recitation.

Mother was—as usual—silently shocked at Vinnie's mimicry but made no remonstrances.

"He looks—and sounds—quite medieval," Austin commented laconically.

At that Emily began to laugh, a robust hilarity that brought tears to her poor eyes. Austin joined with her, a big stirring hurrah of a laugh.

"Oh, dear Emily," Vinnie cried. "Laugh on! It is what is best for you."

Best for what? Emily asked herself, but did not dare say it aloud. But she vowed she would never let the doctor touch her again.

HAVING SLEPT ALL DAY meant that she was awake at midnight, still she did not venture out of the bed. She lay awake fearing to hear once more the horrid knock and feel the house shake and see the piercing white light. A line of poetry ran through her mind: *Me—come! My dazzled face.* But her mind was so befogged that she could not recall if it were her own line or if she had read it somewhere.

At the last nothing more happened and she must have fallen back to sleep some time after two. When she woke it was midmorning and there was a tray by her bed with tea and toast and some of her own strawberry preserves.

She knew she was well again when she realized Carlo was not in the room. He would never have left her side otherwise.

Getting out of the bed was simple. Standing without swaying was not. But she gathered up her dressing gown, made a swift toilette, then went downstairs carrying the tray. Some illnesses she knew, from her months with the eye doctors in Cambridgeport, are best treated like a bad boy at school. Quickly beaten, quicker trained.

If the family was surprised to see her, they knew better than to show it.

"Shall we have Susie and little Ned for tea?" she asked by way of greeting.

SUE CAME OVER PROMPTLY AT FOUR, as much to check up on Emily's progress as to have tea. Austin must have insisted. Heavily pregnant, she walked slowly while Ned, a rambunctious four-year-old, capered ahead.

"Dear critic," Emily said, answering the door herself. She kissed Sue on both cheeks and led her through into the hall. "And who is slower today, you with your royal front or me with my rambling mind."

"Nonsense!" Sue said. "You are indulging yourself in fancies. Neddie, stop jumping about. Your Aunt Emily is just out of a sickbed."

The boy stopped for a moment and then flung himself into Emily's skirts, crying, "Are you hurt? Where does it hurt? Shall I kiss it?"

Emily bent down and said, "Your *Uncle* Emily shall kiss you instead, for I am not hurt at all. We boys never cry at hurts." She kissed the top of his fair head, which sent him into paroxysms of laughter.

Sue made a *tch* sound with her tongue. "And once you said to me that if you saw a bullet hit a bird and he told you he wasn't shot, you might weep at his courtesy, but you would certainly doubt his word."

"Unfair! Unfair to quote me back at me!" Emily said, taking Sue's hands. "Am I not this moment the very pink of health?"

"That is not what Austin said, who saw you earlier today. And there is a white spot between your eyes as if you have lain with a pinched expression all night."

"And all morning, too. Come in here, Sue," Vinnie called from the sitting room. "And do not chastize her any more than I have already. It does no good you know."

They drank their tea and ate the crumbles of the cake from the day before, though it mortified Emily that they had to do so. But she had had no time to prepare more for their small feast. Neddie had three pieces anyway, two of his own and one Emily gave him from her own plate because suddenly the cake was too sweet, the light too bright, the talk too brittle, and Emily tired past bearing it all.

She rose abruptly. Smiling, she said, "I am going back to bed."

"We have overworn you," Sue said quickly.

"And I you," Emily answered.

"I am not tired, Auntie," Ned said.

"You never are," Vinnie said fondly.

"I am in the evening," Ned conceded. "And sometimes in . . ."

But Emily heard no more. The stairs effectively muffled the rest of the conversation as she sought the sanctuary of her room.

I dwell in Possibility—

SHE SAT AT THE DESK and read the wavering line again. But what possibilities did she, indeed, dwell in? This house, this room, the garden, the lawn between her house and Austin's stately "Evergreens." They were all the possibilities she had. Even the trips to Cambridgeport for eye treatments had held no great promise. All her traveling—and what small journeys they had proved—lay in the past. She was stuck, like a cork in an old bottle without promise of wine. Stuck here in the little town where she had been born.

She went over to the bed and flung herself down on her stomach and wept quietly into the pillow until the early November dark gathered around her.

It was an uncharacteristic and melodramatic scene, and when she sat up at last, her cheeks reddened and quite swollen, she forgave herself only a little.

"Possibly the doctor's tonic has a bite at the bottom," she whispered to Carlo, who looked up at her with such a long face that she had to laugh, her cheeks tight with the salty tears. "Yes, you are right. I have the vay-pures." She stood and, without lighting a lamp, found the wash basin and bathed her face.

She was not hungry, either for food or company, and so she sat in the gathering gloom thinking about her life. Despite her outburst, she quite liked the tidiness of her cocoon. She doubted she had the capacity for wings or the ability for flight.

When it was totally dark, she went back to her bed and lay down, not to sleep but to wait till the rest of the household slept.

THE GRANDFATHER CLOCK on the landing struck eleven. She waited another fifteen minutes before rising. Grabbing a woolen shawl from the foot of the bed, she rose ghostlike and slipped from the room.

The house breathed silent sleep around her. Mother, Father, Vinnie, Cook had all gone down the corridors of rest, leaving not a pebble behind for her to follow.

She climbed the stairs up to the cupola for she had not the will nor might to brave

November's garden. Still, she had to get away from the close surround of family and the cupola was as far as she could go.

She knew which risers creaked alarmingly and, without thinking, avoided them. But behind her Carlo trod on every one. The passage was not loud enough to waken the sleepers who had heard it all before without stirring, yet Emily still held her breath till they reached the top unremarked.

Putting her hand on the dog's head for a moment, to steady them both, she climbed up into the dome of the house. In the summer there was always a fly or two buzzing about the windows and she quite liked them, her "speck pianos." But in November the house was barren of flies. She would have to make all the buzz herself.

Sitting on the bench, she stared out of the windows at the glittering stars beyond the familiar elms. How could she have abjured this peace for possibilities unknown?

"Oh, Carlo," she whispered to the dog, "we must be careful what we say. No bird resumes its egg."

He grunted a response and settled down at her feet for the long watch.

"Like an old suitor," she said, looking down fondly at him. "We are, you know, too long engaged, too short wed. Or some such." She laughed. "I think the prognosis is that my madness is quite advanced."

When she looked up again, there was a flash of light in the far-off sky, a star falling to earth.

"Make a wish, Carlo," she said gaily. "I know I shall."

And then the top of the cupola burst open, a great gush of sound enveloped them, and she was pulled up into the light.

A M I DEAD? she thought at first. Then, *Am I rising to Heaven?* Then, *Shall I have to answer to God?* That would be the prime embarrassment, for she had always held out against the blandishments of her redeemed family, saying that she was religious without that great Eclipse, God. She always told them that life was itself mystery and consecration enough. *Oh, do not let it be a jealous God,* she thought. *I would have too much to explain away.*

Peculiarly this light did not hurt her eyes, which only served to convince her that she was, indeed, dead. And then she wondered if there would be actual angels as well, further insult to her heresy. *Perhaps they will have butterfly wings,* she thought. *I would like that.* She was amused, briefly, in her dying by these wild fancies.

And then she was no longer going upward, and there was once more a steady ground beneath her feet where Carlo growled but did not otherwise move. Walls, smooth and anonymous, curved away from her like the walls of a cave. *A hallway,* she thought, *but one without signature.*

A figure came toward her, but if *that* were an angel, all of Amherst's Congregational Church would come over faint! It wore no gown of alabaster satin, had no feathery wings. Rather it was a long, sleek, gray man with enormous adamantine eyes and a bulbed head rather like a leek's.

A leek—I am surely mad! she thought. All poetry fled her mind.

Carlo was now whining and trembling beyond measure. She bent to comfort him; that he should share her madness was past understanding.

"Do not be afraid," the gray man said. *No—the bulbed thing—*for she now saw it was not a man at all, though like a man it had arms and legs and a head. But the limbs were too long, the body too thin, the head too round, the eyes too large. And though it wore no discernible clothing, it did not seem naked.

"Do not be afraid," it repeated, its English curiously accented. It came down rather heavily on the word *be* for no reason that Emily could tell. Such accentuation did not change the message.

If not an angel, a demon—But this her unchurched mind credited even less.

She mustered her strength; she could when courage was called for. "Who—or what—are you?"

The bulb creature smiled. This did not improve its looks. "I am a traveler," it said.

"And where do you travel?" That she was frightened did not give her leave to forget all manners. And besides, curiosity had now succeeded fear.

"From a far . . ." The creature hesitated. She leaned into its answer. "From a far star."

There was a sudden rip in the fabric of her world.

"Can you show me?" It was not that she did not believe the stranger, but that she did. It was the very possibility that she had, all unknowing, hoped for, wept for.

"Show you?"

"The star."

"No."

The rip was repaired with clumsy hands. She would always see the darn.

"It is too far for sight."

"Oh."

"But I can show you your own star."

"And what do you want from me in exchange?" She knew enough of the world to know this.

For a moment the creature was silent. She feared she had embarrassed it. Or angered it. Then it gave again the grimace that was its smile. "Tell me what it is you do in this place."

She knew this was not an idle question. She chose her answer with care. "I tell the truth," she said. "But I tell it slant."

"Ah . . ." There was an odd light in the gray creature's eyes. "A poet."

She nodded. "I have some small talent."

"I, myself, make . . . poems. You will not have heard of me, but my name is . . ." And here it spoke a series of short, sharp syllables that to her ear were totally unrepeatable.

"Miss Emily Dickinson," she replied, holding out her hand.

The bulb creature took her hand in its and she did not flinch though its hand was far cooler than she expected. Not like something dead but rather like the back of a snake. There were but three long fingers on the hand.

The creature dropped her hand and gave a small bow, bending at its waist. "Tell me, Miss Emily Dickinson, one of your poems."

She folded her hands together and thought for a minute of the dozens of poems shoved into the drawer of her writing table, of the tens more in her bureau drawer. Which one should she recite—for she remembered them all? Which one would be appropriate payment for this gray starfarer?

And then she had it. Her voice—ever light—took on color as she said the poem:

> *Some things that fly there be—*
> *Birds—Hours—the Bumblebee—*
> *Of these no Elegy.*
>
> *Some things that stay there be—*
> *Grief—Hills—Eternity—*
> *Nor this behooveth me.*

There are that resting, rise.
Can I expound the skies?
How still the Riddle lies!

WHEN SHE WAS DONE, she did not drop her head modestly as Miss Lyons had taught, but rather stared straight into the starfarer's jeweled eyes.

It did not smile this time and she was glad of that. But it took forever to respond. Then at last it sighed. "I have no poem its equal. But Miss Emily Dickinson, I can expound the skies."

She did not know exactly what the creature meant.

"Give me your hand again."

And then she knew. "But I cannot leave my dog."

"I cannot vouchsafe the animal."

She misunderstood. "I can. He will not harm you."

"No. I mean more correctly, I do not know what such a trip will do to him."

"I cannot leave him behind."

The gray creature nodded its bulb head, and she unhesitatingly put her hand in his, following down the anonymous corridor and into an inner chamber that was something like a laboratory.

"Sit here," the starfarer said, and when she sat in the chair a webbing grew up out of the arms and bound her with filaments of surprising strength.

"Am I a prisoner?" She was not frightened, just curious.

"The lightship goes many miles quickly. The web is to keep you safe."

She thought how a horse starting too quickly to pull a carriage often knocks its passenger back against the seat, and understood. "And my dog?"

"Ah—now you see the problem."

"Can he sit here in the chair beside me?"

"The chair is not built for so much weight."

"Then he may be badly hurt. I cannot go."

The creature raised one of its long fingers. "I will put your dog in my sleeping chamber for as long as we travel." It took Carlo by the collar and led the unprotesting dog off to a side wall, which opened with the touch of a button, letting down a short bed that was tidily made. "Here," the creature commanded the dog and surprisingly Carlo—who ordinarily obeyed no one but Emily—leaped onto the bed. The starfarer pushed another button and the bed slid back into the wall, imprisoning the now-howling Carlo inside.

"I apologize for my shaggy ally," Emily said.

"There is no need." The gray creature bent over a panel of flashing lights, its six fingers flying between them. When it had finished, it leaned back into its own chair and the webbing held it fast.

"Now I will show you what your own planet looks like from the vantage of space. Do not be afraid, Miss Emily Dickinson."

She smiled. "I am not afraid."

"I did not think *so*," the starfarer said in its peculiar English.

And then, with a great shaking, the lightship rose above Amherst, above Massachusetts, above the great masses of land and water and clouds and air and into the stars.

SHE LAY ON HER BED REMEMBERING. Carlo, still moaning, had not seemed to recover quickly from the trip. But she had. All she could think about was the light, the dark, the stars. And the great green-blue globe—like one of Ned's marbles—that was her home.

What could she tell her family? That she had flown high above them all and seen how small they were within the universe? They would say she had had a dream. *If only I could have returned, like Mother from her ramblings, a burdock on her shawl to show where she had been*, she thought.

And then she laughed at herself. Her poems would be her burdocks, clinging stubbornly to the minds of her readers. She sat up in the dark.

The light. The marble of earth. She would never be able to capture it whole. Only in pieces. But it was always best to make a start of it. *Begin*, as Cook often said, *as you mean to go on.*

She lit a small candle which was but a memento of that other light. And then she went over to the writing table. Her mind was a jumble of words, images.

I do not need to travel further than across this room ever again, she thought. *Or further than the confines of my house.* She had already dwelt in that greatest of possibilities for an hour in a ship made of light. The universe was hers, no matter that she lived only in one tiny world. She would write letters to that world in the form of her poems, even if the world did not fully understand or ever write back. Dipping the pen into the ink jar, she began the first lines of a lifetime of poems:

> *I lost a World—the other day.*
> *Has Anybody found?*
> *You'll know it by the Row of Stars*
> *Around its forehead bound.*

BETSY STARK '78

*B*etsy Stark is Business Correspondent for ABC News where she frequently appears on "World News Tonight with Peter Jennings," covering Wall street, the domestic and global economy, and the changing face of Corporate America. Her stories can also be seen on other ABC programs, including "Good Morning America." This assignment follows twenty years of experience covering law, media, politics and the economy for other national news organizations, including The Wall Street Journal. Betsy Stark was for several years Senior Producer of the Journal's television unit and a Correspondent on its weekly syndicated program, "The Wall Street Journal Report." In 1996 her work with Journal Television led to an anchor assignment at the Dow Jones television station WBIS in New York City. There she was Anchor and Editor of the live daily business news program "Heard on the Street."

Betsy Stark has also worked as a documentary producer for the Public Broadcasting System series, "Inside Story," which reported on the media. Her coverage of the controversial libel lawsuit brought by General William Westmoreland against the CBS network won an Emmy for Outstanding Investigative Reporting in 1983. She has earned several other journalism honors, including a second Emmy nomination in 1992 and an ICI/American University award for Excellence in Personal Finance Reporting in 1994.

She began her career as a print reporter for the American Lawyer magazine. She has also worked in radio as a daily stock market reporter and she has freelanced for NBC News, Fox News, and Court TV.

In 1979, a year after graduating from Smith with a degree in government, she married her high school sweetheart, Barney Softness (Amherst '76). Together they have two children, Ben and Sara. Despite a demanding career, she considers family her highest priority and says she has strived throughout her professional life to keep work and family in balance: "I came of age at a time when women were expected to have a career and a family," she says. "But no one told us how we were supposed to do that. I'm still trying to figure it out." The piece she wrote for Smith Voices shows how she juggles career and family.

Having It All

6:15 a.m.
Radio alarm goes off. Continue trying to sleep while performing mental checklist. Barney has late office hours. Ben has tennis. Sara has gymnastics—doesn't want fruit snacks anymore. Other kids have "good snacks." Need quarters for laundry. Anything in freezer for dinner?

7:00 a.m.
Make coffee. Give Ben breakfast and confirm after-school plans. Defer argument on expensive new sneakers he wants by promising to talk about it later. Glance at newspaper. Nothing big breaking. Turn on TV to check indications on stock market opening. Big drop expected in the Dow. World News may want a story.

7:15 a.m.
Make sure Sara is out of bed. Read yesterday's mail. Pick tie for Barney. Say good-bye to Ben. Glad he's still willing to kiss me good-bye. Hope he always will.

8:00 a.m.
Enjoy being all alone at home. Read paper and surf news channels for more on what's moving market. Get ready for work. Change three times.

9:15 a.m.
Take cab to work knowing it would be a lot cheaper to take subway.

9:45 a.m.
Skim several newspapers. Check market open. Looks ugly. Check e-mail. Check regular mail. Smile at letter from viewer with fashion advice not to wear shirt collars open: in television, it's often about how you look.

10:45 a.m.
Worlds News assigns story on stock market. Third story this week. Producers want a minute and 15 seconds on why stocks are down so sharply, what's being sold, impact on small investors. Used to think a story couldn't be told that quickly. Not anymore.

10:46 a.m.
Get into day-of-air "crash" mode. Producer assigned to work with me. Print latest wire copy on what's moving markets. Call favorite sources for quick takes. Talk strategy with producer: who do we want on camera? what pictures do we need to get? what graphics will we want to create? Have to guess now or risk doing without later. Place calls to potential on-camera interviews. Need someone who speaks in soundbites and is available within a couple of hours. Regret not having breakfast now that lunch is unlikely.

12 noon
Interviews booked for 1:15 and 2 p.m. Story line shaping up. Market is not. But anything can still happen. "World News" won't air story unless Dow finishes dramatically lower. Begin writing script with frequent interruptions. Give husband short shrift when he calls to check in. Apologize and hang up. Patience first casualty of daily deadline.

3:30 p.m.
Finish cold coffee, wishing it were Diet Coke, or even better, lunch. Remember that colleague next door usually has extra pretzels. Present first draft of script to Senior Producer. Likes it, but wants more detail in same amount of time. Now a minute fifteen does seem too short.

4:30 p.m.
Submit revised script to Anchor and Executive Producer for editing. Not too many questions. Revisions thankfully minor. Flee area immediately before they change their mind. Remember virtues of having a thick skin during this process.

5:00 p.m.
Go to sound booth to record narration for producer. Discuss outdoor location near office for on-camera close. Return to office and wonder if heavy make-up can conceal fatigue and hunger.

5:30 p.m.
Meet crew. Tape close. Several takes necessary—wind blows hair during one, busses make too much noise in another. Last take usually the best. Worry about time. Broadcast in one hour. Producer needs tape to make air.

6:00 p.m.
Deliver tape to producer. Experience relief—work is done.

6:05 p.m.
Experience sinking feeling. Work not done. Radio and Morning News requesting additional versions of story.

6:10 p.m.
Call Sara at home. Ben still at tennis. Tell Sara to watch me tonight. Tell her I'll be home as soon as I can. Tell her I love her.

6:30 p.m.
Watch story on "World News Tonight." Looks fine. Leave message thanking producer. Quickly rewrite script for Radio and Morning News. Quickly record new narrations.

7:00 p.m.
Take cab home knowing it would be a lot cheaper to take the subway.

7:15 p.m.

Walk through door to hugs—and hunger. Order Chinese food immediately. Set table and get family news of day: Ben aced his math test; Sara did a round-off-back-handspring-back-flip combination. Wish Barney were home to hear it all.

8:00 p.m.

Clean dinner dishes. Negotiate evening schedule for homework, showers, and television.

9:00 p.m.

Get in bed with newsmagazine. Browse catalogues instead. Field random homework questions. Answer phone calls for Ben and Sara. Glad they're not for me. Too tired now to talk.

9:30 p.m.

Wonder what I am forgetting for tomorrow. Sara reminds me she is playing trombone in school concert. Will I be there? Absolutely. Ben reminds me he needs new sneakers. Relent on sneakers. Too tired to resist.

9:45 p.m.

Fall asleep before my children . . . exhausted and content . . . having had it all.

PATRICIA
CLARK SMITH '64

Patricia Clark Smith was born on Valentine's Day in Holyoke, MA, and was the first member of her Micmac/Irish/ French-Canadian family to get a college education. She went from Phi Beta Kappa at Smith to Yale for her PhD (1970), writing a dissertation on Edgar Allan Poe. She taught for a year at Smith, 1968-69, seeing the College from both sides of the desk, after growing up seeing it with the perspective of her grandmother, a maid at Smith. Since 1971 she has taught at the University of New Mexico, where her courses in Native American literature, creative writing, and world literature punctuate her own writing life. Her two grown sons visit her often in Albuquerque where she lives and works with her husband John F. Crawford, a publisher and a college professor.

Her first two books were collections of poems, Talking to the Land *(1979) and* Changing Your Story *(1990). Her third was a two-volume co-edited anthology:* Western Literature in a World Context *(1995). Her fourth is for young people, a somewhat surprising but satisfying turn. With her former student and friend Paula Gunn Allen, Pat Smith has written* As Long as the Rivers Flow: The Stories of Nine Native Americans *(1996) to make readers aware of the range of Native American achievement. Her latest work is* On the Trail of Elder Brother: Glous'gap Stories of the Micmac, *traditional stories about the great hero of her people, retold with co-author, Michael Running Wolf. Her academic essays, short stories, and poetry have appeared in many collections, include* New America Review, Tierra: Contemporary Short Fiction of New Mexico, *and* Studies in American Indian Literature.

The essay that follows was published in an earlier version in Working Class Women in the Academy: Laborers in the Knowledge Factory *(1993), ed. Michelle Tokarcyk and Elizabeth Fay.*

Grandma Went to Smith, All Right, but She Went from Nine to Five: A Memoir

For Nana; for Sandy, Annie, Sharon, and the Heights Kids

"PROPERTY OF SMITH COLLEGE" on Northampton town plats comprises the nearest sizable green space to the house where my family lived until I turned seven, in the same upstairs apartment where my mother was born. That house, 53 Old South Street, was torn down in the mid-1950s, but I like knowing that my mother and I came to consciousness in the same set of rooms, that our eyes first learned to distinguish squares of sunlight shifting across the same kitchen floor, the same tree shadows on the wall.

The Smith campus, too, my mother and I both knew early in our lives. But here there is a difference between my mother's experience and my own, for she explored that place only after she was big enough to go there with her gang of neighborhood kids. Her mother, the grandmother I called Nana, seldom took her there. Smith land and Smith events have traditionally been open to townspeople, but Nana was Quebec-born, with a few years of grade school education, not the sort of Northampton resident likely to assume the college was accessible to her. Besides, even though my mother was her only child, Nana had little leisure for long walks with a toddler. Walks were what Nana took on her way upstreet from our house on the flats to go shopping, to go to Mass, or to go to work; walks were what she took to the bus stop, en route to visit relatives or to nurse them. She and my grandfather, who died when my mother was in her late teens, both came from sprawling and often hapless families, hers French Canadian and Micmac, his Irish. Both sides were riddled with tuberculosis, alcoholism, infant failure-to-thrive—the classic diseases of the poor. The stunning exception, the one success in my mother's family, was one of my grandfather's brothers, who made his way upward through ward politics to a term as mayor of Northampton in the thirties; his success was short, and apparently, unlike TB, it was not catching within families.

For Nana, Smith College was primarily the place where she worked intermittently throughout her life cleaning dormitory bathrooms and hallways. It is easy to see why she did not think of the Smith campus as an arena for leisure or pleasure, as a place to take a baby. My mother was the first in our family to see the grounds of Smith as in some way a part of her turf. She played there as a child; as a grown woman, she ventured into the art gallery, attended public lectures and foreign films, though always with a sense that Smith was special, its delights not her birthright, but privileges graciously extended to her.

As for me, her daughter, I cannot remember a time before the Smith campus was a familiar presence to me. I knew it first through my body, through bare feet and skinned knees, by way of the dirt lodged in the creases of my palms and caked beneath my fingernails, dirt Nana scrubbed off with gritty Boraxo in our slate sink. I learned to walk, and later to ice skate, on the campus; my first bullfrogs hunkered on the margin of the lily pool by Lyman Plant House.

And Smith was where I first understood metaphor, not in any freshman English class, but in the woods at the western edge of the campus heavy in early spring with the rich smell of leaf mold, soaked through by melting snow, where I hunkered down to inspect a jack-in-the-pulpit. On walks there, my parents taught me the wonderfully satisfying names of things: rose-breasted grosbeak, Solomon's seal, nuthatch, dogtooth violet, lady's slipper.

Within the boundaries of the campus, the Mill River widened out and briefly changed its name to Paradise Pond, though Nana said it was really still the same old Mill River. The Paradise Pond skating rink was kept glossy and clear of snow by the Kingsmen, Smith patois for the male groundskeepers and maintenance men. No question of Kingspersons in those days. There were cooks and chambermaids, all women. And then there were Kingsmen. *Kingsman* is said to derive from Franklin King, for fifty years Superintendent of Buildings and Grounds, whose name at full length was also given to the colonnaded neo-Georgian dormitory where Nana worked as a maid. A *chambermaid*.

For me and other Northampton kids whose relatives did service work at the college, *Kingsman* and *chambermaid* were words of double meaning. They meant the ordinary jobs held down by familiar adults. But the words also evoked the quaintly dressed people in the illustrations of Mother Goose books, the world of Humpty Dumpty and Old King Cole and the four-and-twenty blackbirds. When I entered Smith, the information booklet for freshmen commented upon the nice aptness of calling gardeners and janitors *Kingsmen*, for "they help put Smith back together again," no matter what maintenance problems might arise. I don't remember any mention in that booklet of chambermaids, only an oral explanation during some orientation session that those women were not to be tipped and were to be treated with courtesy. There was little danger of anyone tipping them, of course; as for the courtesy, I came to Smith knowing Nana's stories. And I had done some time by then as a waitress myself.

I grew up in a politically progressive family, where unions and strikes were common table talk. But as a little kid, I like most of my friends had no notion of the class assumptions evident in cutely calling working people Kingsmen. It seemed only one more odd conjunction of language, one I might some day figure out – and there were so many of those adult puns and euphemisms to puzzle over. My dad's stepfather, the only grown man I saw regularly during the war years, would chuck me under the chin and pinch my nose, and ask if I wanted to hear the story of Goldilocks and the Three Beers; when my brother Mike was born, and I asked my mother why Pop Noflke called Mike's tiny penis an "erector set," she said it was because the first erector sets were made at the Gilbert factory where Pop worked as a janitor (no "Kingsmen" in the Holyoke mills, to be sure), and Pop loved erector sets, and he loved baby Mike....She trailed off. *Kingsmen* was probably that sort of mystery.

The adult world was full of such secrets, of mysterious imports and double meanings. I took for granted the significance of names, words, multiple identities, even if often I could not guess what the significance might be, whether the doubling of meaning were portentous or playful.

But I knew one thing from an early age: there was some acute difference between being a chambermaid in the way Nana was and the apple-cheeked girls dressed in ruffled aprons and mob caps in the Mother Goose book. In a folklore course at Smith, I discovered the Opies' *Oxford Dictionary of Nursery Rhymes*, where I read avidly about the politics, sex, and class wars secreted in those texts. At four, at seven, I knew only that the chambermaids in the bright pictures seemed spunky, healthy, young, and largely cheerful, even when threatened by blackbirds and crosspatch mistresses. But then, as Nana once remarked when I asked her about the connection between her job and the pictures, those maids didn't have to scrub toilets. In the pastoral vision of the illustrators, maids milked bonny cows; they hung out clothes, they stood prettily all-in-a-row. It was different with Nana.

It is a soft spring evening in 1948. I come upon Nana sitting in her rocker in the darkened kitchen, rubbing her thick ankles. She is crying. I am five: I am terrified. In all the world, she is my steadiest point, steady and beautiful, like her name: Julia Larock Dunn.

What, Nana, what? I ask.

Oh, those girls, she says, and I know she means the students who live at Franklin King House. But what have those girls done?

They called me a bitch, she says, *right to my face!*

She sees I don't know the word, and now she's sorry she's used it, but I press her: *They called you what?*

A bitch, she says. *A she-dog. Like Lady.* And she names the mongrel next door, a very doggy-smelling dog with dangling teats.

I cannot believe this. I am sobbing, and now she is holding me, rocking me, singing to me in her gravelly Quebecois: *Allouette, je te plumerais.* Little skylark, I will pluck your wings. Don't cry: everything is all right.

Two kinds of bitch, two kinds of chambermaids, and the Mill and Paradise the same flowing water; many of my first confusions of language centered around Smith.

In the April after I turned seven, Nana felt poorly one evening, but not yet so poorly that I could not go in to kiss her goodnight. In her room I whispered to her the prayer she taught me, one she perhaps picked up from the Irish in-laws, a prayer I now know is called "The White Paternoster," and is recited in the British Isles as a charm against ghosts:

> Four posts round my bed,
> Four angels o'er my head.
> Matthew, Mark, Luke, and John,
> Bless the bed I lie upon.

And I spoke the names of all whom I wished to bless. By the time my father waked me in the morning, the ambulance had come and gone with Nana. I ran home from school breathlessly that noon, willing myself to hear from the backstairs landing the sounds of her stumping about the kitchen, singing along with the radio tuned to "The Franco-American Hour." I prayed now not for Evangelists to guard me, but to smell tomato soup, baking apples, a chicken roasting, to find everything somehow in place.

Instead, there was only Aunt Anna, trembling, telling me with a terrible false smile that Nana was all gone, that Nana was with the angels now.

For a few years after, I would sometimes wake in the darkness of my room, after an evening when I had gone to bed sad or afraid, to feel a rough hand gripping my thumb beneath the covers. In time, these tactile visitations frightened and disturbed me more than they comforted me, and one night I asked Nana aloud to go away. She did.

I never told anyone of those experiences, and never heard from anyone a comparable story until I read Chapter four of *Moby Dick*, with Ishmael's (and Melville's, I'd bet) memory of the ghostly hand. I was at Smith by then, and I cried after reading that passage, looking out my dormitory window across the darkened quadrangle toward Franklin King House.

The day after Nana's funeral, the gas company property manager called on us to serve an eviction notice. The company owned the house, and they had allowed Nana to continue her lease on grudging sufferance, as she was the widow of a gas inspector; we were only a gas-company widow's survivors. And so Aunt Anna moved to Florence to share a tiny house with three cheerful maiden ladies, as they called themselves, who worked beside her at Pro Brush, and we moved, my father, my pregnant mother, my baby brother, and I, to Hampshire Heights, a low-income veterans' housing project newly built at the edge of Northampton on land carved out of woodlots and farms. In the space of a few weeks, we had become a nuclear family.

The Heights spilled over with 1950s energy, alive, raw-edged, very hopeful, a little dangerous. Many of the fathers, five years after the war's end, were still shaken, given to fits of depression or sudden explosive rage. We kids accepted anger as an adult male norm, the way fathers were. When I think back on our mothers, I remember them pregnant. Kids were everywhere at the Heights; you could not be granted a lease unless you had at least two. The oldest tier was all my age, seven and eight. Most of us had come to the project from wartime homes like mine, homes shared with grandparents, aunts, uncles. Families composed only of parents and children seemed to many of us small, unripe, ingrown, scarily lacking in extra sources of support and comfort, and we older kids bonded fiercely in a large nomadic tribe that transcended gender and ethnicity. We roamed parking bays and clothesline yards, playing hide and seek among wet flapping sheets; we explored woods and fields, each of us in charge of at least one younger sibling. They trailed behind us on foot, or we pulled them in wagons or sleds. We coached them on how to slide under barbed-wire fences, while one of us stood guard to make sure the lethargic bull was preoccupied in a far corner of his pasture; we carried them across the stepping stones of the brook to the Piney Woods, where we built forts of resinous boughs; we took them to the free Christmas production of Humperdinck's *Hansel and Gretel* at Smith, hissing them silent, holding them when they cried at the witch; we warned them away from the construction constantly underway around the project: *Billy Ouimet, Tony Perfito, Mikey Clark. I see you, get over here right now or you'll get a licking!*

Our bond was the stronger because by moving to Hampshire Heights we had become suddenly identifiably lumped together as low-income working-class kids. We older Heights kids rejoiced out loud at how brave, how smart, how strong we were; as it turns out, we seem to have been all those things. Those of us now in our mid-forties who belonged to that first generation of Heights children keep splendid oral histories, and I know of few stories of failure among us.

In our grade school classrooms, it would have been hard for an outsider to pick out us Heights kids. But kids themselves unfailingly know who is who, and on the walks home we needed to band together, fighting, flailing against taunts: *Heights kids: Project kids!* After school it was simply easier not to try to venture beyond our own group, however welcoming other kids who lived outside the project might initially seem.

Joanie lived in a pretty ranch house in the Gleason Road addition just across Jackson Street from the Heights. Joanie said her mom would let us come over until more ranch houses got built on Gleason Road, when Joanie would have more playmates of her own sort. We knew well enough not to report these remarks to our own proud families. And it was tempting to play over at Joanie's house. The best climbing tree in the neighborhood grew there, left over from the time when it was all farmland, a venerable apple tree with sturdy perches we gave names to: The Baby Seat (a foot off the ground); the Lookout (the topmost fork).

I lay stretched out on a middle limb, dreaming, my whole body banked by sweet apple blossoms. That afternoon I was the last Heights kid left over at Joanie's. Suddenly from up in the Lookout, Joanie began her soft chant: *Every kid on this Apple tree is COMing to my BIRTHday party exCEPT PAT CLARK*...and YOU KNOW WHY. And from various nooks around the tree, out of the massed blossoms and sticky new leaves, the refrain came from the mouths of hidden children: *YAH, yah. HAH hah, YOU live at HAMPshire Heights!*

I dropped ten feet to the ground and landed running, yelling up at the whole beautiful tree, *Who cares? Who cares? Who cares about you and your stinking party?* As I ran through the front yard, I glimpsed Joanie's mom and her gentle, Polish-speaking grandma at the big picture window. Her mother's face was set; her grandma waved at me, looking sad. I did not wave back.

Well, who cared, indeed? I cared. Since then, the parties I have attended stretch in a long line from that party I was not invited to, right to the present: high school proms, college mixers, graduate school sherry hours, faculty receptions, museum trustees' dinners in honor of scholarly books to which I've contributed. And I never have, I never will, attend one such function without looking surreptitiously around, checking it out, figuring out who's here, who's like me, trying to spot my kind: *who's here who wasn't born knowing how to do this?*

Always, I am looking around for the Heights kids.

WHEN I WAS TEN, my father was transferred, and we moved straight from Hampshire Heights to an old farmhouse on the outskirts of Portland, Maine, where I lived until I graduated from high school. Those years don't need chronicling here, except for the last summer before I entered Smith, the college I chose because it was the one I knew. And because, though now I cannot recall her ever saying she hoped I would grow up to go to Smith, I wanted to give Nana a Smith girl who knew what Julia Larock was worth. My parents were pleased, but they were also fearful, afraid I might not succeed, afraid I would and alter into some unknowable stranger. I remember two stories from that summer, one told by my mother, the other by my father.

The quote under my mother's Northampton High School yearbook picture, from Thomas Hood, reads "And she had a face like a blessing." And so she did; high-cheekboned and radiant, she smiles shyly there on the page. Other old snapshots show her slender and graceful, even in a shapeless 1930s tanktop swim suit; she is dressed for a dance with an orchid in her hair, à la Rita Hayworth.

One afternoon that last summer while we were shelling peas she told me a story about herself newly out of high school and enrolled at McCarthy's Business School in downtown Northampton, thrilled one October Saturday because she had a date with a college man, a student at UMass. At the last moment she tucked into the picnic basket one of her favorite books, *The Poetical Works of John Greenleaf Whittier.*

I know that book well, and I love it still, uncritically, not just "Snowbound," but the ballads of shipwreck, heroism, love gone astray. Sweet Maude Muller among her hayricks, whom the wimpy judge rejects as a possible wife, and Kathleen's wonderfully wicked stepmother, getting in her licks in the class wars:

> There was a lord of Galway
> A mighty lord was he,
> And he did wed a second wife,
> A maid of low degree.

But he was old, and she was young,
And so in evil spite,
She baked the black bread for his kin
And fed her own with white.

No worse than batches of Keats or Yeats, or whatever my mom's date was reading – D. H. Lawrence, I bet. On the grass by Paradise Pond, that boy pounced not on my mom but on her book; *What's this? Oh, my god, Whittier!* And he read snatches of it out loud, roaring with laughter, his hands greasy from the fried chicken, laughing at Maude and Kathleen, at Mom. When she cried and the picnic was ruined, he called her a bad sport.

My mother told this story without pointing any moral, just as a sad little tale about how things don't always pan out. But by the time I heard this story, I had some idea myself why they might not: college man from Boston suburb, business school townie. I carried the story with me to Smith; I can still hear the cold water running in the sink, the shelled peas pinging down into the colander, as my mother imitated that boy's voice, the way he held the book out of her reach. I think of him every time a college bookstore announces the readers for a poetry series that devalues the lyrical, the narrative, and awards the avant-garde; I think of him every time I hear a teacher criticize a student's taste: "You mean you *like* 'O Captain, My Captain'?"; eyebrow raised, faint smile.

My father also had a story for me that summer of 1960, and his are never told as anything *but* moral exempla.

Late August on the beach of Prout's Neck. I am holding so much joy and fear and expectancy inside this summer, my whole self feels like a brimming cup I am trying not to spill. But now in a voice heavy with import my father commands me to walk with him down the shimmery waterline toward the private beaches of the big Victorian resort inns. It is low tide, and the beach is very wide, strewn with wavey parallel lines of kelp and shells, pebbles and bones, plastic bleach-bottle floats, bits of glass buffed to opalescence, all the old garbage the sea keeps trying to refine.

My mother winces, mutters, "Just get away as soon as you can," and I realize she is guessing better than I can what's coming. And indeed I could not have guessed. What my father wishes to tell me is not about the burden on me as the first to go to college, or even his usual sermon about how though I must certainly *go* to college, I will lose family and soul if I turn into "one of those girls too proud to wipe her own arse." Instead he relates a twisted picaresque epic of the easy sexual conquests he and his buddies made at Smith and Mount Holyoke; about how many girls he knew in high school ended up seduced and abandoned by callous college boys. (Underneath his picture in *his* Holyoke High yearbook they wrote "The girls really fall for the charm of Joe 'Clicker' Clark and the sweet strains of his Hawaiian guitar.") He explains earnestly that (1) college girls are loose, and all townie men know that; (2) college boys believe that all townie girls are loose, and they may well be right; (3) it will be easy for anyone to spot me as not to the manor born, and so therefore (4)....

But I don't stay for (4). I run back along the beach, crying *please, Dad, no*, rubbing at my ears as if that could erase the sounds I have heard, but it is too late. His words reinforce my deepest fears: I am overreaching by going to Smith, condemning myself to a life of being neither duck nor swan, with no true allies, infinitely vulnerable to the worst each "sort" can say about or do to one another in these class wars I've been witness to my whole life.

I gained much from Smith, eventually. But my first years were bewildering, marked more often than they might have been by shame and despair. I lost my freshman scholarship in a dismal welter of C's and D's, though my adviser kept pointing out that I'd entered with soaring College Board scores, hoping perhaps that I'd suddenly say, Oh yeah, now I remember, I'm a good student.

But too many other things compelled my attention. Spellbound, I wandered the campus and the streets I had known as a child, not a college town to me but a landscape of myth whose significance I found it impossible to impart even to the classmates closest to me. I hung out around Franklin King House, too shy to ask the people now working there if they had known Nana. I saw my Heights friends when I could, but they were working, getting ready to be married; I'd met the man I would marry myself. And I was supposed to be studying.

The great gift that first year came through the accident of being placed in a dormitory with a recent reputation as "debutante house" with a lowering scholastic average which the housing office tried to stack with freshmen on scholarship—serious, intellectual, hardworking. My classmates tended to be politically left, socially dim, good at friendship, spirited debate, and high nonsense. The seniors caucused about us; we were so hopeless, there would be little point staging freshman mixers on our behalf. We grinned at each other. It was like the Heights. We had each other. We still do.

Those women got me through. What one of us didn't know, someone else was sure to. In the house dining room set with linen and candles, I learned from them how to manage a knife and fork, how to approach soup. Someone's Canadian graduate student fiancé smuggled Enovid down to blue-lawed Massachusetts; someone else could make thrift-shop hems hang well; all of us shared the stories of where we'd come from, told one another how good we were, supported one another through and beyond the time when we found, as we almost all did, the classes and teachers who mattered, the work we really wanted to do. For me, that took the better part of three years.

As a freshman, I would stay awake all night talking, or devouring books that weren't assigned, while forgetting to study for a biology exam on mitosis. I memorized great swatches of poetry, and yet the trick of the five-part essay eluded me, and I could not seem to avoid the marginal comment of *overly personal response* on papers for my English professors. The first teacher to grant me a B at Smith remarked to another student that he thought it remarkable that I was so perceptive, given that I came of "poor stock." And for those first two years, given that background, I was a listless language student. My dad forced me to take Spanish instead of the French I loved because Spanish was the "language of the future," and because, as he put it, French was spoken only by "fancy diplomats" and "your own relatives who still don't have a pot to piss in." *Aren't you glad?* he asks me, now that I have lived in New Mexico for nearly twenty years. *No*, I say. I'd have learned Spanish here, where I need it. But in that time, in Northampton, at once so strange and so familiar, so haunted with my ghosts, what I required most was to reaffirm my own roots.

My sophomore year, allowed to return on loans, I resolved to dig in and do well. In a creative writing class, I tried to write about my family, my life, not Northampton, not Old South Street or Hampshire Heights, not yet, but about Maine, about summers waitressing or working at Sebago-Moc, hand-stitching the uppers for pricey moccasins such as no Algonquin ever wore; about practicing with my .22 on chunks of paper pulp floating down the Presumpscot River below our house; about my brother coming home bloodied, proud of decking the drunk who tried to mug him at the Riverside Roller Rink, where he managed the concession stand.

My British teacher, pale and anorexically thin, wears huge geometric earrings, nail polish in odd shades of green and fuchsia. My stories come back with C+'s and B-'s, sparse comments in her miniscule handwriting – "inappropriate diction." When I describe Richard Widmark's wiping out a machine gun nest with three grenades, she notes "one would be sufficient surely." She reads to us from D.H. Lawrence, Mary McCarthy, never asking us to talk about our own stories, and I never get to say it took three grenades because the Japanese kicked the first two out of their foxhole. When I showed up timidly at her office hour one day, she asks sharply, "Are you fishing for a change of grade?"

I say no, stuttering, I just want to do better next time. "Give that here, then," she sighs, and she takes from me the story about my brother's fight, the one that contains the description of the Widmark movie. Her fingers are almost translucent in the light through the gothic window of her office. The silence is very long.

"This, here," she says at last, and her blue fingernail taps a sentence where a father is ranting about a "nefarious sod who couldn't find his own arse with both hands." This character, she says, would not use this language.

"How come?" I ask. I truly do not know what she means; is it the profanity? Does she think someone who says "arse" wouldn't use a word like "nefarious?" But she thinks I am being insolent. Or just dumb, hopelessly dumb. She sighs again. If I don't see the point, she says, she doesn't see how she can very well convey it to me. So I don't try to explain about the grenades, about the rolling silver and vulgar eloquence of working-class Irish. I leave her office diffusely ashamed and angry, still not sure of how I've failed. But whatever that failing is, I think, it will surely keep me from being a writer.

My friends kept me together. And there came at last the meaningful classes, Daniel Aaron's American literature, most dramatically, with a syllabus miraculously advanced for 1962; not just Thoreau and Melville, but Chopin, Norris, Harold Frederick's Irish immigrants, Cather's and Jewett's country people, Dreiser's working men and women. And there was Aaron himself, assuring me that I could write; Aaron, upon my shyly mentioning Nana, displaying interest and pleasure: *That's really wonderful, you know: tell me about it. What dorm…?* I cried after I left his office that day from sheer relief, the relief of validation.

When I read the autobiographical accounts in Ryan and Sackrey's *Strangers in Paradise: Academics from the Working Class*, what surprises me is how little they speak of what that experience has meant for them as teachers of their own working-class students. Most of us, I think, carry a sense of not fully belonging, of being pretenders to a kingdom not ours by birthright. In the year I came up for tenure at UNM, I dreamed of leaving the university before I could be asked to leave, taking a job as a waitress in what I call in a poem "my sad downtown that was always waiting." Some teachers bury their sad downtowns deep inside them; they strive to be more punctilious, academic, "objective," more "Ivy League" than most of the professors who actually taught me at Smith or Yale.

But for most of us, I think, our pasts are a strength, a means of connecting with our own students' lives, with literature itself, a talisman to carry into any classroom to remind us of the multiplicity of histories, of the stories we study in that room in addition to the printed ones, the stories that together with the books make up the real text of our class. At a state university in the southwest, those stories are especially multiple.

D has been my problem child in my Whitman and Dickinson course – a body builder, often late, annoyingly macho. A good month into our work on Whitman, after much talk of gender, sexuality, biography, he suddenly exclaims, "Hey, wait a minute: Was Whitman queer?" He cannot, he claims, "seem to feel all this emotion you guys feel when you read poetry." In desperation, trying to help him find a paper topic, I suggest he try *Specimen Days* instead of the poems. I steel myself to read his paper.

But D's paper is a stark account of his childhood as an MIA's son, a fatherless kid trying to figure out how to be a man, manly. It is about using his high school graduation gift money on a fruitless trip to Saigon to look for clues about his father, and his determination now to get on with his own life. And his paper is about the reawakening of all his old questions in reading Whitman's descriptions of released Union prisoners-of-war. D's paper ends by saying, *I love Walt now, but I hate him too. Because he has made me remember. And he wants to be my father.*

C is in the same class, a Pueblo Indian, a shy, attentive single mother living too far from the close-knit community where she was raised. We're on Emily now – my home-girl, from Amherst, Hampshire County, in the state of Massachusetts. I've told the class how I didn't even know she was dead until I was eight or so, because every time we drove down Amherst's main street, my folks would point and say, "There's Miss Dickinson's house."

Last Friday was a beautiful October day when we were all getting a little overdosed on death kindly stopping and looks of agony, and I suggested we just read together the nature poems that often don't get taught because they don't require much teacherly help or comment. It was a wonderful hour of hummingbirds like revolving wheels, leaves unhooking themselves from trees, and the frog who wears mittens at his feet. I smile to myself, remembering the bullfrogs of Smith. C nodded and nodded as we read.

Today, Monday, C comes up after class, and asks, "Did you know I'm Frog Clan?"

No, I didn't. But I do now.

She tells me she brought Dickinson's frog poems home with her over the weekend to show her clan elders back at the pueblo. "They liked them," she says, and adds, grinning, "Frog people are supposed to be good talkers."

I say I think Dickinson would have loved knowing that.

Yeah, she agrees. She's been having trouble writing her paper, but she got the draft done this weekend at home. It felt good, she says: "It was kind of like taking Emily home to meet my folks, you know what I mean?"

Yeah, I do. I do.

MAUREEN HOWARD '52

Being an Irish Catholic from Bridgeport, Connecticut, Maureen Kearns Howard has a rich heritage from which to draw for her fiction as well as for her memoir, Facts of Life (1978), winner of the National Book Critics Circle Award for non-fiction. After graduating from Smith, she entered the publishing field but soon moved into academic circles as a professor's wife. She herself began teaching when her novels attracted the attention they deserve, and she has taught at the University of California at Santa Barbara, the New School for Social Research, Amherst, Yale, and Columbia. Her frequent book reviews appear in The New York Times Book Review and elsewhere, and her articles have been published in The New Republic, Vogue, Vanity Fair, and other national magazines. Her seven novels, each carefully structured and cleverly paced, capture the complexities of modern life and expose the paradox of pleasures flecked with pain: Not a Word About Nightingales (1960), Bridgeport Bus (1965), Before My Time (1974), Grace Abounding (1982), Expensive Habits (1987), Natural History (1992), and A Lover's Almanac (1997). The last three novels have been nominated for the prestigious PEN/Faulkner award.

In 1997 Maureen Howard received the Award in Literature from the American Academy of Arts and Letters, and in 1998 she was inducted into the American Academy of Arts and Sciences. In 1999 she gave the annual lecture for the Friends of the Smith College Libraries. She now lives in New York City with her husband, Mark Probst, a financial consultant and novelist.

The excerpt here is from her latest novel, A Lover's Almanac, reissued in paperback in 1999. The passage reveals some of the ironic pleasures of Shirley Moffett's first holiday alone, solitude Anne Morrow Lindbergh would approve, and culminates in a telephone conversation with her daughter Louise, listening from her artist's loft in New York.

Woman Alone

FROM *A Lover's Almanac*

THE SUN AND THE MOON BLESS SHIRLEY MOFFETT. Warm Winter days on Sanibel are heavenly for a woman from Wisconsin and the soft nights, reaching beyond the white shore, dipping stars into the dark ocean, are bliss. For long hours she swings in a hammock on the balcony of the time-share, baking her bones. The time-share is contractually, delightfully, not a place she can call her own. Shirl knows not one soul, though she nods to the couple who occupy the other half of the condo, folks like us who she does not see until the end of each day, when they wheel in their golf carts. In their distant, protective smiles she sees that they suspect her—a woman alone, divorced or widowed—as a possible prey. She is alone, plopped down on the tidy lawn—barefoot, in jeans—waiting for the spectacular sunset. For the first time in her life alone. A thought which startled Shirley Moffett on her first night in the time-share, when the sporty folks like us (Vermont license plate on the BMW) had not yet arrived. She was alone in a bisected building waiting for Harold's call, figuring there was no time difference—Sanibel to Cincinnati, where the world's largest cheese manufacturer consulted with her husband on the next wave of additives. Harold's old expertise with nitrates and phosphates paid for the pastel walls and rattan furniture which for two weeks are hers alone.

Alone seemed fine, she said to her husband, promising that she would change into her lemon slacks, a bit flashy in the mall at Madison, and take herself out to dinner where folks like us . . . but that first night she did not go beyond the impersonal walls. In her navy blue traveling suit, Shirley shelled peanuts left by the previous time-shares, drank down their Orvieto, the whole bottle with Sun Chips. Alone was surprisingly O.K. *Odey-dokey* came to mind as she stood on the narrow balcony and looked over the cluster of condominiums set at deceptively cozy angles to each other, all uniform grey with tasteful white trim. *Okey-dokey* was her father's expression. As the sun set, the color drained from the flower boxes and bright umbrellas and the grey condos became so like the factory half-houses in Milwaukee. Yes, much like the workers' houses which John McClure condemned to his children. When she was a kid, the McClures drove into the city once a year—Shirl stuffed in the back seat of the two-door sedan, squirming with her brothers and sister. Off the farm, farm children dazzled by the downtown traffic along Wisconsin Avenue, by the lovely hats and dresses in Shusters' big plate-glass windows. Always summer, always unbearable heat in the Chevy. They went to visit an old lady who lived alone in stifling dark rooms with sticky end-tables and tilting lamps. The McClure kids were lined up on a prickly horsehair sofa and served sour lemonade from cheese glasses, rancid cookies that crumbled into the cushions.

The old lady was so alone, yet Shirley could tell not eager to see them in her parlor, polite to her father but not in need of his company. She wore a faded wash dress and black teacher shoes, had been a teacher until . . . . The rest of the story was not told to them as children. It was the end of the Depression and the company half-house in which the woman lived was unpainted, stoop and railings rotted. Black men and white loitered in the streets. Skinny kids in rags played kick the can. "Never live on the dole," John McClure said as soon as they were stuffed back in the car. "Never live with no place to call your own, niggers in the same house—other side of the wall."

As Shirl grew older, maybe eight or ten, there was the war work and no loafers, as John McClure called them, in the scruffy neighborhood. The yearly ride to the city was more to observe the decaying half-houses, more to take heed of her father's instruction, than to visit that lady who did not particularly want them in her parlor with unraveled doilies, the sofa spilling its guts and everywhere yellowed newspapers and stacked magazines. Not the magazines her mother cherished with recipes and dress patterns and colored photos of tables with fancy food they did not eat on the farm.

"What's her name?" Shirley was the oldest and now sat up front where her father's rough hand scraped against her knee as he shifted.

"Her name is a mouthful," he said of his very own aunt born a McClure, a woman he had respected as a child, a teacher. "A fine teacher, now no school will have her."

When she learned the name it was easy, not even Milwaukee German or Polish. Italian, the teacher had married a union agitator, a man who died in a prison riot, Del'Aquilla was his name. The Italian had organized an occasion of terror called the Hunger Strike in which workers and policemen were killed.

"You never went to bed hungry on the farm," John McClure said, though that was not true.

The stern lady who lived alone had lived out of wedlock with Del'Aquilla, had only married him when he went to trial. What he was charged with Shirley never knew, but being wed his wife could not be made to testify against him. Her father had taught his children the meaning of disgrace and she had learned her lesson well, never to speak against John McClure, to shut up as they drove out of the city, back to their poverty, which was okey-dokey, almost a blessing from God their scrubbed-clean, thread-bare isolation on the farm.

Shirley Moffett finds herself alone for the first time in her life, having gone from farm family to farm family. Her two years in college came with sorority sisters, then Harold, then the kids. Her husband's fame beyond the university now leaves her in the house of her own, but there is the farm manager, his assistants, graduate students, a bookkeeper, a parking lot beside the new office, a daily maid. The rooms in the house, the original farmhouse, are peopled with beds, chairs, appliances, window treatments and seasonal coverlets that hold her hostage. Harold plans to convert the old barn, to move them into that empty space with new chestnut beams not needed for support, with the hayloft marked on a blueprint as Library, with entertainment areas and wet bars, plans to move her into this Early American artifact, as the architect terms it, to hang useless old pitchforks and scythes on the wall. Well, it was built in nineteen-ought-nine and she is no one's prize cow.

Each morning at Sanibel, Shirley Moffett hears her neighbors in the back-to-back bathrooms of the condo—his needlepoint shower, the buzz of her electric toothbrush, assigning each their own noise—his early Market report on CNN precedes her *Good Morning America*. Shirl does not wash or dress or plug in the coffeemaker until they are gone so that her noise will not counter their noise. It has been over fifty years since she has given a thought to the old lady about whom she was once so curious, Mrs. Del'Aquilla and her agitator who lived with colored people other side of the wall, a shadow on a blameless family history of Midwestern goodness and good will. But now, now as a nameless time-share woman unknown to her well-preserved neighbors, loving her own silence, Shirl wonders. She wonders what if she had trilled it like a song in the sweltering Chevy—Del'Aquilla, Del'Aquilla, Del'Aquilla, taunting her father with the lovely liquid name. . . .

Well, Shirl is only three days into wondering (a week and a half to go) and will not fulfill a reader's expectation of romance—handsome woman, once handsome, frank streak of silver in her tinted hair; transient lover appears to the faded beauty sleeping late. Shirley Moffett will experience no such poignant encounter, for she is deeply into wondering if, for instance, Del'Aquilla, as her father maintained, was a Communist. If her great-aunt read the accumulation of flaking papers and radical magazines, or if they were the man's like Harold's farm journals.

No, Shirl believes that Mrs. Del'Aquilla read them with the agitator, an exciting thought; and that, being a fine teacher, a graduate of a state normal school, she wrote inflammatory articles in those desperate days when the factory gates were closed, when the McClures went to bed hungry on the farm, their stomachs rumbling. So much conjecture as she walks the shore searching out shells, or is suspended idly in the hammock: why her daughter, for instance, Louise, the late child who wounds her, the one she loves most, must live in a factory and continue to make her living off the manufacture of pictures that distort the farm, its barns, ponds, pastures, the very trees she once painted with care; and wonders why Beatrice Moffett no longer comes to walk her back acres and wail at the moon, now that she heads a department of oncology in Los Angeles. Does she ride the Freeway in helmet and jack books—Harold's little sister being well over sixty? Shirley, with few details of Louise's life or Aunt Bea's, thinks of them as women alone—artist, scientist. As she is alone and happy as the day is long on this island where she avoids folks like us, where the nightly calls from Heidi with the boys' hockey scores, from Harold back at the ranch upgrading the next generation of cow/goat production, might be messages from Mars.

At the end of the first week, she hears the sporty couple arguing through the wall, the woman's gasping cries and the hushed command of the husband, "Quiet. *Quiet down,*" and wonders is the woman is sad to leave this perfect resort in the sun to return to the snows of Vermont, if it is only that which sets her off, for minutes earlier she watched them packing up their golf bags and Vuitton luggage. As though they have been the warmest of vacation friends, they wave to Shirley on her balcony, a woman they do not know—silent, self-contained in her half-house. Shirley Moffett sees them off, hail and farewell, delighted that she has a week coming to her, a week of the next time-sharers with new moans and sighs on the other side of the wall.

DOOMDAY FOR SHIRLEY MOFFETT, packing to go home while, in New York, Louise steals out of bed, where Artie dreams a twitchy wake-up dream of his résumé written in invisible ink. In chalky morning light, the days lengthening at last, Louise answers the phone. The second week of the time-share has been heavenly, Shirley proclaiming it pure bliss, which is not exactly what she means. She does not have the heart to tell her daughter of her discovery, that it is pleasurable alone. And though she loved farm and family once, it seems once upon a time, so her call, her one call out from the impersonal pastel haven, is to Louise, who detects not bliss, but hysteria in her mother's nattering on.

"The second week *not* folks like us, not at all. Dilly and Moe know *exactly* the block you live on in the city with the Tong and the Mafia clam house. Folks who write letters to *stop* the nitrates and phosphates contaminating our food and could not abide your father, poor man, he's not here. Not here, thank God, no time to waste with the sand and the sea, Hal has no time for the time-share and believe me not a moment to waste on folks like Dilly and Moe."

"Mom?"

"Dilly was *detained* in '69. Moe split for Canada."

"Daddy's war?"

"Exactly."

Louise peevish: "Mom, I had to read about the quartermaster in *The New York Times*.

"Exactly. We never spoke of Nam. Nam. Nam, I was alone with two cows, a new baby and a barn full of cats. Forget that picture in the *Times*. Hal sat at a desk in Washington, believe me."

"I do."

Shirley up at farmers' hours on her island, her time sadly at an end. Lou believes her mother's complaints, though the postcard words, *heavenly* and *bliss*, do not reflect Shirley's agitation. She believes that Dilly and Moe know shit-all of disorganized crime on lower Broadway. She believes about the people on the other side of the wall, folks like and unlike us, the latter story incorporating a poor woman in Milwaukee who married into a Commie slum, a courageous woman alone who served stale cookies and warm lemonade in the Great Depression, her couch sprouting "coarse pubic hair."

"Mom?"

She believes that her mother in Sanibel has missed choir practice for the Easter service at First Methodist, but sang the "Hallelujah Chorus" on the balcony, her soprano to Dilly's alto, the woman through the wall detained briefly in the war, "bravely imprisoned while Harold Moffett shipped what order of untested crap. . . ."

"Mom?"

"Crap with what lethal preservatives, that did not preserve diddly-squat in the jungle." This radical alto and Shirley going it *a capella* during the gold-to-purple sunset, though Moe and Dilly were atheists from Brooklyn, which did not diminish their appreciation of Handel. Moe says screw the hallelujahs—art is art.

"Mom. Mom?" Louise looks down the length of the loft. Yesterday, the hearts, roses, wedding signifiers of her manufacture were shipped off to the back rooms of the gallery to await installation. Now her cleared space, call it home with Artie, seems cluttered with her mother's anger and elation. The words assaulting her have no place in her mother's mouth, a woman who does not belong with a godless couple from Brooklyn.

"Your father was one good looker, the body of a god." Louise does not believe that, but believes that he was taken from his desk in the Pentagon, costumed in combat gear and photographed for a patriotic promo pushing chemical foodstuffs, and that home on leave he begat . . . To her daughter Shirley Moffett sounds like one of those shrill women on a talk show, unburdening themselves of a lifetime of injustice. And Harold begat Louise out of Shirley while on leave, abandoning the farm and the university for the patriotic service he was exempt from, having the cats, cows, etc., two kids and a breeding wife. What is there not to believe in? Shirl's history of blood relatives who lived in prehistoric condominiums? . . . .

"Mom! You want me to come down there?"

"Certainly not. My time is up." The hard edge to Shirley Moffett's voice softens, "It's been heaven," she says dreamily to her daughter, "pure *bliss*."

HELEN EUSTIS '38

*B*y the time Helen Eustis won the Edgar Allan Poe award for The Horizontal Man (1946), the best first mystery novel of the year, her marriage to
Professor Alfred Fisher at Smith was over, she had a young son to raise, and she
had just remarried. The novel is certainly revenge more cruel than alimony, as
Gail Mazur '59 remarks in the poem in the next selection. But the novel is more
than revenge. It not only kills off the campus Lothario at "Hollymount College," a
clever pseudonym for Smith by way of Mount Holyoke, but it also elevates undergraduate students to detectives, with profound perceptions worthy of practicing
psychologists whose intuitions outpace their curiosity. Here are students empow-
ered by the president to head off a tabloid journalist; students who can solve a
murder by exposing the private lives of the faculty; a sick student who can defy
infirmary nurse, Springfield psychiatrist, and college president to find the truth.
Yet these same students fall in love with professors as replacements for real fathers,
get drunk on beer or brandy alexanders well before the ten o'clock curfew, and
shirk their academic work for the thrill of a date or the danger of an investigation.
The paradoxical youth and maturity of students creates much of the humor and
more of the suspense than does the working out of the murder of the fictional Kevin
Boyle. In short, these students have wisdom, while their professors have more
knowledge and pathology than libido. In the excerpt here, as the grieving Molly
Morrison approaches Mr. Hungerford to ask him for a copy of one of the dead
Kevin Boyle's poems, she conquers both fear and grief, illusion and insanity, only
to be plunged again into darkness.

Helen Eustis prepared herself to write this novel by writing a series of short
stories published in national magazines like The New Yorker, Harper's Bazaar, and Mademoiselle, and collected in The Captains and the Kings
Depart (1949). Another novel followed her first success. The Fool Killer
(1954) describes a twelve-year-old runaway boy, an appealing tale appropriate
for film. Following her writing career, Helen Eustis became a professional counselor in New York City.

Something in Common

FROM *The Horizontal Man*

S HE HAD MADE THE DECISION. She had been very brave. She had been brave almost beyond her own power. She had taken her coat and scarf and put them on. She had walked to the front door. She had opened it. "Where are you going, Molly?" Miss Justin had cried from the desk, with hygienic cheer. "For a walk," she had answered. For a walk. She had stepped out on the stoop. She did not look down the street, she only looked down at her brown moccasins, her tan socks, her cold bare legs. She watched her own feet walking down the brick walk. She was very tired. She walked slowly and dragged her feet. She was cold, too. Her teeth chattered and her muscles contracted against the wind. She heard a group of girls pass on the other side of the street. She did not look up from her feet. She heard them begin to laugh. They were laughing at her, at what a fool she was, walking there all hunched over with cold, looking at her feet. A lunatic. In the Infirmary because she was crazy. But she wasn't really. If she had been really crazy there would have been some excuse. She was just indulging herself, saying: I can't stand it, when what was really true was that she wouldn't try hard enough. But something had to be worth trying for. You couldn't try in a vacuum, try for nothing. Now she had something to try for—something to take a walk for. She knew where she was going. It took a great deal of courage, but courage was what she must force herself to have. Oh, how she despised the coward that she was!

It was getting to be evening. The winter sun was nearing the horizon, salmon-coloured among violet clouds, promising snow. For a moment Molly looked up from the ground; it seemed to her the world was turned to a vast, ominous, but beautiful dream landscape. The white frame houses took on a luminousness in the evening light, standing in their drab dead lawns among the skeletons of trees. She had reached the corner and turned out of the side street. Now there were a few more passers-by, bundled against the cold, intent upon their secret errands. And she knew that, as in a dream, though their faces seemed strange to you, you knew that somehow they were your enemies; secretly they peeped at you from under their eyelids, from over their furs, and mentally noting your appearance, your patent guilt, they hurried on with news of your treason to the great mysterious one who held your fate in the hollow of a palm, who totted black marks against you, and would at last pounce, strike . . . . She walked faster, hearing footsteps behind. If she walked quickly, got to where she meant to go, warmed herself with a fire, perhaps, and talked—the kind of talk she longed for so, then everything would not seem so threatening and evil.

She recognized the house, set back on its lawns with a dark antique elegance. For a moment when she first saw the iron Saint Bernard, she was stricken with a new fear, thinking that it was real, and she would have to pass it. But as it continued to stand so still, with one paw raised, she saw it was only a statue, and let her breath puff out, milky on the cold air. Now she was close enough to see the lamp gleaming amethyst and ruby through the coloured glass panes of the front door. The house towered above her, high and stern, with its flat roof, its beetling eaves, its cupola. It seemed to hold her at a distance, to ask her business. Her heart pounded, she could not catch her breath. "Courage!" she whispered to herself, and turned up the walk. The bell at the high double door was the sort you have to pull. At last she found the trick of it, and heard it pealing, far back in the hollow reaches of the house. Oh please . . . she prayed. She waited a long, long time before footsteps sounded within, far away and slow, then closer and shuffling. Finally the door opened and an old, old woman peered out. She said nothing, but stared at Molly, as if she, too, were participating in the dream.

"Please," said Molly faintly, after a long silence, "is Mr. Hungerford . . . ?"

Still the old woman did not answer, but stood there staring at her in the twilight. At last it seemed true—this was a nightmare, the horror was about to come. Then the old woman spoke. "Well, Miss, speak up!" she said sharply.

Don't be a fool, said Molly to her pounding heart. She's only deaf! "Is Mr. Hungerford in?" she said loudly.

"Doesn't live here any more," said the old woman flatly, and began to close the door.

"Oh, please!" cried Molly, "can you tell me where he lives?"

The old woman drew the door a little farther open again. "He moved over to West Street," she said grudgingly. "He moved in where that young man lived who got murdered. I don't recollect the number." And closed the door.

S HE HAD TO STOP and press her mittened hands against her breast, standing there on the high step, panting in the cold. He lived at Kevin Boyle's house . . . He had moved there . . . . It was beautiful—like a gift! Now she could go, could ring his bell, could go in the room where he had stood, had lain . . . lain dead. She ran down the steps lightly before her weariness caught up with her again. She crossed the street and took the short cut down the hill toward where she knew so well.

As she walked toward Kevin Boyle's house she had no choice but to think of the thing that had brought her out—out of her hole. It was a strange thing, something new, something she could not understand, something terrible, a new kind of death. In the last days she had forgotten Kevin Boyle.

She had forgotten the way he looked. Or how it felt to walk to The Coffee Shoppe with your heart exploding like electric shocks because you did not know if he would be there. Or how it was in class, watching him talk, seeing the way his hands moved. She could remember *that* it had been, but *how* it had been was gone.

The thing that had come over had begun with grief, but it had been worse than grief, worse than any live pain. It had been like a stone on her heart, a negation of life, of love. She began to wish fiercely that she could feel grief as she had felt it in those first days after his death, but even the memory of the sharpness of it was gone from her. Grief had been a thing like love—clear, and with a certain purity. Depression, Dr. Forstmann would say, who always had the word for everything. Almost she could hate him too, though he was her only friend. Sometimes she felt that if she had not talked to him she might have preserved the beauty of her grief and kept the life from running from it. Now she had two things to mourn—the death of Kevin Boyle and the death of her grief. And since the first was irreparable, it seemed the second was harder to bear. She would not, *could* not bear it. So she had tried to think of what would be a restorative for her dead grief. She thought if she had a picture of him . . . but she could not think where she would get one. Or a letter he had written—just some impersonal thing . . . but that was just as hard. And then the perfect thing had come to her. A poem. Just a copy of one of his poems. And she knew where she could find that, too. Only—how many ages ago?—two weeks ago she had heard him tell, sitting in the booth at The Coffee Shoppe, Mr. Hungerford was reading his book of poems, was kind enough to offer to submit it to his publisher. Mr. Hungerford. He had a kind sad face. And a poem. A poem was like a painting. In it you said a thing so dear and tender and secret you could not venture it straight out in plain words . . . . If anything could revive her dead grief, it would be Kevin Boyle's poem. She had begun to long and long for it. Longing had made her brave. Longing had drawn her out . . . .

It seemed strange to her to see the college girls pushing their bicycles up the hill past her or walking in long, striding steps. A long time ago she had been one of them—in name at least— sharing their common routine, their meaningless activities. What meaning could they have? To go in a library, to look in a book, to write words on a paper . . . . Was that life? Was that any sort of preparation for life? Once in her father's studio there was a young man with a beard, one of the wild-talking ones who made her want to hide for not knowing what to say. "What do *you* do for a livelihood?" he had asked, looking down his crooked nose patronizingly, stroking his too thin beard. "I—I'm going to college in the fall," she had stammered. Suddenly he began to pace around the studio as if he had gone mad. "College!" he had cried. "Education! All they care for is knowledge—all knowledge and no wisdom!" At that moment she had scorned him, had heard her mother's voice speaking in her own thoughts, saying, why do artists think they have to behave like maniacs? Yet he had been right. That was all that was here. Knowledge, and no wisdom. Now that Kevin Boyle was dead . . . .

She was at the corner of West Street. There was a hedge full of red berries, running along by the walk. Then the house. What was she to say? Yet she must speak. She had come so far . . . . She would blind herself to everything . . . . She could scarcely gasp air into her lungs as she plunged round the corner, ran up the steps on to the porch. His name was still on the mail-box on the card tacked over the bell. She pushed it desperately, and closed her eyes. She heard the door open and looked quickly. There was Mr. Hungerford, his thick grey hair rumpled, his tie loosened, his face haggard. "Yes?" he said in a strange, faraway voice. Now she was here. Now she must begin.

"Mr. Hungerford?" she said. But of course she knew him. "I'm Molly Morrison. I'm the girl who . . ." but she trailed off, not knowing how to say, "I'm the girl whose name was in the paper, I'm the girl who confessed to murdering Kevin Boyle, only it wasn't true, I'm the girl . . . ."

"Oh," he said, "yes, of course. Come right in."

Now she knew it was a dream. This was the strangest thing of all. He acted as if he had been waiting for her, as if he had known she was coming. *Of course what?* she wanted to demand of him. But she followed him into the dim hall. This was not a nightmare part of a dream. This was a warm, good part. This was the way she would have wished to be welcomed to Kevin Boyle's rooms, as if she belonged there, as if it were natural that she should come.

French doors with glass panes opened off the hall. One of them stood ajar. Preceding her, Mr. Hungerford stood in the entrance and said, "Won't you come in?" She followed him. He turned to her. His face seemed very tired and very kind and very sad. "Excuse the mess," he said. "I'm not properly moved in yet. I was just lying down for a moment." He passed his hand across his eyes. "Then you rang, and I was glad. I couldn't sleep. I can't seem to sleep here—not any more."

She stood clutching her hands together in front of the dying fire. For the first time in days, feeling assailed in her heart, as if a half-healed wound had broken, and warm beautiful blood were pouring out once more. She saw everything with terrible intensity, as if each object were surrounded by a ring of light. It was Kevin Boyle's room she was standing in—where he had stood; perhaps where he had died. And Mr. Hungerford there, his face hanging in such weary and despairing folds . . . . How she knew that look! How she had lived with it! It was her father's look, standing at the easel, his brush dropped to the floor, staring out of he dirty panes of the slanting skylight . . . ."Can't you work?" she asked softly.

"Oh," said Mr. Hungerford, a sudden little smile of surprise lighting one corner of his mouth, "that. No. Not for years. My God, child, how did you know?"

She tossed her head in embarrassment. "I just knew."

"Here," he said, "take your coat off. Pull up to the fire. Get warm. Are you one of my students? To tell you the truth, I don't yet know one face from another."

Then she grew cold again inside. No, it was not a dream. It was only a mistake. He thought she was one of his students. She must tell him at once, even if then he would not like her any more. Her face contracted with anxiety. "No," she said, "I'm not one of your students. I'm—I mean—I—" and against all her most fervent intentions, she began to cry. She put her mittens up to cover her face.

"Oh, my goodness, child!" she heard his worried voice saying. "Don't cry. Just tell me what it's all about. You're very welcome, you know. You don't have to be one of my students to call on me!" he gave a little laugh. "I'm very delighted to have a strange young woman in . . . my . . ." His words trailed off strangely. She took her hands down from her tear-smeared face. He was looking off into space as if something were behind her shoulder, as if he were haunted. Again her heart grew hot with pity for him.

"Mr. Hungerford," she said reassuringly, sniffling at the remains of her tears. "Is it embarrassing for you to have me here? I'll go away. I didn't know students weren't supposed—"

"My goodness, no!" he said, with heartiness to counteract her sadness. "Take your coat off like a good girl and tell me what it is you want." He put his hand to the knot of his tie and pulled it closer. "Tell you what," he pushed on, "this is really against rules—to offer a student alcohol—but let's have a glass of sherry; by now we both need it." He did not wait for her answer, but took a decanter from the top of a bookcase and filled two of the glasses that stood by it. She took off her coat and laid it on the couch, then sat down on a stool by the fire, pushing close to the warmth. She stared at the hearth. On these bricks Kevin Boyle had lain. His blood had flowed here. And the truth was . . . the truth was she had forgotten him. Her heart had gone dead. In all the confusion, the drugs, the confession, the weepings to Dr. Forstmann, she had lost the wood in the trees. Nothing was about her but the confusion of the trees of her thought—her mother, her father, the shame of living among the girls at Birnham, Miss Justin, Miss Sanders, the newspaper reporter, the policeman—she wanted to make a sweep of them! She wished she could take a wet cloth and wipe her mind clean as a blackboard. She wanted to go back—go back to the sense of her love. She had lost her love—first she had lost Kevin Boyle, and then her love for him. The second loss was more desolate than the first. The first was human and bearable, in a terrible way. The second she could not stand. She could not bring back Kevin Boyle, but she must bring back her love for him . . . . "Here's your sherry," said Mr. Hungerford's voice.

She looked up at him, almost startled, and took the glass. "Thank you," she said.

He pulled forward the chair opposite her and sat down. "Now," he said, raising the glass in silent toast before sipping from it. She sipped too, staring at him. His face was so drawn, so weary. And there was a strange indecency about seeing him with his streaked grey hair, usually so smooth, disarranged. He moved his lips together in little mumbling motions, like an old man.

"What's your name?" he asked kindly. "I'm afraid I didn't listen when you told me before."

"Molly Morrison."

He looked at her, waiting for her to go on, she knew, but she was unable . . . . "What class are you—shall I call you Miss Morrison or Molly?"

"Oh, Molly, of course," she said, her tongue suddenly loosened. How kind he was! He seemed—he seemed so much more human, more understanding—something . . . . "I'm a Freshman, I was in—I was—" she wanted to say she had been in a class of Kevin Boyle's but her voice faltered and broke.

"And you aren't in any of my classes, but you came to see me—is it a guessing game?" There was an edge of asperity in his voice at last. His patience was going to end in a moment. She gathered herself together frightenedly. She did not know what to say, though—how to begin. She couldn't just ask him baldly.

"I've been in the Infirmary," she said abruptly. "They seem to think—I've been acting—they think I'm rather unbalanced." But she did not want to give him a false impression. "I may be, you know," she said earnestly.

Suddenly he laughed, startling her. For a moment she thought her heart had stopped at the thought that he was laughing at her. Then he looked at her very, very kindly. "That makes a pair of us, Molly," he said. "We should be friends, alone together in this neurasthenic garden spot."

She did not know what he meant, except that they had something in common, and he looked so very kind, so very sad. "I didn't mean to be," she said, saying at last to him what she had wished to say to all of them. "I wanted everything to go right when I came to Hollymount—I wanted to be different, to make people like me, not be shy. But then I wasn't and I couldn't seem to make it change—they hated me, and laughed at me, and then when—when Mr. Boyle died—" She had done it again. She had begun to cry. She put her face down in her hands and let the tears trickle through her fingers. She cried a moment in silence. Then suddenly she heard a glass crash on the bricks of the hearth, and looked up, all tear-stained as she was.

She had heard the girls talk about the way his face twitched sometimes—how he would have to stop dead in the middle of a lecture to wait for it to be over—but she had known it was as bad as this. The whole side of his face was drawn together in the most grotesque way—it was so strange and horrifying it almost shocked you to laughter. She saw his hands were shaking, and that the sherry glass lay in fragments on the hearth. She felt terribly terribly sorry—she almost had risen to touch him, to comfort him—when suddenly the dream was back. Inwardly she shook herself, she implored herself not to let it come again, but inexorably—as inexorably as if she were asleep—she felt its atmosphere closing in. The warmth of the fire, the warmth of the sherry, the warmth of Mr. Hungerford's kindness—all evaporated until her very bones were shuddering with cold at the knowledge that she was alone in a threatening world, a room in which each object of furniture conspired against her. Outside unknown pursuers were closing in; wicked enemies were ambushed behind the berry-red hedge; and here inside, even Mr. Hungerford, even with his kind sad face, his tragic tic, his trembling hands, his hopelessness . . . . She should never have come out. She should have stayed in the safe white room at the Infirmary, where she lay like a corpse, with Miss Justin and Dr. Forstmann praying at her wake. She got to her feet nervously. "I came," she said, because she must get it out at once, "because I heard him—I heard Mr. Boyle say once you had some poems of his. I came to ask—I came—" She was shaking all over, uncontrollably.

On the other side of the fire, Mr. Hungerford got to his feet. Was it true that he was shaking too, or did she only imagine it was so because she shook herself? In any case, his face had not relaxed from its contorting grip, it stared at her gargoyle-like. Impossible to separate true from false—was he glaring at her, or did her fear read anger into kindness? Then suddenly it seemed to her something strange had happened to him. The tic left his face, but left it different, slacker, in strange new lines. His posture changed; everything was different, because of what she imagined she saw. She thought, quite carefully, I am going mad. She thought she must pick up her coat and scarf and leave here before she lost her mind in front of Mr. Hungerford—as if she had to get to the bathroom before throwing up. She knew it was madness now, because suddenly, instead of the sad worn intelligence so like her father's that had first clothed his face, she now saw on his features the fierce, peering cruelty of her mother—the slack jowls, the drawn brow . . . . She slung her coat over her shoulders, mumbling foolishly, keeping her eyes on him, trying not to let him notice. "I'll just—" she said. "I'd better go now, I don't—I'm not feeling very—you'll excuse me . . . ."

It was useless. Whatever it was that had been holding her together snapped loudly, like a log on a fire and he—she—Mr. Hungerford—her mother—who?—took a step forward, hands raised, the way she had always feared. "Why," said a strange voice, a voice she had never heard before, coming from she knew not where, "you little—it was you—" She closed her eyes to shut herself in darkness. Hands were at her throat as she had always known they would be. Her own hands were wrestling at them—or was it her own hands at her throat? A fingernail drew a thin line of pain over her wrist. Back and forth she was battered, like a boat in a storm, battered by waves, caught in undertow—what? "Oh, Mr. Hungerford!" she gasped. She wanted to say she begged his pardon, but she had no breath.

Then at last she was loose. Something had fallen to the floor—someone—an inert lump. She could not stop to see what it was. It might even be herself lying on the floor there. She flung open the door and fled. The cold night air tore in her lungs. And all the time she ran she was thinking foolishly, He'll never believe me. Meaning Dr. Forstmann. Meaning she was mad.

GAIL MAZUR '59

*G*ail Mazur is the founding director of the nationally recognized Blacksmith House Poetry Reading Series, which brings hundreds of admirers and aspirers to Cambridge, MA, to see and hear the best poets of our time. As a leading poet herself, Gail Mazur has been the Bunting Fellow in Poetry at Radcliffe and the Poet-in-Residence at Emerson College in the MFA Program in Writing, Literature and Publishing. She has been on the faculty of the Harvard University Extension School and on the graduate faculty in the MFA Program at the University of Houston, and she has taught at Wellesley College and the University of Massachusettts at Boston. Her poetry workshops in the Fine Arts Work Center in Provincetown attract poets and students from around the world.

Her poems, often first appearing in literary reviews, have been published widely in anthologies, including Best American Poetry, The Pushcart Anthology, The Ploughshares Poetry Reader, Agni, Slate, and New American Poets of the '90's. Three books show her range and her development, beginning with Nightfire (1978), The Pose of Happiness (1986), and The Common (1995). Many of her poems have an elegiac quality, rich with memory but ripe with promise and humor. She has won several awards for her work, including the National Endowment for the Arts Award in Creative Writing. Her poetry, essays, and reviews have appeared in Poetry, Paris Review, Ploughshares, The Hudson Review, The Harvard Review, The New Republic, and The Atlantic Monthly among many others.

From The Pose of Happiness, her second book, "The Horizontal Man" recalls the novel by Helen Eustis '38, excerpted in the prior selection, as well as the poet's undergraduate years at Smith. "Foliage" and "The Common," from The Common, transform the ordinary into the extraordinary through the poet's keen imagination.

The Horizontal Man

Surely it was too awful to be real.
The darkened library, the buildings full of empty classrooms,
the threatening olive-green shape of the mailbox under the lamp at the centre of the campus . . .
—Helen Eustis, *The Horizontal Man*, 1946

On the second page,
my old professor's murdered with a poker.
His black curls, matting with blood
on the shabby rug,
                    were wild and gray
when he lectured to the Shakespeare class
on Sputnik and Ophelia. We'd all heard
of his affairs, and of this novel,
already out-of-print, written by a former wife

who killed him with a pen—revenge
more cruel than alimony
to young things on allowances . . .

When he recited "O, what a rogue
and peasant slave am I," we thrilled
to the alcoholic timbre of his brogue . . .

This reissued mystery
brings the whole semester back.
Fat, and pining for a boy,
I ate and smoked and slept most days away,
convinced I'd end up lonely, and alone.

For Professor F, I studied
"O that this too too solid flesh would melt,"
and earned the isolated A that failed
to keep my parents' hopes for me alive.

I recognize the Infirmary—
it's at the end of Paradise Road.
The demented freshman's dragged there
in the second chapter babbling about love;
the nurse thinks she's the "perpetrator."

I remember the unwomanly physician
stricken by the vagaries of menstruation—
Is the psychiatrist from Springfield
the one they called the night my mind
was slipping, and the dean suspected
that wasn't all I'd lost that term?

In the spring nocturnes of my sophomore year,
I lay on my restricted cot,
confined to campus for my indiscretion—
my confession. I memorized soliloquies
for Doctor F—"To be or not"—
as if my life depended on my memory.
There was nothing I was going to *be* . . .

My teacher died, exhausted,
in a rest home late last year.

I've read all night again.
This *roman á clef*, with its bloody weapon
on the cover, is like the dream I stay up
to avoid, the classic college nightmare:
a gothic building, and months
of literature unready, the unversed girl

I never stop becoming, dragging
her cold feet through the scrollery
iron gate, past Paradise Pond
to the examination hall silently
filling with victims and perpetrators.

Foliage

Even the man who dozes on cardboard
in the Common, wearing a bright knit cap,
has picked Clover and Ladies' Thumb to stick
in the cosmos of his shopping cart.
These last warm days, wanting to deny
what's frozen and gray ahead, I admire
the star turns of my town's great trees.
Sunbursts, and the alizarin crimson

of our maples' explosions, a kind of payoff
(I want to think) for all the dying,
yet something I'm part of—part of me—
like my feet, planted deferentially
in this old park, my hands red at my sides,
my head nodding and shaking in the leafy air.

The Common

Iron cannons from the Revolution. Ghost music—
folk songs, rock concerts, Sunday demonstrations.
A granite slab for the elm where Washington

took command. A new wood plaque, already rotting,
for Margaret Fuller Ossoli—the city fathers'
minimal nod to the life of her mind.

The black trunks of old maples brushed with snow,
their strong lines rephrased by snow's finery.
From a concrete gazebo, Abraham Lincoln

gazes down at the cobbled plaza where raffish
bands plugged in, and stoned crowds gathered;
my small son and daughter skipped ahead

of me, hand in hand, to the swings, the jungle
gym, the roundabout, and at home, pre-season
jonquils dazzled in a white crockery jug.

Stringed beads—necklaces, earrings—for sale
by a woman who's sat cross-legged on folded blankets
since those days, those days.

The season's worst cold brewing this early morning.
Two men huddled in damp sleeping bags spread out
on newspapers; convulsive dreams of their war.

The oaks. The maples. In the near-zero day
I take on faith, faith in Nature, that life's
machinery groans and strains in the frozen limbs.

NANCY FRANKLIN '78

*B*orn in Cincinnati as the youngest and only girl in a family of four children, Nancy Franklin came to Smith from Larchmont, NY, just in time to celebrate Smith's Centennial; she still has her vintage t-shirt proudly announcing "A Century of Women on Top." Thinking she wanted to be a doctor, she majored in cell and molecular biology. The class of '78, she remembers, was the first not have a gym requirement and first not to have to undergo competence exams in their major field of study, making them, as another t-shirt infamously declared, "The First Incompetent Class."

Following graduation she joined the editorial staff of The New Yorker as an assistant in the typing pool. Two years later, she became a fact checker, and in 1985 she began a ten-year stint as an editor of non-fiction. The first thing she published, a collaboration with Daniel Menaker, was a moving "Notes & Comment" in January 1989 about Martin Luther King Day, celebrated at Smith that year with a talk by Yolanda King '76. The second was a "Talk of the Town" story about her infatuation with the movie Gone With the Wind, which she saw three times in one weekend during her freshman year.

In 1994, after the retirement of long-time theatre critic Edith Oliver (who had, in the 1930s, attended Smith for two years), Franklin was asked by the magazine's then editor, Tina Brown, to try writing theatre criticism. "Tina Brown made me a writer," she says, "because she liked my memos about editing more than she liked my actual editing. She thought I had a voice." The voice is startlingly unpretentious and unquestionably honest. In her first year of theatre reviewing, she covered a revival of Uncommon Women and Others by Wendy Wasserstein (Mount Holyoke '72), later the subject of a Franklin feature, who says prophetically: "Nancy could become legendary."

Besides a host of distinguished theatre reviews and other short pieces, now including television reviews, Franklin has published feature stories on singer Jo Stafford and Katharine S. White, a founding editor of The New Yorker and the wife of E. B. White. The essay on her New York apartment, which follows, was published in The New Yorker on 16 October 1995.

How Did I Get Here?

I NEVER REALLY DECIDED TO MOVE TO NEW YORK, and I never really decided to stay, but I've lived here, in the same apartment, for sixteen years, which is longer than I've lived anywhere else. In that time, my parents and my three brothers have moved twenty-four times. My last move was from my parents' house in Westchester County, ten months after I graduated from college. With a roommate who was a friend of a college friend, I got a two-bedroom apartment on the Upper West Side which rented for four hundred and seventy-five dollars a month; half that amount was about as much as I could afford on my take-home pay, which was a little less than two hundred dollars a week. I was working in the typing pool of this magazine, at a time when career advice to young women included an admonition that if you started out with a job that involved typing all you would ever do was type. But I didn't believe that. I dared to type. Over the years, things between me and my apartment deteriorated to the point where we barely acknowledged each other's existence. I kept waiting for it to change into something that it wasn't, and it kept waiting for me to give it the attention it deserved. By the time this year rolled around, we had both had enough. It was clear that one of us had to go.

For most young people who come to New York, having a roommate is not a matter of choice. I was lucky in that my apartment was well laid out for sharing: the two bedrooms were at opposite ends of the apartment, with the bathroom, kitchen, and living room in between. Nobody had to go through anybody else's space. My room was almost twice as big as the other bedroom—big enough to fit the double bed I'd bought for twenty dollars a few months after I moved in, from someone who was leaving the building, and the twin bed I brought from home, which I used for guests until I stopped having guests. There was plenty of space left over for my desk, my stereo, and the bookcase that had been next to my bed at home when I was growing up and that I had spent hours staring at, reabsorbing the contents of the books by gazing at their spines.

I don't know how I ended up with the better room, but I'm pretty sure we didn't flip a coin. I think I just took it. My decorating scheme was a big map of Scotland and a framed Manet poster on the walls, a big straw mat on the floor, and matchstick blinds. Since my room was on the fire escape, my father made me buy a metal gate for the window. The gate made my room look like a prison and cut down on the little light my window lets in, but I was glad I had it a few years ago, when, one fall night at about 3 a.m., a guy who was the boyfriend of someone who lived next door at the time tried to climb into my window, thinking it was his girlfriend's. I stood in the dark in my nightgown a few feet away from him, safe behind the gate, and delivered a somewhat louder and more detailed assessment of him than was strictly necessary.

I MAY NOT HAVE EVER LOVED MY APARTMENT, but I've always loved my address: Riverside Drive. It sounds great. My building has an even number, so my address has a round, satisfying sound, and I like the way it calls up a long-ago kind of bourgeois prosperity and comfort, and connects me to the life of the river. I used to love to say it out loud. When people asked me where

I lived, I would practically bellow my address, as if I were telling them they had just won the grand prize on "Truth or Consequences." My building went up in 1904 and consisted of nine- and ten-room apartments, all of which have since gone under the knife at least once. Elegance inside and out was standard then on Riverside Drive, but there are no clues now to whether my building met that standard on the inside. (The exterior is unremarkable to the point of unnoticeability, like a bicycle that works but that no one would ever think of stealing.) The only room that has survived intact from the apartment that mine was part of is the bathroom, and the only vestige of its originalness is a row of tiles in a pink-and-blue floral pattern which runs around the room at armpit level. Tenants of yore painted the bathroom pink and then blue, and though there are now many layers of white covering the walls, a chip with a colorful underside still occasionally falls, providing the only evidence that anyone else ever lived here.

During my first few years in the apartment, I did everything the way my mother did. (She herself had lived on Riverside Drive for a couple of years in the forties; *her* entry-level job in publishing, which was also her exit-level job, since she quit to get married, was at *Life*.) I used the same household products, baked chicken the way she did, got charge cards at all the same department stores. Altman's card was the hardest to get: I had to go to the credit department in person and get checked out, because my income didn't quite cut it, and only because my mother was an old customer did the woman there decide to give me a card. I had a London Fog trenchcoat, a junior version of my mother's Burberry—something I now associate with sad commuters with comb-overs and clunky briefcases. When I rode up in my elevator alone at night after work, wearing the trenchcoat and carrying my book bag, I always became flooded by a melancholy vanity, as if I were being watched through a hidden camera. "Here is a young woman living in New York. It's the end of the day, and she's going home to her apartment." To me, my self-conscious weariness was cinematic and fascinating. It made me feel like an adult. Now I mostly get that feeling when I'm going home in a taxi late at night, but I don't know whether the feeling is still really mine or whether I ripped it off from "My Dinner with André."

After a few years, I thought from time to time about moving, and for the past five or six I thought about it constantly. But I had a sense of pride about my stability, and believed that if I stayed in the same apartment long enough the time I'd spent there would acquire weight and meaning. I would have a history, and I would be able to look back on it and see that it all made sense. I would stand out in people's address books among all the other addresses that had been crossed out or erased. My friends and family would know my phone number the way they knew their own birthdays. In the meantime, I was waiting for something to happen—for something or someone to come along and give me the signal that my adult life had officially begun.

FOR THE LAST TWELVE YEARS, for about four thousand days and nights, I have had the apartment to myself. My first roommate moved to the East Side after two years; my next, and final, roommate was a friend from work who after two years moved to Texas. I put the twin bed in the other bedroom, and I would tell people who asked what I did with the extra room that I slept there when I was having a fight with myself.

Gradually, I became obsessed with the idea of spatial integrity. Old Upper East Side and Upper West Side apartments usually have it; parlor-floor apartments in brownstones never do. The test for it is physiological as well as visual: if your body relaxes when you walk into an apartment, if you're drawn in by a sense that a human being with a heart created it, it has spatial integrity. I began to notice—and to be unable not to notice—that my apartment was a misbegotten shell of a space, and I took it personally. It's impossible to figure out what the layout and the dimensions of the original apartment were, even though I have been in two of the other apartments that are its offspring, but I started to fantasize about what no longer existed. The ghost pains I felt about what was missing made me acutely aware of the inadequacy of what I had. (Memo to studio dwellers: yes, it *is* unseemly to complain about having a two-bedroom apartment.) Aside from the bathroom, which is the best room in the apartment, nothing feels right. My bedroom is unnecessarily big, and the other one is too small. There is no hall closet; in fact, there is no hall. There is no counter space in the kitchen; there are no counters, or drawers. The kitchen is a squared-U shape, like a staple, and is about the same size. The closets jut into the bedrooms like clumsy afterthoughts. The closets themselves are all right, though—they are the second- and third-nicest rooms in the apartment.

I dream about my apartment all the time, the same two dreams over and over. One is a bad dream: I wake up and realize that I have no front door, or that the door doesn't lock, or that the door is a Dutch door, and the top part doesn't lock, so anyone can get in. Nothing terrible actually happens to me, but I have the terrible awareness that I've never been safe, that I've ignored threats and warnings, that I haven't lived right. The other dream is, on the surface, a good one: I find a door at the far end of the second bedroom which I've never noticed, and when I open it I find several more rooms. (There's always a room with a washer and dryer, which for someone who shares five washers and four dryers with a hundred people is the height of erotic wish fulfillment.) More space, if I'd only known to open the door; but, then, I didn't know the door was there.

Lately, I've begun to dream that the people who live next door are my roommates, which in a way they are. Many people have passed through the apartment next to me, and I know a little something about all of them, even the ones I never met, because hand in hand with my apartment's lack of spatial integrity is its lack of structural integrity. The wall that separates my living room and bedroom from my next-door neighbors' apartment is so thin that it's more of a membrane than a wall—an imperfect, porous barrier, through which sound and bad vibes pass freely. The trend next door has been from older to younger, from couples to transient groups of single people, from bohemian to corporate, from people who make their own music to people with powerful stereos. My first neighbors were a couple with a baby, whose teething cries used to wake me up at night. I didn't mind that; it made me feel that, if the day ever came when I had children myself, my maternal instincts would be ready to roll. But I did mind hearing the husband's cello and, every Tuesday night, the string quartet that gathered there for several hours and played in the living room, directly behind my bedroom. (The living room has since been sliced in two; now there's a small bedroom behind mine, with a very different sonic menu.) One night, I came home from work at about ten o'clock—I was by then a stressed-out fact checker—and when I heard the music coming through the wall I lost it. I thought, I'll see your string quartet and raise you a Bruce Springsteen. I put on "Darkness on the Edge of Town," which was the most thunderous of all my albums, and turned the volume and the bass way up. Within a couple of minutes, the cellist was banging on my door—a metal door, whose position in the doorframe he altered slightly but permanently, despite his having no visible muscles—and yelled at me to open up, which I refused to do. "What do you want?" I yelled back, as if I didn't know. He ordered me to turn my stereo down. I told him that I didn't want to hear his music, either. I then did turn my stereo down, the quartet stopped playing for the night, and that was that. My dislike of these people continued until they moved, a couple of years later, because I knew that they knew I had behaved badly. I remember this incident with great shame but no regret: I like to think that, having snapped once, I now have antibodies against snapping and won't snap again, and so far I haven't. . . .

When I say that I've always hated my next-door neighbors and that they've ruined my life, I mean it as a tribute—an acknowledgment that my outsized feelings about the noise that comes through the wall have more to do with me than with any unneighborly activity on their part. But when you live alone and yet don't have the one advantage that's supposed to come with the territory—real, true privacy—you end up not so much living alone as feeling alone. Wherever I am in the apartment, I can hear the neighbors come and go, so I'm always aware of their presence. And the fact that they almost always slam the door (young people today), which startles me and makes the pictures on my living-room wall shake, means to me that they are indifferent to my presence. So I'm stuck with irritatingly contradictory feelings that thrive by feeding on each other—the feeling that I've been invaded and the feeling that I don't exist. If I'm reading in bed and someone next door closes any door in that apartment, the wall behind my head gives a little shudder, and when someone walks down the long hallway next to the wall my floor creaks. I can hear sneezes, the ringing of a telephone, light switches being flipped, the clatter of pots and pans. I hear voices all the time, though only once have I been able to catch a complete sentence: "Oh, my God, I forgot to iron a blouse for tomorrow!" When I'm out walking around the city, I'm alert but not edgy; at home, though, I have to maintain a semi-tense readiness for the shock of unexpected sounds from next door. Except when I'm sleeping, I exist in two modes at home: either I'm about to be startled or I've just been startled. There was one sound from next door that I liked, but I don't hear it anymore, because the perpetrator is gone, and I sort of miss it—a cat padding down the hallway.

Of course, I have had my moments. I am not exactly a day at the beach. I'm more like a night on Bald Mountain. I wouldn't have wanted to live next door to me during, say, my Judy Garland phase, which lasted for about three years. I was going through a long stretch of emotional numbness, and treated it by self-medicating with large volumes—and high volumes—of Judy Garland. The album of her Carnegie Hall concert was particularly effective, since it's live, and Garland, who normally emotes enough for two, practically smothers the frenzied audience with feeling. For quite a while, I couldn't leave home in the morning without the energy boost provided by listening to "Swanee" about eight times. I can't listen to Garland anymore. The emotional overkill is too much, all wrong for my life now. Just looking at the CDs, and remembering how I almost drowned in them, makes me wince. But my immersion in Judyism served its purpose, and I would have liked to be able to go through it without having to worry whether my neighbors, who could surely hear every note (there is no wall that can stop Judy Garland), thought I was out of my mind.

BEGINNING IN THE EARLY EIGHTIES, so many new buildings went up on Broadway between Eighty-sixth Street and Ninety-sixth Street that for several years you couldn't go more than two blocks at a time without having to walk under three blocks of scaffolding. Other areas of the Upper West Side have gone through several incarnations as well. Columbus Avenue boomed, then became dead; now there are once again young people out at night all over Columbus and on Amsterdam, which until a few years ago was simply a speedway for taxis and trucks. Your favorite restaurant probably wasn't here five years ago, and it probably won't be here five years from now. You get to the point where it would be foolish to be surprised at anything. A sports bar opens. Then it closes. Whatever. A movie theatre undergoes fission and becomes a magnet. Another movie theatre opens twenty blocks south of it, and suddenly the first one becomes passé, a dumping ground for action movies and duds. The only stores that never go out of business are the Korean markets. . . .

My place was a lot like my neighborhood: the more it changed, the more it stayed the same. When the crummy couch that a friend had given me (she was already its third owner) got even crummier, I covered it with a nice Indian cloth. When that got crummy, I did nothing. For a long time, the amount of space I had and my frequent-enough attacks of fastidiousness (it's 2 a.m., time to clean the bathroom; can't go another minute without putting those photographs in an album) masked the fact that I had no plan for the apartment, no design for living, no idea about what I wanted my home to be like. Eventually, after I'd spent several years living alone, the thick coats of discipline that my parents had applied to me began to peel off in large chunks, revealing a psychic infrastructure with progressive mettle fatigue. Does it really matter if I make the bed? Mmm, let me think. . . .No. I used to be incapable of leaving dishes in the sink overnight, but I gradually loosened up to the point where I could ignore them for days. So what? I'll get to them. Is there any reason I should pick up that Lord & Taylor flyer announcing a sale that ended three months ago off the floor and throw it away? Name one. And if I'm done with the ironing board, wouldn't it be a good idea to put it away, so I don't have to do a subway-turnstile hip swivel every time I walk by it? I guess.

I didn't think of this as any kind of rebellion; I knew it was slippage. I stood outside it, watched it happen, was a little bit in awe of the creeping chaos. I could hear my father's maxims being broadcast over my private public-address system: "If you put something where it belongs, you'll always be able to find it"; "If you want something done right, do it yourself"; "If you've got a problem, fix it." The principle of accountability had seeped in and set firm. My sense of responsibility (and culpability) made it hard for me to help myself and even harder for me to ask for help. I was ground down by the oppressive ideals of self-sufficiency: it—whatever "it" was—didn't count unless I did it myself, and if I didn't do it myself it didn't get done. I suppose this idea makes some people bound out of bed in the morning, but I am not the wouldn't-it-be-fun-to-go-swimming-in-Long-Island-Sound-at-the-crack-of-dawn-in-the-middle-of-winter-like-Katherine-Hepburn type. Domestically speaking, I found it easier and easier to roll over and play dead. My life wasn't adding up; it was just piling up. It was like the headline of a story about Bette Davis that I'd clipped from the *Star* and sent as a joke to a friend in California, which said, "SHE'S LIVING ON COFFEE AND CIGARETTES AND IS TIRED OF EVERYTHING.'"

Part of the problem is that I like stuff. Except for plastic souvenir pens, which I have a huge collection of, I don't deliberately collect anything, but I automatically accumulate everything. (In duplicate, if possible. I have only one piano and one fiddle, but I do have two harmonicas and two banjos.) I'm especially drawn to things that nobody wants anymore. When I get off the elevator on my floor, or while I'm waiting for the elevator, I always look at the stuff that people have thrown out. Among the magazines and hangers and broken appliances and old clothes (all clothes that get thrown away seem to be orange) have been some eyebrow-raisers—two of the dirtiest dirty magazines I have ever seen; the manuscript of an unpublished and unpublishable autobiographical novel written by someone on my floor—and some keepers. I didn't have a fez. Now I do. I also have a set of three-pound dumbbells. Once, I came upon a big clear plastic bag filled with more than a dozen soccer trophies. Stuff at its finest. I took a few of them home, thinking they might come in handy someday. Incredibly, they didn't, and late one night I carried them down to another floor, so the person who had thrown them away wouldn't see them back on the garbage pile two years after she got rid of them. I also pick up any college alumni magazine I happen to see, even if I don't know anyone who went to that college. Yale is a good one, not just because of the rah-rah, old-boy nicknames—Inky, Bunky, Chili, Sport, and Tiger all make an appearance in the class notes of the latest issue—but because it provides me with precious information about a certain shrink I know. Recent revelations are that she attended her twentieth reunion (travel and hotel accommodations paid for by Nancy Franklin, Smith '78) and that Joyce Maynard was in her class—the same Joyce Maynard whose journalistic career I have been a rapt spectator of for more than twenty years, beginning with her famous 1972 *Times Magazine* article about Her Generation (you wanted to smack the title: "An 18-Year-Old Looks Back on Life") and continuing at least to an article in *Self* two years ago about why she'd decided, at the age of thirty-six, to get breast implants. ("My journey into the land of large breasts" was how she put it.) I have a lot of stuff like this in my head, just as I have a lot of stuff in my apartment. In fact, by the time I was about thirty, the inside of my head and the inside of my apartment had become a lot alike—a mess I didn't know how to clean up. But the thought of getting rid of stuff was unthinkable: my stuff was how I knew myself, it was who I was, and how would anyone else know who I was in the absence of my stuff? My stuff was my hedge against anxiety—never mind that it was, even more, a source of anxiety, as the inhabitable space in my apartment grew smaller and smaller. I was relieved that a boyfriend I had a couple of years ago was not bothered by the disorder my stuff created, but I found his lack of interest in my stuff disturbing—it meant he would never really understand me. I was missing the point. It was me that he was interested in, and I finally saw that I was more than the sum of my stuff. For the first time, I had the feeling that there was a way out.

Of course, the way out was literally out—out of the apartment, out of the building. This year, after fending off most people from seeing how I lived ("No one's allowed in my apartment," I would say, as if I were warning them away from an abandoned mine shaft), I asked a friend from work whom I've known for ten years but who had never been here to come over and help me—to perform, in effect, an intervention. I made her promise that she would still like me when she saw the piles of multimedia clutter—records, CDs, books, magazines, old mail, videotapes, newspaper clippings—and then I gave her free rein. At the end of five hours, we had filled fourteen garbage bags with clothes to go to the Salvation Army and eight bags with stuff to go on the garbage pile by the elevator. We had a few disagreements. When she pulled my lab coat from college out of the closet and said "Why would you keep this? Are you going to wear it?" I said "Why wouldn't I keep it?" Her stare of incomprehension was too powerful for me; I threw it out. We also clashed over a three-year-old issue of *New York* that I was keeping under the couch in case I ever needed to refer to the cover story, which was "Getting Fired: How to Survive." After a brief tug-of-war, her world view prevailed, and out it went. Into the garbage went outdated travel brochures from Norway, British Columbia, the Shetland Islands, Ireland, Montana, South Dakota, and Cape May. Eight shopping bags filled with other shopping bags—out. Clothes I knew I would never wear again and clothes my friend urged me never to wear again—out. I was allowed to keep a few mementos of my old self—two Laura Ashley dresses ("Maybe I'll make pillows or something out of them," I lied), and my Frye boots from 1979. Four of my five pairs of flip-flops—out. More than a dozen pairs of shoes, some of which were ugly, some of which were worn out, some of which had shrunk a size in the closet and were too small—out. A few weeks later, my friend came back and we picked up where we had left off. We didn't finish (I'll have to decide on my own what to do with my mother's Burberry, which she gave me a few years ago, and which is too small for me), but we'd made a big dent. For the first time in years, my apartment was livable—and, even more important, leavable.

I HAVEN'T MOVED YET, but I've bought an apartment, and I already miss my life here. I've made good friends in my building: people I actually hang out with, watch "Melrose Place" with, go to Happy Burger with, talk about the other tenants with. People I've trusted with my keys, people whose cats I've fed, people who have given me some of the peanut-butter cookies they just baked. People I can call from the Minneapolis airport and ask to turn on my air-conditioner, so the apartment will be cool when I get home. And then there are the people I hardly know but share a comfortable, long-term esprit d'elevator with. I'm staying on the Upper West Side, but I'm moving inland, and I'll miss the seasons here at the edge of the city. I'll miss seeing the river every day when I leave my building, and when I lean out my kitchen window and look west. Wherever you go, there you are, they say, but when I move I'm hoping to give the slip to whatever it was in me that didn't get the oven fixed for two years; kept paying the cable bill but didn't call the cable company for two and a half years to come fix the problem that kept me from getting most of the channels I was supposed to get; didn't have the drip in the bathtub fixed; didn't have the ceiling repainted when a radiator above me sprang a leak six years ago; didn't get a new couch, because I didn't know how long I'd be staying here.

I don't know what it was, exactly, that enabled me to break up with my apartment. But I suppose I knew about a year and a half ago that I was preparing my exit. I forgot to renew my lease—the real-estate equivalent of not showing up at my own wedding—and found an eviction notice taped to my door one morning. I straightened things out, but in my mind it was the beginning of the end. Economics also had something to do with it. Unlike most of the buildings on Riverside Drive, my building never went co-op, so I never had the springboard of an insider's price to give me a foothold on the lower rungs of the ladder of ownership, even though I'd been saving money since I was in second grade, in my elementary school's banking program. Instead, I settled into domestic unhappiness, renewable every two years, in exchange for a rent that was too good to give up. Finally, though, I was able to dislodge the idea that buying a place equaled disaster, and that spending my savings would inevitably make me a bag lady down the road. (I also came to the more profound conclusion that not spending my savings would not necessarily prevent me from becoming a bag lady; in any case, I already was a bag lady—a bag lady with a two-bedroom, rent-stabilized apartment.)

Age has something to do with it, too. The worst year of my thirties was not the year after I turned thirty, but the year after I turned thirty-one; until then, I had believed that once I touched thirty I'd get to turn around and do my twenties again, with a clean slate that this time I would mess up in the right ways. It was a shock to discover that the mistakes I hadn't made would now never be made but would exist as negative shapes, cast in a kind of lost-wax process. At this point, I took half-a-year off from my job—I was by now a stressed-out editor—and from New York, not to find myself but, I hoped, to lose myself. (It turns out that running away from your problems sometimes does work.) I'd always known how lucky I was, always been told how lucky I was, but when I came back to the city I *felt* lucky for the first time. Still, it took me most of my thirties to adjust to being in my thirties, to come to terms with the knowledge that the inability to make decisions had had a decisive effect on my life, that time is unidirectional, and that I wouldn't be getting extra credit for refusing to live in the present. This is the year before the year I will turn forty, and now the idea that if I don't do something it won't get done mostly acts as a propellant instead of inducing paralysis. The great, unexpected realization I've made during the last few months has been that by deciding to stay in New York I am now also free to go.

CAROLINE CLARKE
GRAVES '85

Caroline Clarke Graves was born and raised in New York City. The only child of a public elementary school teacher and a chemistry professor, her childhood home was one in which familial devotion and academic performance topped a short list of high expectations. Her love of writing began at The Bronx High School of Science, where she dabbled in poetry and song lyrics. She went to Smith with a strong desire to major in English, but no clue of how to translate her passion for writing into a career. Soon after graduating, she locked in on journalism as a way to get paid for doing what she loved.

After earning a master's degree with honors from Columbia University Graduate School of Journalism (1987), she spent a few years as a newspaper reporter in New Jersey and Connecticut before becoming a staff writer at The American Lawyer *magazine. She joined* Black Enterprise *magazine as a senior editor in 1992. In 1995 she was awarded the New York Association of Black Journalists Award for her feature, "Moment of Truth for the Class of '70," and she has received several annual Unity Awards from Lincoln University for her editorial direction of* Black Enterprise, *notably that of the twenty-fifth anniversay issue.*

Today, as an editor-at-large, she still writes and edits for the magazine while also serving as editor of Blake Enterprise Books, a division that publishes business books targeted to African Americans. She lives in New Rochelle, New York, with her husband (and college sweetheart), John Graves, and their two young children. She is now working on her own first book for the Blake Enterprise series, tentatively titled Take a Lesson: A Mentoring Guide for African Americans, *in which fifty black achievers share the greatest career lessons they ever learned.*

The essay, "A Courageous Choice," was first published in the Smith Alumnae Quarterly *(Winter 1995-96), an issue devoted to the newsmaking appointment of Ruth Simmons as president.*

A Courageous Choice

I CAN BARELY REMEMBER WHOM I MET with or what I ate yesterday, but I have not forgotten the moment nine months ago when I heard that Ruth Simmons had been named to lead Smith.

It was 7:27 a.m. on Friday, December 16, 1994. (I know because I checked the clock as I dashed to catch the phone.) At the time, Smith College could not have been farther from my mind. All I could think as I grabbed the receiver was, 'I'm late.'

"Hello," I offered, with more impatience than I intended.

My mother-in-law's voice was breathless with excitement. "Hi. Did you hear?"

"No. What?"

"Smith College has appointed a black woman president!"

My verbal reaction was involuntary and immediate: I squealed, long and loudly, although her words were still slowly processing in my head. Smith College? My alma mater? A black president? Was she sure? I was stunned, elated, incredulous.

As I hung up the phone, I felt the heat of tears on my cheeks. But my grin was whole-face wide and the realization that I was crying made me laugh out loud. What was this reaction about? In the ten years since graduating, I hadn't much cared what went on at Smith. I was the type who assumed anything in an envelope with a Smith College return address was a call for cash. In the trash they went, unopened. The vibrant newsletters usually got a glance-through, and the *Smith Alumnae Quarterly* (before I recently agreed to join its editorial board) found me heading straight to the news about classmates and the obits.

So in the dark about Smith was I, that I was only vaguely aware that Mary Maples Dunn was stepping down. Her appointment, which was announced during my senior year, hadn't struck much of a chord with me either. To be blunt, I didn't much care. Jill Ker Conway seemed to have kept the shine on Smith's sterling reputation while also keeping the coffers brimming. I was supremely confident that her successor would do the same, and I didn't have to read tarot cards to know two things: her successor would be a woman, and she would be white. No big mystery there.

I don't mean to sound glib. Smith was a wonderful place, but it never captured my heart. Although I was a fairly active member of the community, much of the time, I felt more like a visitor. It wasn't that I didn't fit in, but that where I fit was on the periphery. And there's no question that my being African American was part of the reason why. So, leaving 10 years ago wasn't hard to do. And staying away has been even easier.

Yet, here I was, moved to tears of pure delight by the news that Ruth Simmons, an African-American woman, was going to be Smith's ninth president. I wasn't sure which thrilled me more—that Simmons had shattered the ceiling for African Americans at Smith or that Smith had been the first to break boldly with the exclusionary tradition of elite liberal arts colleges. In choosing Simmons, the board of trustees had clearly placed the life and integrity of the college first, and it came up sparkling like new. As I hung up the phone on that cold, sunny morning, I couldn't have been more surprised, nor had I even been more proud to claim Smith as my own.

I looked at my seven-month-old daughter, Veronica, who smiled back at me, oblivious to the flood of thoughts and questions swirling through my head. "Maybe you'll go to Smith one day, after all," I told her.

I devoured the *New York Times* cover story on Simmons that day as well as the special edition of *News-Smith* I received later that week, but they weren't enough. I wanted to know more about Ruth Simmons. I wanted to meet and to touch her. Luckily, my line of work gave me license to do so. I got the go ahead to do a profile of Simmons for my magazine, *Black Enterprise*. A few weeks after the announcement, I was on my way to interview her.

En route to Princeton, I was excited, but nervous—which is out of character for me. I wasn't sure what to expect—or what I hoped to find. I studied the questions I had prepared over and over. They sounded ridiculous. She'll think I'm an idiot, I thought, then realized I felt more like the interviewee than the interviewer. I had been overly concerned about how I looked, being on time, making the right impression. She knew I was a Smith alumna. I felt pressure to do Smith—and myself—proud. When had I ever felt that way before?

Meeting her, although she was warm and welcoming, didn't ease the pressure. There's a look that certain teachers and your mother have. It says, I care about you, I believe in you. But you'd better sit up straight and do the right thing or else. . . . So, I tried, launching into my questions.

For a reporter, there's nothing worse than a stilted interview. Cryptic answers, non-answers, rhetorical answers, bored answers: this is the stuff of writers' nightmares. Simmons, by contrast, was a dream.

By the time I sat with her, she had been interviewed no less than fifty times, I'm sure. No doubt, she had heard my questions before. Yet, she was thoughtful, candid, and engaging in her responses. Her answers to even the most mundane questions were unpredictable. Like most people who rise to prominence, Ruth Simmons speaks her mind. But, having interviewed several corporate heads and business leaders (I work for a business magazine), Simmons has a quality I've found rare in people at her level: she listens.

We talked about her childhood in rural Texas, about what it was like to be the youngest of twelve, seven of whom were boys. Clearly, it was during those earliest years that Simmons learned to speak up and out. In a brood that size, the baby's only other option would have been to settle into oblivion—and oblivion would have no place in this feisty child's future.

In Simmons's family, attending college was so far-fetched a notion that to call it a pipe dream would be pushing it. But Simmons stood out early academically and caught the attention of caring teachers. Ultimately, she earned a scholarship that, literally, took her far—all the way to New Orleans, where she attended an all-black college, Dillard University. A standout at Dillard, as well, she was hand-picked to spend her junior year at Wellesley. Simmons says she was "an oddity" there, but didn't mind. "For the first time, women were in charge, and that was magical," she said. I mentioned that I often felt like an oddity at Smith. She seemed to understand, but added with a smile, "I do not expect to feel like an oddity at Smith."

Although still consumed with her work at Princeton, and carefully keeping her distance as Mary Maples Dunn finished her term, Simmons seemed to have already made Smith her own. She spoke of the college with a tenderness and respect usually expressed by only the most reverent alumnae.

She was still marvelling over her appointment. Having always fashioned herself as a worker-bee ("I'm not your average gung-ho leader. I don't think I have the ego that a lot of leaders have," she said), she had to coax herself into envisioning the role. The length of the search process helped. But key, she says, was what she realized about Smith during that process.

"I knew there would have to be a special place to make me consider the role [of president]," said Simmons, who declined even to participate in several other presidential searches. "It would have to be a place with a unique mission. What impressed me about the Smith search is that they spent a lot less time asking me to conform to their ideas or a presidential ideal than they did trying to learn about me. So, in appointing me, there are affirming me as I am."

REFLECTING ON OUR MEETING on the train ride back to New York, I don't know that I did Smith proud, but Ruth Simmons did. It was one of the most memorable interviews I have conducted. No doubt, after meeting with her, the presidential search committee felt the same way.

It is not easy to describe what it means to me, as an African-American woman and a Smith alumna, to know that another African-American woman—a supremely capable, brilliant, and insightful one—is taking the helm of my alma mater. Suffice it to say that Simmons's appointment in and of itself has radically changed my view of Smith College. For the college I knew—or thought I knew—would not have placed a black woman at its helm, no matter how capable, how brilliant, or how insightful.

Having said that, for anyone who might have assumed (as one classmate of mine expressed to me) that Smith College set out to find a black woman to "make some sort of statement," and lucked up on one who just happened to be accomplished and dynamic, let me assure you, that was hardly the case. Smith College set out to find the very best person to lead it into the next century and that person just happens to be black. And that Smith hired her finally affirms who I am.

So, there it is, the reason for my spontaneous tears of joy. In appointing Ruth Simmons president, Smith has finally acted on the message it preached throughout my undergraduate years—that I, not just a woman but an African-American woman, can do anything, be anything, achieve any post, and that I deserve an equal shot at any opportunity. I always believed it. But I didn't think Smith believed it. There simply wasn't enough evidence to show that it did. There weren't enough black professors or instructors; the artists, scholars, and speakers brought to campus were rarely African American; there wasn't enough emphasis placed on the contributions of African Americans—or those of other non-European cultures—built into the curriculum; there wasn't enough action behind Smith's spoken commitment to diversity to separate it from the pack of so-called progressive colleges, corporations, and communities talking that talk but doing little else.

My resentment over this put me at a determined distance from my school, even while I was a student living there. That gap widened during the ten years since. It has now begun to lessen. But the greater challenges for Smith and for Simmons in trying to fashion a diverse and dynamic community remains.

Near the end of our interview, Simmons recounted for me her final meeting with the search committee. Upon accepting their nomination she asked, "Are you ready for this? Not just for the first black woman president, but a president who is really black—unself-consciously, unapologetically black?"

Given the overwhelming reaction the college community gave Simmons last winter when she was introduced for the first time, I would venture that, yes, Smith is ready. But as an African-American woman, well aware of what unforeseen reactions my skin color can inspire, I say, ready or not Smith College, it's time.

JANNA MALAMUD
SMITH '79 MSW

Janna Malamud Smith grew up in a literary family in Corvallis, OR, Bennington, VT, and finally, as a teenager, in Cambridge, MA. She did her undergraduate studies at Radcliffe/Harvard in American history and literature, earning her AB in 1973 before taking a Master's in Social Work from Smith. For twenty years, she has been a clinical social worker at the Cambridge Health Alliance where she sees patients, supervises, and trains graduate students. She is also in private practice in Cambridge and Milton, MA, where she lives with her husband, a teacher at Milton Academy, and her two children. She is a sometime contributor to The New York Times, The Boston Globe, The Los Angeles Times, *and she is heard on "Fresh Air," "Talk of the Nation," "On the Media," Voice of America," and "The NewsHour with Jim Lehrer."* Private Matters: In Defense of the Personal Life *(1997), her first book, ranges widely and intuitively from cultural criticism to a personal plea that private matters be respected in life, art, and literary biography.*

As the daughter of Bernard Malamud, Janna Malamud Smith has often asked "Where does a writer's family draw the line?" the title and subject of an essay in the New York Times Book Review *(5 November 1989). She recalls her own fascination with literary biography like Anne Sexton's by Diane Middlebrook or Henry James's by Leon Edel, but she describes her reluctance, after her father's death, to have the person she knew transformed by biographers. In her own work, she writes powerfully on why mothers are so often blamed for whatever ails a child and why her own children lack something of her own idealism. The essay here was published in an abbreviated form in* The Alumnae Quarterly *(Fall 1998), and it has been reprinted in* How We Want to Live: Seventeen Distinguished Writers on the Meaning of Progress in Their Own Lives *(1998), ed. Susan Richards Shreve and Porter Shreve. Her literary sensibility and her sense of her own history and that of her own time strike chords in us all.*

Beyond Bread and Roses

I T IS RARE THAT I CRY AT DINNER. Certainly not with guests present. I cannot remember what we were eating, or whether the wine was red or white. I don't think I'd had more than a glass all evening, so it is unlikely that these were wine tears. They were, however, startling, unexpected to me as much as to my dinner companions. I had casually set out to talk about James Carroll's Sixties era memoir, *An American Requiem*, which I had just finished reading. Before I knew it, I was crying about the Vietnam war. More exactly, I was recalling the loss of a large youthful sense of social hope that the civil rights movement had awakened and that had crashed in the course of the next decade, like a car falling slowly from a high cliff.

Review the film of the loss frame by frame, and you will see the vehicle tumbling through large events: Martin Luther King's death, Robert Kennedy's, Watts, the Chicago convention, Mylai, accompanied by a near infinity of smaller ones: Fred Hampton's murder, the napalmed girl, the nightly body counts on television news, the clubbed and tear-gassed protesters. By the early Seventies, there was the Cambodia invasion, the Watergate hearings, Nixon's resignation, finally ending with photos of Vietnamese men desperately grasping the wings and wheel axles of the planes they had hoped would carry them out of Saigon ahead of the conquering North Vietnamese troops. "Ho Ho Ho Chi Minn," we used to chant during the protests, "NLF is gonna win." And finally, when we no longer saw meaning in the event, it did.

The experience of protest was of torment and futility. The hope that began the effort gave way to weary cynicism. Yet read history and you will conclude that anti-war protesters shortened the Vietnam war and saved lives. We changed the world and we would continue to do so. Our lives would be about change, some of it brand new, some of it a legacy inherited almost unexplored from recent generations. As a woman I have the opportunity to manage my money, write this essay, vote, divorce, control my child-bearing, travel alone, choose my partner, and marry across race, class, and religion. I am the beneficiary of efforts by women of my generation, my mother's and my grandmother's, and can say sincerely that change has been abundant, and that it has constituted progress. So too, the social protest of my own lifetime starting with the Civil Rights Movement, then the Vietnam war, the women's movement and the anti-nuclear movement, has yielded many important changes—among them the diminution of racism and sexism, the shortening of an unjust war, and the lowering of the total number of nuclear missiles in the world.

How is it, then, that the result of protest and progress appears to be a widespread silence about the future, a kind of "aw shucks" embarrassment about idealism or visions of social change? I don't think that the mostly middle-class or affluent—largely white—professionals who were once the student war protesters, by and large feel a personal hopelessness, or a sense of despair for their own children's actual prospects. Private life is full of possibility for people who control such a large piece of the world's resources. Yet, my generation has been almost totally unable to provide ourselves or our children with a horizon on which to focus a collective vision of meaningful social progress or hope.

The teenagers—friends of my sons—who come in and out of our house every day are lively and bright, likely as adults to improve computer technology and protect the ozone. But, as far as I can tell, not one of them would be caught dead dreaming aloud of a better world. Their idealism lacks a shared public language or goal. Not for them a city on a hill, or the uniting of the world's workers. Their youth makes them blind to the struggles which have preceded them. Yet their intuition is like Braille-trained fingers with which they rub their surroundings and perceive that they are the puzzled legatees of others' ambitious dreams, utopian plans, and ideological disappointments. They are not sure what they have inherited, or how to name—beyond more money and things—what they might want.

How do you make dreams of progress for people who—by every historical and conventional measure—have arrived? And recently arrived at that. As opposed to *nouveau riche*, which some might be, the more important but less noticed truth is that many are *nouveau libéré*—newly liberated. Racial prejudice is virulent in America, as are economic and class barriers. But place most people beside their grandparents, and the amount of personal freedom and choice they have is greatly enlarged. More often than not the immigrants who landed here—even those neither indentured nor enslaved—brought little with them, and made what they could with what they found. My neighborhood in a suburb south of Boston is filled with Irish families who live in freshly renovated houses and own new cars. Their grandparents crowded into the Boston tenements, their great grandparents arrived in steerage, forced—as Andrea Barrett reminds us in *Ship Fever*—to abandon the bodies of loved ones who had starved en route. For years during the 19th century help-wanted advertisements read "n.i.n.a.": No Irish need apply.

And often this past was not that long ago. The literary phenomenon of 1997 is *Angela's Ashes*, Frank McCourt's memoir of growing up in awful poverty in Ireland in the years before the Second World War. The book has sold over a million copies in hardcover and is still high on the bestseller list. Just as *Fiddler on the Roof* offered Jewish audiences of the 1960s a narrative which explained how they got to Long Island, *Angela's Ashes* has done the same for the Irish—and both works speak to many Americans. These artistic inventions draw mass audiences because people experience them as prosthetic limbs for pasts amputated by the discontinuity of assimilation and prosperity. They strap on in place of the real missing stories of earlier old world generations. They stand in for the personal history that is lost. Audiences flock to *Angela's Ashes* and *Fiddler on the Roof* seeking reassurance that the present is better. It is comforting to be reminded that the world left behind was often filled with suffering and terrible choices. At the same time, by entering these dramas, people enjoy the restoration of a familiar, delicious, and now lost hope for progress and a better life. (The musical and the memoir both end with emigration. Unencumbered by experience, the characters behold the new land's promise.) Oh, for the days—one can say sentimentally from the safety of plenitude—when people knew what they wanted, when dreams of progress were of food, shelter, freedom, and a large, new world for one's children. Now that the real accompanying terrors are safely in the past, we enjoy revisiting such dreams. Several years ago I watched my son's sixth-grade class perform a rousing chorus of "Food, Glorious Food," from the musical *Oliver*. These affluent children delighted in their role as starving orphans in search of better gruel. Nothing relieves the soul like a borrowed wish; particularly since in prosperity we have lost the sufferer's prerogative of earned righteousness about our own desires.

"Ah," Ralph Waldo Emerson wrote in *Nature* (1903), "if the rich were rich as the poor fancy riches." We resist the notion that arrival includes mourning the loss of the dream of arrival, but it does. When the poor fancy riches, two imaginative acts occur at once. People dream of real solutions to the economic problems that consume their lives. But the particular hope for money is fused to a wish for escape from the present, and perhaps from the very confines of the psychological self. However much images of the future are set in material terms, at heart they are also fantasies of emotional release. In them, surroundings are altered, and people are too. One seeks to feel new, to dissolve the restrictions of convention, habit, worn landscape, and familiar love. One dilemma of arrival is that the mind loses—but still insists upon—a fantasy of arrival. The real present remains imperfect. Yet once basic needs have been satisfied, the props to fill dreams become more rarefied, elusive, idiosyncratic, and diffuse.

Middle-class Americans are—for the moment—sheltered from all the conventional terrors: political oppression, genocide, poverty, starvation, homelessness, and diseases that wipe out half a neighborhood in a day. In such a context, what is progress's rallying cry? History suggests that in time, either from adversity or purpose, new ideas will stir. Gradually, they will ready and lift off. But now the flock—perhaps worn from the last long lap—is consumed in feeding and sleeping, oblivious to larger imperative.

And what of the grief that welled up that night at dinner? I think it had two sources. The first was feeling a long suppressed and carefully denigrated passion for social justice come back unexpectedly. The second was the memory of what a painful era the Sixties and early Seventies had been. Caring about the direction the world took had turned out to include opening oneself to bad surprises. The poet W.D. Snodgrass describes finding a picture of his first wife in a pile of old papers he is sorting. For him, it is like turning up a severed hand while raking leaves.

I was sixteen when Robert Kennedy was murdered. A young woman teacher at my high school and I, made restless by the proximity of summer, had driven up to camp overnight by the ocean. At dawn we turned on the car radio and heard the news of the assassination as we peered out through dew-covered windows at sand dunes and beach grass. We drove back in a daze of anguish. All weekend I lay in bed with an awful stomach ache, and spoke to no one about my grief. I was ashamed to admit I had fallen for the virile, suntanned man in the white shirt with the rolled up shirtsleeves who drew huge crowds, and promised a better world. But the truth was that I believed in the world he was describing, a place freed of racism, poverty, and pointless wars. A place where we could sacrifice personal gain for the sake of social fairness.

To lose someone who in reality has no connection to you, but in fantasy has captured you, is a particular kind of loss. For even as you are pummeled by grief, you never feel fully entitled to your mourning. Rather, you feel embarrassed, caught out caring when you should have known better. What kind of naïve girl were you anyway to admire such a compromised, uneasy man? Or worse, to believe that a different world was possible? To see virtue in voluntary poverty?

But my feelings about Robert Kennedy are important here only insofar as they were emblematic. Our emotional experience during the era was often of an exquisite vulnerability that is as difficult to name, describe, or recapture as it was to live through. By agreeing to care, we opened ourselves to pain. Suffering by choice for causes not obviously our own—the fate of the Vietnamese people, the well-being of the American downtrodden—gradually made us feel mistaken, even foolish.

I had suppressed all this until I read Carroll's memoir. Or more precisely, I had blamed myself for feeling too much, and decided that it was a personal problem. Carroll's book made me weep because it declared that that era's anguish and the participants' grief had been legitimate and widely felt. Like a parent who refuses to enter the room where a beloved child has died, I had tried to shut away the memory of how much we had cared—and how perhaps the best thing about us was that we did. Carroll took me back into that room, and I remembered the child's touch and smell, the overwhelming bond, and what it still held of my own passion.

Vietnam was a bad war, and our protest was enlightened even as it contributed to the anguish, the father-against-son fury, that Carroll describes. The accompanying pursuit of greater social and economic equality was also right. But at the time it felt too hard. Our leaders had been killed. Adulthood was waiting. We put down the placards, returned to graduate school, and found professions. There were children to raise, and mutual funds to worry over. So much was possible. We concentrated on sampling the fruit before us—figs, apricots, tangerines— crates overflowing with worldly delights. And we quietly abandoned our large idealism. Left it, shook it off, took it to the edge of the woods and instructed it not to follow us home. Drowned it in a stream. Held it under the water until we thought it was still. For a while, life seemed better without it.

MEG GREENFIELD '52

*B*orn and raised in Seattle, Mary Ellen Greenfield excelled at Smith College, being elected to Phi Beta Kappa and graduating summa cum laude in 1952. Following a year as a Fulbright Scholar at Newham College, Cambridge, Meg Greenfield returned to the United States and began a career in journalism at the now-defunct Reporter Magazine. She began as a researcher, working her way up to appointment as Washington editor in 1965. In July of 1968, she joined The Washington Post and became deputy editor of the editorial page in 1969. Again, her talents as a writer and editor propelled her through the ranks; she was named editor of the editorial page in 1979, a year after winning the Pulitzer prize for Editorial writing.

Meg Greenfield also contributes a fortnightly column to Newsweek, which many readers peruse from back to front to get her enlightening and often entertaining take on current events. A resident of Washington, DC, Meg Greenfield is noted for her insightful observations on the political atmosphere within the capital, but she has become a model of reason, integrity, and understanding on the broader human condition as well. She was given an honorary doctorate of humane letters by Smith in 1978 at Rally Day. Among her many commitments, Meg Greenfield is a member of the American Society of Newspaper Editors, and holds membership on the Pulitzer Board and on the Board of Shakespeare Theater at The Folger.

The two columns featured in this selection reflect both her humorous and serious sides in characteristically spare and witty prose. The "Oppression of the Aunts" takes a look at the everyday discrimination against aunts throughout history and literature and Meg Greenfield's own life. "'Paperizing' Policy" has a more serious bent with wry observations on the proliferation of paper and the lack of action to right any wrong. Both columns appeared in the regular Newsweek magazine feature, "The Last Word."

Oppression of the Aunts

FROM *Newsweek*

I BECAME A GREAT-AUNT THIS SUMMER. I realize this may not be accounted much of a personal achievement—and talk about feeling old. But talk about something else, too—namely about being socially and culturally oppressed. You heard right, so stand back: I believe I have uncovered the last remaining area of group discrimination, not to say group persecution, that has not had its day in federal court. Let us call it "auntism." It is a virulent scourge.

Auntism (why should the name be any prettier than ageism, sexism and the rest of those newly named but ancient isms?) may in fact be the single unswept corner in the great modernistic mansion of feminism. Even "women drivers," after all, have been vindicated and pretty much let alone by the male gag writers ever since woman-jokes got just a little chancy to tell and the spoilsport joke-police accurately pointed out that it is men, not women, according to insurance statistics, who are the lousy drivers. But aunt-bashing proceeds apace.

Who or what is the aunt figure in our literature and our lingo, anyway? I'll tell you. At her most promising she may be Auntie Mame—the elegant, engaging, adored and risqué family member who is a beacon to the unruly young and a shock to her contemporaries in the family ("We don't talk about your Auntie Mame"). She is the one that auntdom most fervently aspires to be, though usually without success. Slightly less desirable, but still at least tolerable, is Aunt Em from "The Wizard of Oz"—capacious, gentle, white-aproned, a surrogate mom. If you don't qualify as one of these, you're pretty much on your own, and the outlook is not good. From Aunt Em to Tom Sawyer's Aunt Polly—lovable but gullible, ineffective and dithery—is but a short step. And frankly it's downhill from there.

I offer as the first article in our indictment the observation that the mere prefix "aunt" does something dimly ridiculous to your name. Generally, the aunt—or aunt figure—is: priggish, unbeautiful, archaic, demanding and altogether a person whose departure from the party is required before the rest of the family can have any fun. Aunts are etiquette-maniacs in an age of chili dogs. But the fact is that even before there were chili dogs, way, way back when there were actually knives and forks and spoons and napkins on the table, aunts had this noxious reputation. Our oppression is of ancient standing.

At this point I expect to hear outraged bleats of self-pity and complaint from the charter members of uncles' lib. And I agree that sometimes the poor class of creatures derided as "uncle" gets it, too. The uncle as a figure of speech and a figure of fun is, to be plain about it, a lush. He may also be a little bit *off*. "Dotty," we would say; lives in the attic; Uncle Amos, Uncle Arthur. I am aware that you're probably not supposed to use the word "lush" anymore or any of these other terms either, some variants on "alcoholic" or "mentally ill" being thought right. However, the errant-uncle figure is not thought of as sick at all, but rather as weak—a lush, off in the head. Even so, he is not nearly so universally exploited for comic relief or dismal example as is his counterpart, the dread and dreary aunt. And the word "avuncular," after all, though somewhat condescending in implication, does on the whole convey something benign.

In the course of talking to legislators, administrators, lawyers and business people who preside over the nation's far-flung enterprise, whenever you get off policy questions and onto the quirky or obstructive or trivial case, you will start hearing about aunts—depend on it. This or that provision (you will be told) of course doesn't cover the "Aunt Mathilda cases." Or perhaps the provision was put in explicitly to deal with her funny little problems. The aunts always have these antique, vaguely forbidding, spinster-sounding names. I have a quote here from a recent *Wall Street Journal* to illustrate my point for those who are not aunts and may therefore need guidance. I could have found one in any publication, including those I write for, but this from a *Journal* editorial on airline deregulation was at hand: "With regulated profits, airlines didn't have to care about efficiency or fares. Business types didn't care either; their companies simply wrote the expense off against taxes. Aunt Mabel couldn't afford the fares, so she had to drive or take the bus, or not travel at all."

Now try to tell me that Aunt Mabel didn't appear to you as you were reading those words: a stout, shelf-bosomed old party in a 30-years-out-of-date wool suit, dumb hat and flattened iron-gray hair; she was descending from the bus, for her unwanted summer visit. You got the sinking feeling. The poor old aunt, in other words, exists only on the periphery of other people's lives, a marginal creature at best; she is either a statistical aberration or a little window on pathos where the big policy questions before the society are concerned. She is also a stickler (having incorporated the old schoolteacher/scold image into her own), and she wears a permanent expression of her disapproval on her face related to the single true drama in her, on the whole, drama-starved life.

This, of course, as anyone who has ever been an aunt or had one knows, is the drama of the unreceived thank-you note. It is what we aunts were born for, what God had in mind when he put us on this earth: "Hello there, Charley. My, what a big boy you have become and how fine you look carrying around that . . . what is it, a radio? I'll bet you bought it with the $25 I sent you when you graduated from junior high school two years ago. You did get the check, didn't you, dear?"

Having been at both ends of this unrewarding exchange, or at least a version of it, I can sympathize with both aggrieved parties. I also think the mere fact that, as an aunt, one finds oneself uttering the phrases hauntingly familiar from childhood demonstrates how grave the auntism crisis is and how thoroughly deserving of another of our national rooting-out campaigns, one of our many total-mobilization "wars." We need a war against auntism because people like me find themselves sounding like that. We become our stereotype. We don't want much—just a few new role models. Aunt Raquel. Aunt Cher. Aunt Fergie. Think of it this summer as you head for the airport to pick up Mabel. She needs help.

'Paperizing' Policy

I DON'T EVEN KNOW YOU, but I'm willing to bet you have had it up to here with the avalanche of unsolicited mail-order catalogs the post office dumps in your mailbox every day. It occurred to me once that I might start saving mine and stacking them up, one on top of the other, on the first of the year and then have my picture taken standing beside the result 365 days later. But I was afraid the thing might topple over and kill me.

Now, as improbable as this will seem, such a sky-high pile of unwanted catalogs would be as nothing to a comparable pile of the unwanted studies, reports, polemics, and assorted other policy propaganda that thuds down on my desk every day at roughly four-hour intervals, when the office mail is delivered. Most of it is vacuous junk parading as "findings," albeit junk that has been festively decked out in bright binders with millions of tabs and graced with titles that are stunning in their pretension: "The Fate of Our Children," "Roadmap for the Next Millennium." I rarely lift this stuff; I push it across my desk from the in-box side to the out-box side, whence it is quickly dispatched to the Ultimate Out Box from which there is no return—with one final thud.

As the volume of this incoming printed material has risen exponentially over the past few years I have taken to wondering what the reason is. It can't just be that so many people are working in the lobbies, advocacy organizations, PR companies and the rest. I think it is more likely that the booklet-and-binder boom represents just one part of a larger phenomenon. That is the permutation of much of our public life from action into talk, its reduction from concern with a threatening, obligation-creating reality to concern with a kind of inert, abstract format in which everyone can argue and expostulate without danger of getting hurt or, more importantly, having to do anything at all that has real-life consequences. We tune in to see and hear the participants in our interminable national arguments expressing verbal violence on this or that, contending stubbornly over whose vision of social justice is the right one, who is a miscreant and who a victim.

But their arguments leave both us and them unscathed, like that form of fencing where no one can get hurt. That is because the arguments amount to substitutes for engagement, not real engagement that bears a cost or can be expected to change anything. We all just unhook our little microphones at the end of the contention and go home. We've done our duty by NATO or Rwanda or immigration law or whatever it is, and now we don't have to think about it anymore till we bone up for the next impassioned debate. Periodically, an administration will get tripped up when it's expected to make good on these theoretical, verbal-only policies—foreign policy ultimatums, campaign promises—that it cannot fulfill, and thus it must be seen in the ungainly act of backing down the ladder that led to the 32-foot board, step by step by step.

But mostly, and conveniently enough, it doesn't come to that. Troubles can be resolved on paper or in skillful rhetoric (although in ways that resolve nothing) by evading or simply being ignorant of nondebating, nonverbal reality. I can illustrate with a couple of stories from my journalistic past. One concerned an itinerant expert on Northern school-integration plans in the '60s who worked out what he considered a suitable desegregation scheme for Gary, Indiana, that, as I learned at the time, would have had the children traversing land that was crossed by three U.S. highways, the Little Calumet River and the tracks of nine different railroads, including the Pennsylvania and Wabash main lines. The other story is of a moment in an editorial meeting when we were concluding in our characteristic collegial fashion that the solution to the problem of a costly, ugly government building in midconstruction on Capitol Hill was to wait until spring and then reconsider whether or not to go ahead. One newly among us who had studied science, not Shakespeare, in school said, "You can't do that; it's winter; the girders are already up, and they'll rust." The girders will rust? Now, there was a novel thought. *Girders?* Hey, we're making *policy* here. What's this stuff about girders? Can't they put something on them like you squirt on lawn furniture?

One reason, I think, that printed polemics (including columns and editorials) and verbal hassling have managed to supersede real engagement with public issues is that the argument seems to have become, in so many instances, more important to the arguers than the subject they are purportedly arguing about. Words are more malleable than actual people or actual fiscal fact or actual well-armed tyrants overseas. There is a lot of self-congratulation, moral posturing and feel-good stuff in the truckload of paper that is dropped on my desk, for example—mostly theoretical material that has contrived to present a solution to some abiding national problem, but only by virtue of having left out the really hard part.

So some considerable portion of the growing "paperization" of policy and involvement in public issues is about contrived self-justification (especially on the part of tax-exempt paperizers). And the same may be said of the often vitriolic disputes among journalists and political/governmental people. You can make a case if you're not in danger of having to acknowledge and live with its results. True, the participants love to point out how they were luminously right and their antagonists were disastrously wrong about the subject three weeks or three months ago. But that is just an aspect of the intractably gamelike nature of the proceeding. Any possible consequences of the rightness or wrongness of prior analysis will be either denied, reconfigured beyond recognition or said to have been mooted by the fact that the opponent was equally wrong on some other subject.

And then we all move on. That's the nice thing for the wranglers: these arguments have no staying power. I mean, Rwanda is still there in all its bereavement and misery, but we are somewhere else. We have finished our argument about whether Bill Clinton could or should have done more and what he really knew about the massacres and when he knew it. That was weeks ago. The distinguishing thing about paper-policy fights is that they just move by you and are heard of no more, except for that one last telltale thud.

TERRY MAROTTA '70

*C*aroline Theresa Sheehy Marotta, who was born in Boston, spent the single-digit years, she says, "across from the Monkey House at the local zoo, then moved to Jack Kerouac's town of Lowell, MA, where, along with the thousand other members of the high school class, she collected a diploma, kicked her locker shut, and said good-bye to childhood." She followed her mother to Smith (Class of '30), earned a magna cum laude degree, and married shortly after graduation. She taught for seven years, while her husband, David Marotta, finished Harvard Business School, and soon she had two daughters and a son to raise, along with three or four honorary children. She says she looked in her high school yearbook one day and saw that her English teacher had written, "I hope you do write." Then she began to write seriously and for syndication in over forty newspapers. She describes her 650-word columns as "funny, mainly, except for the ones that make you cry. The target of humor is myself, hypocrisy, consumerism, and now and then, my spouse."

Her first collection, I Thought He Was a Speed Bump and Other Excuses from Life in the Fast Lane (1994), won her a writing award from Parents Magazine and two for humor from the National Society of Newspaper columnists. In 1986 she was also a finalist for the Journalist in Space competition. She sells stories to national magazines for women and special features to papers ranging from the St. Petersburg Times to the Christian Science Monitor. She teaches writing to senior citizens and published a collection of their reminiscences in The Mountains I Raise (1997). She is self-effacing and lighthearted about the source of her inspiration for her varied subjects, saying she gathers information in the check-out line. "In my writing, I stick up for love and sex and the planet. I believe in not riding when you can walk, in eavesdropping with the intention of catching people at their best, and in the great font of collective wisdom that resides in the common people. I don't mind mentioning God now and then. And I think we are all capable of a higher sort of thought than we're normally invited to engage in by the media."

In 1997 Terry Marotta was the distinguished alumna lecturer at the second reunion in May, reading from a memoir of her remarkable mother. Two daughters, one honorary and one real, are currently at Smith. Terry Marotta writes often for the Smith Alumnae Quarterly, but the essays here are new ones.

Sisters

W HEN WE WERE LITTLE and our mom was in the world, my sister and I would go out each Mother's Day morning, and find an apple tree, and pick us some blossoms.

You know how these blossoms are, all bunched like popcorn on their spidery branches, soft-pink when folded in the bud but exploding slowly into whiteness. We would make from them a corsage, a thing of safety pins and crinkle-ribbon, and present it to our mom, choking with the inexpressible love of children for their mother.

It was years later when I learned of that other custom for the second Sunday in May, whereby you wear a red carnation if your mother is still held in Time's tight hug, and a white one if she flies now beyond Time.

It was later still when I myself became a mother, for seven years a mother to daughters only.

I left a job I loved to have that first child. A new job mothering was absorbing and difficult, lively and relentless, delightful and sometimes lonely.

When the second child came, it grew easier. Sure, the older one dominated and teased; sure, the little one tattled and whined. But they were friends.

Once, it was the older one whining, hanging on her parents as we tried to talk, asking me, in a whole parkful of playground equipment, "What can I do *now*, Mom?"

Exasperated, I answered flippantly. "Go play with your sister! That's why we had two of you!"

Back then, our daughters and I had a game we sometimes played at bedtime. All tucked in and ready for a kiss, they would ask in turn, "What am I like?"

"You're like Snow White, of the two-sisters fairy tale," I would tell the elder, pale and slender as she was, quiet and thoughtful. "You're like the lily."

"You're like Rose Red," I'd say to her little sister, rounder and louder, quicker both to laughter and to tears. "You're like the geranium."

They liked this game. I guess I liked it pretty well too.

So time passed, and their own tightly-folded buds opened slowly into blossom. Snow White grew and changed her hue; became merrier and more outspoken; became in her heart a warrior and a seeker for justice.

Rose Red changed too; grew wise and insightful beyond her years; became a great listener to her friends and a fearsome source of insight. She turns 18 this year. Her sister turns 21.

Last fall, the older one decided to take six months off and drive across the country, working small jobs, even touching the Arctic Circle if she could.

She could and did. But two weeks before Christmas, she was exhausted, sick with a bad flu, and facing alone the long drive home.

Just about then, her younger sister began making her Christmas gift: an original drawing, hand lettered with four lines of verse by T.S. Eliot: "We shall not cease from exploration," this verse goes, "And the end of all our exploring will be to arrive where we started, and know the place for the first time."

When the older one reached home and opened this gift, she gasped.

"I *know* this passage!" she exclaimed. "All through my trip I kept it in my glove compartment! The day I finally turned my car east, I took it out and taped it to the dashboard!"

They looked at one another in amazement.

And right then I knew two new things I did not know before: That home is more than the place where you once lived with your parents.

And that until that day comes when my children themselves must put on the White Carnation, I will remember how one of them took a piece of verse and used it to call the other home.

And how the other felt the call; placed the same piece of verse before her own eyes; and came there.

Hap and Cal

I WAS 8 WHEN OUR MOTHER WAS 50, and sometimes, standing among the young moms with their skin like rose petals, she said she felt like our grandmother.

For Cal, as everyone called her, had married late—because there was a Depression, she said, and no one had money. Because there was a war, she said, and the men were all gone. We had heard both reasons as she described her young life as one of five children of a widower-judge, as high-minded an idealist as the good Woodrow Wilson.

They may not have had money, but they sure had fun, to hear the tales of evening dress at the Ritz and raccoon coats at the Harvard-Dartmouth game.

And yes, there were men at these events: young singles and the brothers of friends. "But to be honest," she said of them all, looking back, "there was no yeast in the bread." By which she meant they didn't attract her.

Then, during the war she met our father, a man called Hap for his mild and cheery way. This time there was plenty of yeast in the bread.

She married him. He had wavy hair and red cheeks and bright blue eyes. I know because I've seen snapshots; he left us before I was born.

It was when I was 8 and my mother was 50 that my sister and I first began to understand the misshapen quality of our little family.

"Where is *our* father?" we asked her.

"I don't know," she said truthfully.

"Our dad's dead," we told neighborhood kids. "He kicked the bucket," a friend tells me we said once, though we both plotted in secret to get him back; even wrote "Queen For a Day," the TV show that measured women's hardships by audience applause, then chose one, put her in robes and a crown and made her Dream Come True. Our dream was finding our dad, little realizing he preferred to stay lost.

So Mom raised us without him, in her father's house with her two elderly aunts. Each night she fed and bathed and tucked us in alone, the three old folks being past all that. She crouched between our beds to stroke both our childish brows simultaneously, and sang us to sleep nights.

Often, we were naughty. But often we sensed her sadness too: turned down her bed for her and wrote notes raw with love and apology.

She told jokes and drove fast and made great faces. She also had a temper, kept her desk a mess and was late for everything all her life.

I was 18 when she was 60. She sent me to college and listened, on semester break, as I told her everything I was doing. It never occurred to me to lie to her.

But I did lie once: said I was going south for spring break to see a friend…I saw the friend, all right. But I looked for the man with the blue eyes, too.

When I got back, I told her how I'd found him. She listened, tears running down her face. One day toward the end of that week, the phone rang at home. I picked it up and said hello. It was Mom, calling from work. "Tell me again what he looks like," was all she said.

I was 28 when she was 70. My sister had a baby and I had two, just when she was beginning to think we never would. Shortly before my third came, she moved to a retirement home in my town, where she hosted sherry fests and ignored the fire drills and nearly drowned, in her little room, in subscriptions to every magazine from *Prevention* to *Ms.*

I was 38 when she died at 80, all unexpectedly. I felt wholly a kid at the time of her passing and no more equipped to do without her than in the days of the early bedtimes.

But I am better now.

And I hear from her in odd ways: one child has her very teeth; one, her sense of humor.

And one, listening to this story complete for the first time today, said, in dead earnest and with shining eyes, "I will call my first boy Hap."

Some cold thing in me melted, hearing that.

And it causes me to say, "Here's to you, Cal, who held out for love, and got it, for a while at least, and two kids who adored you, too."

And "Here's to you too, Hap, wherever you may be, redeemed from blame at last, as we all would wish to be redeemed, deserving it or not."

ELIZABETH BILLER
CHAPMAN '65

*T*he daughter of Sylvia K. Burack, Smith '38, and Abraham S. Burack—longtime editors of The Writer magazine—Elizabeth Biller Chapman was born in Boston in 1943. She graduated from Smith summa cum laude and received the prestigious Marshall Scholarship for graduate study in the United Kingdom. She received an MA in Renaissance Literature from the Shakespeare Institute, University of Birmingham, in 1967 and returned to the United States to earn a PhD in English and Comparative Literature from Columbia in 1969. Her dissertation was awarded the F. J. E. Woodbridge Prize for the outstanding humanities thesis.

Her individual poems (more than 100 of which have appeared in print) have been published by such journals as Poet Lore, Yankee, Santa Clara Review, Poetry, and Prairie Schooner. Chapman's book publications include Creekwalker and Backbone of Night, limited edition chapbooks published by (m)öthêr Tøñgué Press, Salt Spring Island, British Columbia. Her full-length collection, First Orchard, will be issued in June 1999 by Bellowing Ark Press, Seattle, WA. Chapman has been the recipient of the Poet Lore/John Williams Andrews Poetry Prize (1996) and the annual poetry award of the California State Poetry Society (1997). Creekwalker was the winner of the (m)öthêr Tøñgué Press International Poetry Chapbook Competition in 1995.

A Californian since 1970, Chapman is the mother of two daughters, Katherine and Margaret Biller. She currently lives in Palo Alto, CA, with her husband, Richard F. Chapman, MD.

"It snowed" was written immediately after a 1997 visit to Smith, where she read her poems and led a memorable poetry workshop. "Wintering On" is reprinted from Backbone of Night. Both illustrate the verbal invention and precision of image that characterize her work.

It snowed

last night in the high forest
huge crystals lying on stumps
and shake roofs I woke fearing
a wolverine the future
my life a bone fractured twice
and mended more than half gone
climbing from the Happy Isles
starting upward steeply till
a patch of white frazzle-ice
turned me around I never
got to the Emerald Pool
Instead a warming met me
on the bridge the precise blue
of Steller's jays ruffling their
dark crests losing their shyness
in the sun the wake-robin
spills his blood by the river
Winter dissolves her body
cascading over granite
as I hope I will some day
I am changing becoming
part of the Vernal Fall these
fissures a water-ouzel
running on the bottom with
slate colored wings half open
nesting season past I am
not yet finished with singing

Wintering On

My husband says I often look
bemused these days,
and he is right—
all these departures—
our olive tree, felled; a friend
dying too soon. I blink
in the light left behind,
the season's chiaroscuro:
creekwater moving swiftly
itself an aquatic animal
with a brown, leaf-spotted hide;
a north wind driving cold tears of sleet
against the window.
It is the penumbra of things
I am feeling.
When my mostly grown daughter
excited about her new job
comes for supper, we linger at table
as the Sap Moon rises.
I describe the colt I saw this week,
just a few hours old—
the sooty shape of responsibility—
his hair the char-brown
of cypress bark;
how he got to his feet
and found the right position, anchored
for milk.
All at once I find myself saying
It's hard to spin a world
out of your own guts.
She writes it down.
And, before leaving, she tells me
her old room looks much better
without all that children's furniture.
I go to bed
thinking of the new stallion,
his white blaze
a teardrop, transfigured;
one vernal cloud. Falling asleep
I am unreasonably happy.

GLORIA STEINEM '56

Gloria Steinem, now a member of the Board of Trustees of Smith College, came to Smith from Toledo, OH. She describes herself as a Midwesterner still despite her many years in New York City. Following her graduation, she studied for two years in India, and upon her return to the United States established herself as a journalist. In 1963 she received national recognition for a two-part exposé in Show magazine of the New York Playboy Club, where she had infiltrated the ranks of the Playboy Bunnies. The Beach Book (1963), an anthology of excerpts with fresh comments from Gloria Steinem, was followed by a series of essays in Life, The New York Times Magazine, and regular columns on politics, profiles, and the national scene, first in Look and later in New York magazine.

As a founder of the Women's Action Alliance and the National Women's Political Caucus, Gloria Steinem took a leadership role in the cause of active feminism. In 1972 she launched Ms. magazine, the most popular feminist periodical in the United States, and continued lecturing and organizing around the country. In 1983 she reprinted twenty-six of her essays in a stirring collection, Outrageous Acts and Everyday Rebellions, introducing the whole with a moving analysis of her own growth as a journalist and feminist. A few years later Gloria Steinem enlarged an essay on Marilyn Monroe, first published in Ms. and reprinted in Outrageous Acts into a full biography, called Marilyn (1986). In 1992 she published Revolution from Within: A Book of Self-Esteem, complete with meditative exercises and a wise chapter on romance versus love informed by her reading of Charlotte and Emily Brontë. Her most recent collection is Moving Beyond Words: Age, Rage, Sex, Power, Money, Muscles: Breaking the Boundaries of Gender (1995), a collection of six essays. She is now the subject of a biography by Carolyn G. Heilbrun, who had access to Steinem's papers in the Sophia Smith Collection at Smith College. The following 1983 essay, "Ruth's Song (Because She Could Not Sing It)," first published in Outrageous Acts and reprinted in Family Portraits: Remembrances by Twenty Distinguished Writers (1989) describes her family, particularly her mother.

Ruth's Song (Because She Could Not Sing It)

FROM *Outrageous Acts and Everyday Rebellions*

HAPPY OR UNHAPPY, families are all mysterious. We have only to imagine how differently we would be described—and will be, after our deaths—by each of the family members who believe they know us. The only question is, Why are some mysteries more important than others?

The fate of my Uncle Ed was a mystery of importance in our family. We lavished years of speculation on his transformation from a brilliant young electrical engineer to the town handyman. What could have changed this elegant, Lincolnesque student voted "Best Dressed" by his classmates to the gaunt, unshaven man I remember? Why did he leave a young son and a first wife of the "proper" class and religion, marry a much less educated woman of the "wrong" religion, and raise a second family in a house near an abandoned airstrip; a house whose walls were patched with metal signs to stop the wind? Why did he never talk about his transformation?

For years, I assumed that some secret and dramatic events of a year he spent in Alaska had made the difference. Then I discovered that the trip had come after his change and probably been made because of it. Strangers he worked for as a much-loved handyman talked about him as one more tragedy of the Depression, and it was true that Uncle Ed's father, my paternal grandfather, had lost his money in the stockmarket Crash and died of (depending on who was telling the story) pneumonia or a broken heart. But the Crash of 1929 also had come long after Uncle Ed's transformation. Another theory was that he was afflicted with a mental problem that lasted most of his life, yet he was supremely competent at his work, led an independent life, and asked for help from no one.

Perhaps he had fallen under the spell of a radical professor in the early days of the century, the height of this country's romance with socialism and anarchism. That was the theory of another uncle on my mother's side. I do remember that no matter how much Uncle Ed needed money, he would charge no more for his work than materials plus 10 percent, and I never saw him in anything other than ancient boots and overalls held up with strategic safety pins. Was he really trying to replace socialism-in-one-country with socialism-in-one-man? If so, why did my grandmother, a woman who herself had run for the school board in coalition with anarchists and socialists, mistrust his judgment so much that she left his share of her estate in trust, even though he was over fifty when she died? And why did Uncle Ed seem uninterested in all other political words and acts? Was it true instead that, as another relative insisted, Uncle Ed had chosen poverty to disprove the myths of Jews and money?

Years after my uncle's death, I asked a son in his second family if he had the key to this family mystery. No, he said. He had never known his father any other way. For that cousin, there had been no question. For the rest of us, there was to be no answer.

FOR MANY YEARS I also never imagined my mother any way other than the person she had become before I was born. She was just a fact of life when I was growing up; someone to be worried about and cared for; an invalid who lay in bed with eyes closed and lips moving in occasional response to voices only she could hear; a woman to whom I brought an endless stream of toast and coffee, bologna sandwiches and dime pies, in a child's version of what meals should be. She was a loving, intelligent, terrorized woman who tried hard to clean our littered house whenever she emerged from her private world, but who could rarely be counted on to finish one task. In many ways, our roles were reversed: I was the mother and she was the child. Yet that didn't help her, for she still worried about me with all the intensity of a frightened mother, plus the special fears of her own world full of threats and hostile voices.

Even then I suppose I must have known that, years before she was thirty-five and I was born, she had been a spirited, adventurous young woman who struggled out of a working-class family and into college, who found work she loved and continued to do, even after she was married and my older sister was there to be cared for. Certainly, our immediate family and nearby relatives, of whom I was by far the youngest, must have remembered her life as a whole and functioning person. She was thirty before she gave up her own career to help my father run the Michigan summer resort that was the most practical of his many dreams, and she worked hard there as everything from bookkeeper to bar manager. The family must have watched this energetic, fun-loving, book-loving woman turn into someone who was afraid to be alone, who could not hang on to reality long enough to hold a job, and who could rarely concentrate enough to read a book.

Yet I don't remember any family speculation about the mystery of my mother's transformation. To the kind ones and those who liked her, this new Ruth was simply a sad event, perhaps a mental case, a family problem to be accepted and cared for until some natural process made her better. To the less kind or those who had resented her earlier independence, she was a willful failure, someone who lived in a filthy house, a woman who simply would not pull herself together.

Unlike the case of my Uncle Ed, exterior events were never suggested as reason enough for her problems. Giving up her own career was never cited as her personal parallel of the Depression. (Nor was there discussion of the Depression itself, though my mother, like millions of others, had made potato soup and cut up blankets to make my sister's winter clothes.) Her fears of dependence and poverty were no match for my uncle's possible political beliefs. The real influence of newspaper editors who had praised her reporting was not taken as seriously as the possible influence of one radical professor.

Even the explanation of mental illness seemed to contain more personal fault when applied to my mother. She had suffered her first "nervous breakdown," as she and everyone else called it, before I was born and when my sister was about five. It followed years of trying to take care of a baby, be the wife of a kind but financially irresponsible man with show-business dreams, and still keep her much-loved job as reporter and newspaper editor. After many months in a sanatorium, she was pronounced recovered. That is, she was able to take care of my sister again, to move away from the city and the job she loved, and to work with my father at the isolated rural lake in Michigan he was trying to transform into a resort worthy of the big dance bands of the 1930s.

But she was never again completely without the spells of depression, anxiety, and visions into some other world that eventually were to turn her into the nonperson I remember. And she was never again without a bottle of dark, acrid-smelling liquid she called "Doc Howard's medicine": a solution of chloral hydrate that I later learned was the main ingredient of "Mickey

Finns" or "knockout drops," and that probably made my mother and her doctor the pioneers of modern tranquilizers. Though friends and relatives saw this medicine as one more evidence of weakness and indulgence, to me it always seemed an embarrassing but necessary evil. It slurred her speech and slowed her coordination, making our neighbors and my school friends believe she was drunk. But without it, she would not sleep for days, even a week at a time, and her feverish eyes began to see only that private world in which wars and hostile voices threatened the people she loved.

Because my parents had divorced and my sister was working in a faraway city, my mother and I were alone together then, living off the meager fixed income that my mother got from leasing her share of the remaining land in Michigan. I remember a long Thanksgiving weekend spent hanging on to her with one hand and holding my eighth-grade assignment of *A Tale of Two Cities* in the other, because the war outside our house was so real to my mother that she had plunged her hand through a window, badly cutting her arm in an effort to help us escape. Only when she finally agreed to swallow the medicine could she sleep, and only then could I end the terrible calm that comes with crisis and admit to myself how afraid I had been.

No wonder that no relative in my memory challenged the doctor who prescribed this medicine, asked if some of her suffering and hallucinating might be due to overdose or withdrawal, or even consulted another doctor about its use. It was our relief as well as hers.

But why was she never returned even to that first sanatorium? Or to help that might come from other doctors? It's hard to say. Partly, it was her own fear of returning. Partly, it was too little money, and a family's not-unusual assumption that mental illness is an inevitable part of someone's personality. Or perhaps other family members had feared something like my experience when, one hot and desperate summer between the sixth and seventh grade, I finally persuaded her to let me take her to the only doctor from those sanatorium days whom she remembered without fear.

Yes, this brusque old man told me after talking to my abstracted, timid mother for twenty minutes: She definitely belongs in a state hospital. I should put her there right away. But even at that age, *Life* magazine and newspaper exposés had told me what horrors went on inside those hospitals. Assuming there to be no other alternative, I took her home and never tried again.

I N RETROSPECT, perhaps the biggest reason my mother was cared for but not helped for twenty years was the simplest: her functioning was not that necessary to the world. Like women alcoholics who drink in their kitchens while costly programs are constructed for executives who drink, or like the homemakers subdued with tranquilizers while male patients get therapy and personal attention instead, my mother was not an important worker. She was not even the caretaker of a very young child, as she had been when she was hospitalized the first time. My father had patiently brought home the groceries and kept our odd household going until I was eight or so and my sister went off to college. Two years later when wartime gas rationing closed his summer resort and he had to travel to buy and sell in summer as well as winter, he said: How can I travel and take care of your mother? How can I make a living? He was right. It was impossible to do both. I did not blame him for leaving once I was old enough to be the bringer of meals and answerer of my mother's questions. ("Has your sister been killed in a car crash?" "Are there German soldiers outside?") I replaced my father, my mother was left with one more way of maintaining a sad status quo, and the world went on undisturbed.

That's why our lives, my mother's from forty-six to fifty-three, and my own from ten to seventeen, were spent alone together. There was one sane winter in a house we rented to be near my sister's college in Massachusetts, then one bad summer spent house-sitting in suburbia while my mother hallucinated and my sister struggled to hold down a summer job in New York. But the rest of those years were lived in Toledo, where both my mother and my father had been born, and on whose city newspapers an earlier Ruth had worked.

First we moved into a basement apartment in a good neighborhood. In those rooms behind a furnace, I made one last stab at being a child. By pretending to be much sicker with a cold than I really was, I hoped my mother would suddenly turn into a sane and cheerful woman bringing me chicken soup à la Hollywood. Of course, she could not. It only made her feel worse that she could not. I stopped pretending.

But for most of those years, we lived in the upstairs of the house my mother had grown up in and that her parents left her—a deteriorating farmhouse engulfed by the city, with poor but newer houses stacked against it and a major highway a few feet from its sagging front porch. For a while, we could rent the two downstairs apartments to a newlywed factory worker and a local butcher's family. Then the health department condemned our ancient furnace for the final time, sealing it so tight that even my resourceful Uncle Ed couldn't produce illegal heat.

In that house, I remember:

. . . lying in the bed my mother and I shared for warmth, listening on the early morning radio to the royal wedding of Princess Elizabeth and Prince Philip being broadcast live, while we tried to ignore and thus protect each other from the unmistakable sounds of the factory worker downstairs beating up and locking out his pregnant wife.

. . . hanging paper drapes I had bought in the dime store; stacking books and papers in the shape of two armchairs and covering them with blankets; evolving my own dishwashing system (I waited until all the dishes were dirty, then put them in the bathtub); and listening to my mother's high praise for these housekeeping efforts to bring order from chaos, though in retrospect I think they probably depressed her further.

. . . coming back from one of the Eagles' Club shows where I and other veterans of a local tap-dancing school made ten dollars a night for two shows, and finding my mother waiting with a flashlight and no coat in the dark cold of the bus stop, worried about my safety walking home.

. . . in a good period, when my mother's native adventurousness came through, answering a classified ad together for an amateur acting troupe that performed biblical dramas in churches, and doing several very corny performances of *Noah's Ark* while my proud mother shook metal sheets backstage to make thunder.

. . . on a hot summer night, being bitten by one of the rats that shared our house and its back alley. It was a terrifying night that turned into a touching one when my mother, summoning courage from some unknown reservoir of love, became a calm, comforting parent who took me to a hospital emergency room despite her terror at leaving home.

. . . coming home from a library with three books a week into which I regularly escaped, and discovering that for once there was no need to escape. My mother was calmly planting hollyhocks in the vacant lot next door.

But there were also times when she woke in the early winter dark, too frightened and disoriented to remember that I was at my usual after-school job, and so called the police to find me. Humiliated in front of my friends by sirens and policemen, I would yell at her—and she would bow her head in fear and say, "I'm sorry, I'm sorry, I'm sorry," just as she had done so often when my otherwise-kindhearted father had yelled at her in frustration. Perhaps the worst thing about suffering is that it finally hardens the hearts of those around it.

And there were many, many times when I badgered her until her shaking hands had written a small check to cash at the corner grocery and I could leave her alone while I escaped to the comfort of well-heated dime stores that smelled of fresh doughnuts, or to air-conditioned Saturday-afternoon movies that were windows on a very different world.

But my ultimate protection was this: I was just passing through, a guest in the house; perhaps this wasn't my mother at all. Though I knew very well that I was her daughter, I sometimes imagined that I had been adopted and that my real parents would find me, a fantasy I've since discovered is common. (If children wrote more and grown-ups less, being adopted might be seen not only as a fear but also as a hope.) Certainly, I didn't mourn the wasted life of this woman who was scarcely older than I am now. I worried only about the times when she got worse.

Pity takes distance and a certainty of surviving. It was only after our house was bought for demolition by the church next door, and after my sister had performed the miracle of persuading my father to give me a carefree time before college by taking my mother with him to California for a year, that I could afford to think about the sadness of her life. Suddenly, I was far away in Washington, living with my sister and sharing a house with several of her friends. While I finished high school and discovered to my surprise that my classmates felt sorry for me because my mother *wasn't* there, I also realized that my sister, at least in her early childhood, had known a very different person who lived inside our mother, an earlier Ruth.

She was a woman I met for the first time in a mental hospital near Baltimore, a humane place with gardens and trees where I visited her each weekend of the summer after my first year away in college. Fortunately, my sister hadn't been able to work and be our mother's caretaker, too. After my father's year was up, my sister had carefully researched hospitals and found the courage to break the family chain.

At first, this Ruth was the same abstracted, frightened woman I had lived with all those years; though now all the sadder for being approached through long hospital corridors and many locked doors. But gradually she began to talk about her past life, memories that doctors there must have been awakening. I began to meet a Ruth I had never known.

. . . A TALL, SPIRITED, AUBURN-HAIRED HIGH SCHOOL GIRL who loved basketball and reading; who tried to drive her uncle's Stanley Steamer when it was the first car in the neighborhood; who had a gift for gardening and who sometimes, in defiance of convention, wore her father's overalls; a girl with the courage to go to dances even though her church told her that music itself was sinful, and whose sense of adventure almost made up for feeling gawky and unpretty next to her daintier, dark-haired sister.

. . . A very little girl, just learning to walk, discovering the body places where touching was pleasurable, and being punished by her mother who slapped her hard across the kitchen floor.

. . . A daughter of a handsome railroad engineer and a schoolteacher who felt she had married "beneath her"; the mother who took her two daughters on Christmas trips to faraway New York on an engineer's free railroad pass and showed them the restaurants and theaters they should aspire to—even though they could only stand outside them in the snow.

. . . A good student at Oberlin College, whose freethinking traditions she loved, where friends nicknamed her "Billy"; a student with a talent for both mathematics and poetry, who was not above putting an invisible film of Karo syrup on all the john seats in her dormitory the night of a big prom; a daughter who had to return to Toledo, live with her family, and go to a local university when her ambitious mother—who had scrimped and saved, ghostwritten a minister's sermons, and made her daughters' clothes in order to get them to college at all—ran out of money. At home, this Ruth became a part-time bookkeeper in a lingerie shop for the very rich, commuting to classes and listening to her mother's harsh lectures on the security of becoming a teacher; but also a young woman who was still rebellious enough to fall in love with my father, the editor of her university newspaper, a funny and charming young man who was a terrible student, had no intention of graduating, put on all the campus dances, and was unacceptably Jewish.

I knew from family lore that my mother had married my father twice: once secretly, after he invited her to become the literary editor of his campus newspaper, and once a year later in a public ceremony, which some members of both families refused to attend as the "mixed marriage" of its day.

And I knew that my mother had gone on to earn a teaching certificate. She had used it to scare away truant officers during the winters when, after my father closed the summer resort for the season, we lived in a house trailer and worked our way to Florida or California and back by buying and selling antiques.

But only during those increasingly adventurous weekend outings from the hospital—going shopping, to lunch, to the movies—did I realize that she had taught college calculus for a year in deference to her mother's insistence that she have teaching "to fall back on." And only then did I realize she had fallen in love with newspapers along with my father. After graduating from the university paper, she wrote a gossip column for a local tabloid, under the name "Duncan MacKenzie," since women weren't supposed to do such things, and soon had earned a job as society reporter on one of Toledo's two big dailies. By the time my sister was four or so, she had worked her way up to the coveted position of Sunday editor.

IT WAS A STRANGE EXPERIENCE to look into those brown eyes I had seen so often and realize suddenly how much they were like my own. For the first time, I realized that she might really be my mother.

I began to think about the many pressures that might have led up to that first nervous breakdown: leaving my sister whom she loved very much with a grandmother whose values my mother didn't share; trying to hold on to a job she loved but was being asked to leave by her husband; wanting very much to go with a woman friend to pursue their own dreams in New York; falling in love with a co-worker at the newspaper who frightened her by being more sexually attractive, more supportive of her work than my father, and perhaps the man she should have married; and finally, nearly bleeding to death with a miscarriage because her own mother had little faith in doctors and refused to get help.

Did those months in the sanatorium brainwash her in some Freudian or very traditional way into making what were, for her, probably the wrong choices? I don't know. It almost doesn't matter. Without extraordinary support to the contrary, she was already convinced that divorce was unthinkable. A husband could not be left for another man, and certainly not for a reason as selfish as a career. A daughter could not be deprived of her father and certainly not be uprooted and taken off to an uncertain future in New York. A bride was supposed to be virginal (not "shopworn," as my euphemistic mother would have said), and if your husband turned out to be kind, but innocent of the possibility of a woman's pleasure, then just be thankful for kindness.

Of course, other women have torn themselves away from work and love and still survived. But a story my mother told me years later has always symbolized for me the formidable forces arrayed against her.

"IT WAS EARLY SPRING, nothing was open yet. There was nobody for miles around. We had stayed at the lake that winter, so I was alone a lot while your father took the car and traveled around on business. You were a baby. You sister was in school, and there was no phone. The last straw was that the radio broke. Suddenly it seemed like forever since I'd been able to talk with anyone—or even hear the sound of another voice.

"I bundled you up, took the dog, and walked out to the Brooklyn road. I thought I'd walk the four or five miles to the grocery store, talk to some people, and find somebody to drive me back. I was walking along with Fritzie running up ahead in the empty road—when suddenly a car came out of nowhere and down the hill. It hit Fritzie head-on and threw him over to the side of the road. I yelled and screamed at the driver, but he never slowed down. He never looked at us. He never even turned his head.

"Poor Fritzie was all broken and bleeding, but he was still alive. I carried him and sat down in the middle of the road, with his head cradled in my arms. I was going to *make* the next car stop and help.

"But no car ever came. I sat there for hours, I don't know how long, with you in my lap and holding Fritzie, who was whimpering and looking up at me for help. It was dark by the time he finally died. I pulled him over to the side of the road and walked back home with you and washed the blood out of my clothes.

"I don't know what it was about that one day—it was like a breaking point. When your father came home, I said, 'From now on, I'm going with you. I won't bother you. I'll just sit in the car. But I can't bear to be alone again.'"

I THINK SHE TOLD ME that story to show she had tried to save herself, or perhaps she wanted to exorcise a painful memory by saying it out loud. But hearing it made me understand what could have turned her into the woman I remember: a solitary figure sitting in the car, perspiring through the summer, bundled up in winter, waiting for my father to come out of this or that antique shop, grateful just not to be alone. I was there, too, because I was too young to be left at home, and I loved helping my father wrap and unwrap the newspaper around the china and small objects he had bought at auctions and was selling to dealers. It made me feel necessary and grown-up. But sometimes it was hours before we came back to the car again and to my mother who was always patiently, silently waiting.

At the hospital and later when Ruth told me stories of her past, I used to say, "But why didn't you leave? Why didn't you take the job? Why didn't you marry the other man?" She would always insist it didn't matter, she was lucky to have my sister and me. If I pressed hard enough, she would add, "If I'd left you would never have been born."

I always thought but never had the courage to say: *But you might have been born instead.*

I'D LIKE TO TELL YOU that this story has a happy ending. The best I can do is one that is happier than its beginning.

After many months in that Baltimore hospital, my mother lived on her own in a small apartment for two years while I was in college and my sister married and lived nearby. When she felt the old terrors coming back, she returned to the hospital at her own request. She was approaching sixty by the time she emerged from there and from a Quaker farm that served as a halfway house, but she confounded her psychiatrists' predictions that she would be able to live outside for shorter and shorter periods. In fact, she never returned. She lived more than another twenty years, and for six of them, she was well enough to stay in a rooming house that provided both privacy and company. Even after my sister and her husband moved to a larger house and generously made two rooms into an apartment for her, she continued to have some independent life and many friends. She worked part-time as a "salesgirl" in a china shop; went away with me on yearly vacations and took one trip to Europe with relatives; went to women's club meetings; found a multiracial church that she loved; took meditation courses; and enjoyed many books. She still could not bear to see a sad movie, to stay alone with any of her six grandchildren while they were babies, to live without many tranquilizers, or to talk about those bad years in Toledo. The old terrors were still in the back of her mind, and each day was a fight to keep them down.

It was the length of her illness that had made doctors pessimistic. In fact, they could not identify any serious mental problem and diagnosed her only as having "an anxiety neurosis": low self-esteem, a fear of being dependent, a terror of being alone, a constant worry about money. She also had spells of what now would be called agoraphobia, a problem almost entirely confined to dependent women: fear of going outside the house, and incapacitating anxiety attacks in unfamiliar or public places.

Would you say, I asked one of her doctors, that her spirit had been broken? "I guess that's as good a diagnosis as any," he said. "And it's hard to mend anything that's been broken for twenty years."

But once out of the hospital for good, she continued to show flashes of the different woman inside; one with a wry kind of humor, a sense of adventure, and a love of learning. Books on math, physics, and mysticism occupied a lot of her time. ("Religion," she used to say firmly, "begins in the laboratory.") When she visited me in New York during her sixties and seventies, she always told taxi drivers that she was eighty years old ("so they will tell me how young I look"), and convinced theater ticket sellers that she was deaf long before she really was ("so they'll give us seats in the front row"). She made friends easily, with the vulnerability and charm of a person who feels entirely dependent on the approval of others. After one of her visits, every shopkeeper within blocks of my apartment would say, "Oh yes, I know your mother!" At home, she complained that people her own age were too old and stodgy for her. Many of her friends were far younger than she. It was as if she were making up for her own lost years.

She was also overly appreciative of any presents given to her—and that made giving them irresistible. I loved to send her clothes, jewelry, exotic soaps, and additions to her collection of tarot cards. She loved receiving them, though we both knew they would end up stored in boxes and drawers. She carried on a correspondence in German with our European relatives, and exchanges with many other friends, all written in her painfully slow, shaky handwriting. She also loved giving gifts. Even as she worried about money and figured out how to save pennies, she would buy or make carefully chosen presents for grandchildren and friends.

Part of the price she paid for this much health was forgetting. A single reminder of those bad years in Toledo was enough to plunge her into days of depression. There were times when this fact created loneliness for me, too. Only two of us had lived most of my childhood. Now, only one of us remembered. But there were also times in later years when, no matter how much I pled with reporters *not* to interview our friends and neighbors in Toledo, *not* to say that my mother had been hospitalized, they published things that hurt her very much and sent her into a downhill slide.

On the other hand, she was also her mother's daughter, a person with a certain amount of social pride and pretension, and some of her objections had less to do with depression than false pride. She complained bitterly about one report that we had lived in a house trailer. She finally asked angrily, "Couldn't they at least say 'vacation mobile home'?" Divorce was still a shame to her. She might cheerfully tell friends, "I don't know *why* Gloria says her father and I were divorced—we never were." I think she justified this to herself with the idea that they had gone through two marriage ceremonies, one in secret and one in public, but had been divorced only once. In fact, they were definitely divorced, and my father had briefly married someone else.

She was very proud of my being a published writer, and we generally shared the same values. After her death, I found a mother-daughter morals quiz I once had written for a women's magazine. In her unmistakably shaky writing, she had recorded her own answers, her entirely accurate imagination of what my answers would be, and a score that concluded our differences were less than those "normal for women separated by twenty-odd years." Nonetheless, she was quite capable of putting a made-up name on her name tag when going to a conservative women's club where she feared our shared identity would bring controversy or even just questions. When I finally got up the nerve to tell her I was signing a 1972 petition of women who publicly said we had had abortions and were demanding the repeal of laws that made them illegal and dangerous, her only reply was sharp and aimed to hurt back. "Every starlet says she's had an abortion," she said. "It's just a way of getting publicity." I knew she agreed that abortion should be a legal choice, but I also knew she would never forgive me for embarrassing her in public.

In fact, her anger and a fairly imaginative ability to wound with words increased in her last years when she was most dependent, most focused on herself, and most likely to need the total attention of others. When my sister made a courageous decision to go to law school at the age of fifty, leaving my mother in a house that not only had many loving teenage grandchildren in it but a kindly older woman as a paid companion besides, my mother reduced her to frequent tears by insisting that this was a family with no love in it, no home-cooked food in the refrigerator; not a real family at all. Since arguments about home cooking wouldn't work on me, my punishment was creative and different. She was going to call up *The New York Times*, she said, tell them that this was what feminism did: it left old sick women all alone.

Some of this bitterness brought on by failing faculties was eventually solved by a nursing home near my sister's house where my mother got not only the twenty-four-hour help her weakening body demanded but the attention of affectionate nurses besides. She charmed them, they loved her, and she could still get out for an occasional family wedding. If I ever had any doubts about the debt we owe to nurses, those last months laid them to rest.

When my mother died just before her eighty-second birthday in a hospital room where my sister and I were alternating the hours in which her heart wound slowly down to its last sounds, we were alone together for a few hours while my sister slept. My mother seemed bewildered by her surroundings and the tubes that invaded her body, but her consciousness cleared long enough for her to say: "I want to go home. Please take me home." Lying to her one last time, I said I would. "Okay, honey," she said. "I trust you." Those were her last understandable words.

T HE NURSES LET MY SISTER and me stay in the room long after there was no more breath. She had asked us to do that. One of her many fears came from a story she had been told as a child about a man whose coma was mistaken for death. She also had made out a living will requesting that no extraordinary measures be used to keep her alive, and that her ashes be sprinkled in the same stream as my father's.

Her memorial service was in the Episcopalian church that she loved because it fed the poor, let the homeless sleep in its pews, had members of almost every race, and had been sued by the Episcopalian hierarchy for having a woman priest. Most of all, she loved the affection with which its members had welcomed her, visited her at home, and driven her to services. I think she would have liked the Quaker-style informality with which people rose to tell their memories of her. I know she would have loved the presence of many friends. It was to this church that she had donated some of her remaining Michigan property in the hope that it could be used as a multiracial camp, thus getting even with those people in the tiny nearby town who had snubbed my father for being Jewish.

I think she also would have been pleased with her obituary. It emphasized her brief career as one of the early women journalists and asked for donations to Oberlin's scholarship fund so others could go to this college she loved so much but had to leave.

I KNOW I WILL SPEND the next years figuring out what her life has left in me.
I realize that I've always been more touched by old people than by children. It's the talent and hopes locked up in a failing body that gets to me; a poignant contrast that reminds me of my mother, even when she was strong.

I've always been drawn to any story of a mother and a daughter on their own in the world. I saw *A Taste of Honey* several times as both a play and a film, and never stopped feeling it. Even *Gypsy* I saw over and over again, sneaking in backstage for the musical and going to the movie as well. I told myself that I was learning the tap-dance routines, but actually my eyes were full of tears.

I once fell in love with a man only because we both belonged to that large and secret club of children who had "crazy mothers." We traded stories of the shameful houses to which we could never invite our friends. Before he was born, his mother had gone to jail for her pacifist convictions. Then she married the politically ambitious young lawyer who had defended her, stayed home, and raised many sons. I fell out of love when he confessed that he wished I wouldn't smoke or swear, and he hoped I wouldn't go on working. His mother's plight had taught him self-pity—nothing else.

I'm no longer obsessed, as I was for many years, with the fear that I would end up in a house like that one in Toledo. Now I'm obsessed instead with the things I could have done for my mother while she was alive, or the things I should have said.

I still don't understand why so many, many years passed before I saw my mother as a person and before I understood that many of the forces in her life are patterns women share. Like a lot of daughters, I suppose I couldn't afford to admit that what had happened to my mother was not all personal or accidental, and therefore could happen to me.

One mystery has finally cleared. I could never understand why my mother hadn't been helped by Pauline, her mother-in-law, a woman she seemed to love more than her own mother. This paternal grandmother had died when I was five, before my mother's real problems began but long after that "nervous breakdown," and I knew Pauline was once a suffragist who addressed Congress, marched for the vote, and was the first woman member of a school board in Ohio. She must have been a courageous and independent woman, yet I could find no evidence in my mother's reminiscences that Pauline had encouraged or helped my mother toward a life of her own.

I finally realized that my grandmother never changed the politics of her own life either. She was a feminist who kept a neat house for a husband and four antifeminist sons, a vegetarian among five male meat eaters, and a woman who felt so strongly about the dangers of alcohol that she used only paste vanilla; yet she served both meat and wine to the men of the house and made sure their lives and comforts were continued undisturbed. After the vote was won, Pauline seems to have stopped all feminist activity. My mother greatly admired the fact that her mother-in-law kept a spotless house and prepared a week's meals at a time. Whatever her own internal torments, Pauline was to my mother a woman who seemed able to "do it all." "Whither thou goest, I shall go," my mother used to say to her much-loved mother-in-law, quoting the Ruth of the Bible. In the end, her mother-in-law may have added to my mother's burdens of guilt.

Perhaps like many later suffragists, my grandmother was a public feminist and a private isolationist. That may have been heroic in itself, the most she could be expected to do, but the vote and a legal right to work were not the only kind of help my mother needed.

The world still missed a unique person named Ruth. Though she longed to live in New York and in Europe, she became a woman who was afraid to take a bus across town. Though she drove the first Stanley Steamer, she married a man who never let her drive.

I can only guess what she might have become. The clues are in moments of spirit or humor.

After all the years of fear, she still came to Oberlin with me when I was giving a speech there. She remembered everything about its history as the first college to admit blacks and the first to admit women, and responded to students with the dignity of a professor, the accuracy of a journalist, and a charm that was all her own.

When she could still make trips to Washington's wealth of libraries, she became an expert genealogist, delighting especially in finding the rogues and rebels in our family tree.

Just before I was born, when she had cooked one more enormous meal for all the members of some famous dance band at my father's resort and they failed to clean their plates, she had taken a shotgun down from the kitchen wall and held it over their frightened heads until they had finished the last crumb of their strawberry shortcake. Only then did she tell them the gun wasn't loaded. It was a story she told with great satisfaction.

Though sex was a subject she couldn't discuss directly, she had a great appreciation of sensuous men. When a friend I brought home tried to talk to her about cooking, she was furious. ("He came out in the kitchen and talked to me about *stew!*") But she forgave him when we went swimming. She whispered, "He has wonderful legs!"

On her seventy-fifth birthday, she played softball with her grandsons on the beach, and took pride in hitting home runs into the ocean.

Even in the last year of her life, when my sister took her to visit a neighbor's new and luxurious house, she looked at the vertical stripes of a very abstract painting in the hallway and said, tartly, "Is that the price code?"

She worried terribly about being socially accepted herself, but she never withheld her own approval for the wrong reasons. Poverty or style or lack of education couldn't stand between her and a new friend. Though she lived in a mostly white society and worried if I went out with a man of the "wrong" race, just as she had once married a man of the "wrong" religion, she always accepted each person as an individual.

"Is he *very* dark?" she once asked worriedly about a friend. But when she met this very dark person, she only said afterward, "What a kind and nice man!"

My father was the Jewish half of the family, yet it was my mother who taught me to have pride in that tradition. It was she who encouraged me to listen to a radio play about a concentration camp when I was little. "You should know that this can happen," she said. Yet she did it just enough to teach, never enough to frighten.

It was she who introduced me to books and a respect for them, to poetry that she knew by heart, and to the idea that you could never criticize someone unless you "walked miles in their shoes."

It was she who sold that Toledo house, the only home she had, with the determination that the money be used to start me in college. She gave both her daughters the encouragement to leave home for four years of independence that she herself had never had.

After her death, my sister and I found a journal she had kept of her one cherished and belated trip to Europe. It was a trip she had described very little when she came home: she always deplored people who talked boringly about their personal travels and showed slides. Nonetheless, she had written a descriptive essay called "Grandma Goes to Europe." She still must have thought of herself as a writer. Yet she showed this long journal to no one.

I miss her, but perhaps no more in death than I did in life. Dying seems less sad than having lived too little. But at least we're now asking questions about all the Ruths and all our family mysteries.

If her song inspires that, I think she would be the first to say: It was worth the singing.

JANET FISH '60

*T*he cover of Smith Voices may recall Friday afternoon tea in student houses, that weekly pause that fortifies the flesh and sustains the spirit at the end of the academic week. But the painting was not meant to typify Smith so much as to make a strong, clear visual situation linking objects with light. "Herb Tea" is a luminous reminder of the artistic significance of common objects.

Janet Fish came to Smith from Bermuda where she grew up and where she found a density of vegetation which may have led her toward the very active surfaces she now paints. She went from Smith to the Yale University School of Art and Architecture for her BFA and MFA (1963). After her first year at Yale she attended the Skowhegan School of Art in Maine for the summer. She now spends half the year in Vermont, the other half in New York. Early in her career she chose the still life as a favorite form, often with subjects like glassware that catch the light. Her point is to keep the whole painting very active, "to keep a kind of movement going across the entire surface."

Her grandfather was an Impressionist, and her mother and uncle are sculptors. She works primarily in oil, but also watercolor, pastel, and printmedia. Since 1982 she has included people in her paintings, often children, friends, and occasionally television images. Many of her settings speak of summer, with its vibrant light and vital life.

Her work has been exhibited throughout the United States, Canada, and Australia, and it is now part of the permanent collections at major museums as well as corporate headquarters. Recently she has received the Adolf and Clara Obrig Prize from the National Academy of Design in New York (1995), the Academy Award in Art from the American Academy of Arts and Letters (1994), Girl Scouts Woman of Distinction (1993), and the Outstanding Woman Artist Award from the Aspen Art Museum (1992). She occasionally lectures at her alma mater and held the Albert Donne Visiting Professorship at the University of Bridgeport in Connecticut in 1991. She has enjoyed three MacDowell Fellowships, and her Australian sojourn was supported by the Australian Council of the Arts.

MONICA VACHULA '73

*M*onica Vachula was born in Hatfield, MA, as was Sophia Smith, the founder of Smith College and the subject of Jane Yolen's Tea with an Old Dragon (1998), where this illustration of a child knocking on Sophia Smith's door, imaginatively restored to its original colors, was first published. With characteristic self-effacement and humor, she includes a self-portrait in Tea with an Old Dragon, where she imagines herself Sophia Smith's maid. But she is far more likely to drink tea from the chinoiserie china of the teacup shown in the 3" x 4" detail on the back jacket of this book.

She attended the local schools and graduated from Smith as an art major. Her jewel-like paintings have been exhibited at the Francesca Anderson Gallery in Boston, the Concord Art Association, and the St. Botoph Club in Boston and at many museums in New England and down the East Coast. Juried competitions have won her numerous awards at the museums in Springfield, Worcester, Fitchburg, and Concord. Her work has also been exhibited in group and one-person shows in Northampton at Smith College, Dasenks Gallery, Sync Gallery, and Gallery 112; Barracca Gallery in North Hatfield; Gallery 9 in Chatham, NJ; the Fitchburg Museum, and many other New England museums. Loring Coleman says "she renders objects with incredible feeling, weight, color, texture . . . minute facets of color are like the planes of a cut gem."

Although she is truly a painter, Monica Vachula has illustrated several books for young readers, including The Crest and the Hide (1982) by Harold Courlander and In Bikole: Eight Modern Stories of Life in a West African Village (1978) by Tom Gilroy. Her illustrations have also appeared in Cricket Magazine and her work has been used on the cover of the Massachusetts Review and covers for the publishing firm of Victor Gollancz, Ltd. in London.

Monica Vachula makes her home with her husband in Harvard, Massachusetts, and in Hatfield, where their house is just a few doors from the "old" and "new" houses of Sophia Smith. She is now working on Paul Revere's Ride for Boyds Mills Press with a publication date of 2000.

ACKNOWLEDGMENTS

Excerpt from a speech— "Dare to be Creative!"— Madeleine L'Engle made at the Library of Congress on November 16th, 1983. Reprinted by permission of the author.

"The Good Mother Who Put a Shoe in the Icebox" from *You've Got to Dance with Them What Brung You* © 1998 by Molly Ivins. Reprinted by permission of the author and Random House, Inc.

"Robin" from *Barbara Bush: A Memoir* © 1994 by Barbara Bush. Reprinted by permission of Charles Scribner's Sons.

"Moon Shell" from *Gift from the Sea* © 1955, 1975 by Anne Morrow Lindbergh. Reprinted by permission of Random House, Inc.

"Nantucket" from *Cheaper by the Dozen* © 1948 by Frank B. Gilbreth, Jr. and Ernestine Gilbreth Carey. Reprinted by permission of HarperCollins Publishers.

"About the Television Series" from *The French Chef Cookbook* © 1968 by Julia Child. Reprinted by permission of Alfred A. Knopf, Inc.

"Oslo" from *Dream State: Stories* © 1995 by Moira Crone. Reprinted by permission of the University Press of Mississippi.

"A Civic Duty to Annoy" first appeared in *The Atlantic Monthly* (September 1997) © 1997 by Wendy Kaminer. Reprinted by permission of the author.

"The Scapegoat" first appeared in *Smith College Monthly* (October 1941) in a slightly abbreviated form. Reprinted by permission of the Smith College Archives.

"The Point" from *The Party: A Guide to Adventurous Entertaining* © 1997 by Sally Quinn. Reprinted by permission of Simon & Schuster.

"Tomorrow at Tara" from *Gone With the Wind* © 1936 by Macmillan Publishing Company, a division of Macmillan, Inc. Copyright renewed © 1964 by Stephens Mitchell and Trust Company of Georgia as Executors of Margaret Mitchell Marsh. Reprinted by permission of William Morris Agency, Inc. on behalf of the Author.

"The Local Train" from *The Tiger in the Grass* © 1995 by Harriet Doerr. Reprinted by permission of Viking Penguin, a division of Penguin Putnam Inc.

"Purdah" by Sylvia Plath is from the Mortimer Rare Book Room, Smith College, and from *The Collected Poems of Sylvia Plath* (1981) © Estate of Sylvia Plath. Reprinted by permission of Faber & Faber, London, and by HarperCollins Publishers.

TLs. (typed letter signed) January 26, 1955 to Enid Epstein Mark '54 and TLs. 9 April 1957 to Elinor Friedman Klein '56 are from the Mortimer Rare Book Room, Smith College © Estate of Sylvia Plath. Reprinted by permission of Faber & Faber, London, and by Enid Epstein Mark '54 and Elinor Friedman Klein '56, recipients of the letters.

M. Richard Fish, photographer, for *Wild Dill* by Pamela See, Three Forms from the *Brooklin Series* by Grace Knowlton, Illustrations from *Tea with an Old Dragon* by Monica Vachula, *Shattering Glass* by Enid Mark.

Stephen Petegorsky, photographer for *The Poetic Body*, *Poem Dress of Circulation* by Lesley Dill

Smith Voices

Designed by Elizabeth Pols '75,
North Pols Design of Belchertown, Massachusetts.
Printed by Thames Printing Company, Inc. of Norwich, Connecticut.
Bound by Acme Bookbinding of Charlestown, Massachusetts.